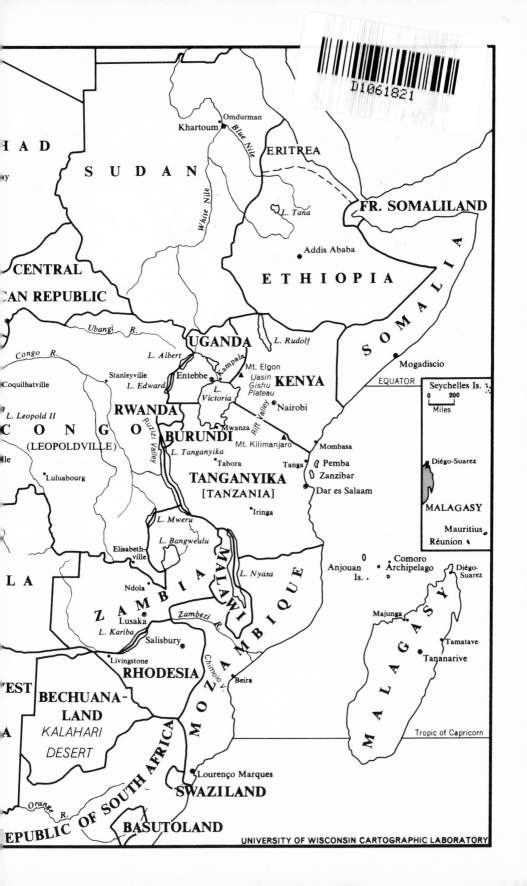

HAD

ay

SUDAN

Khartoum Omdurman

Blue Nile

ERITREA

White Nile

FR. SOMALILAND

L. Tana

CENTRAL

AN REPUBLIC

Addis Ababa

ETHIOPIA

SOMALIA

Ubangi R.

Congo R.

UGANDA

L. Rudolf

Stanleyville
L. Albert
Coquilhatville
L. Edward
Entebbe

Kampala

Mt. Elgon

Uasin
Gishu
Plateau

KENYA

EQUATOR

Mogadiscio

Seychelles Is.

0   200

Miles

L. Leopold II

le

CONGO

(LEOPOLDVILLE)

Luluabourg

RWANDA

BURUNDI

L.
Victoria

Ruzizi Valley

Mwanza

Mt. Kilimanjaro

Nairobi

Rift Valley

Diégo-Suarez

L. Tanganyika

Tabora

TANGANYIKA

[TANZANIA]

Iringa

Tanga

Mombasa

Pemba
Zanzibar

Dar es Salaam

MALAGASY

Mauritius

Réunion

L. Mweru

L. Bangweulu

Elisabeth-
ville

ZAMBIA

MALAWI

L. Nyasa

MOZAMBIQUE

Anjouan
Is.

Comoro
Archipelago

Diégo-
Suarez

Ndola

Lusaka

Zambezi

Majunga

LA

L. Kariba

Livingstone

Salisbury

MALAGASY

Tamatave

Tananarive

RHODESIA

Chimoio V.

Beira

EST

BECHUANA-
LAND

KALAHARI

DESERT

MOZAMBIQUE

REPUBLIC OF SOUTH AFRICA

Lourenço Marques

SWAZILAND

Tropic of Capricorn

Orange R.

EPUBLIC

BASUTOLAND

UNIVERSITY OF WISCONSIN CARTOGRAPHIC LABORATORY

MAIZE IN TROPICAL AFRICA

MAIZE

IN TROPICAL

AFRICA

MARVIN P. MIRACLE

The University of Wisconsin Press

Madison, Milwaukee, and London

1966

PUBLISHED BY THE UNIVERSITY OF WISCONSIN PRESS

MADISON, MILWAUKEE, AND LONDON

P. O. BOX 1379, MADISON, WISCONSIN 53701

COPYRIGHT © 1966 BY THE

REGENTS OF THE UNIVERSITY OF WISCONSIN

PRINTED IN THE UNITED STATES OF AMERICA

BY THE NORTH CENTRAL PUBLISHING COMPANY

ST. PAUL, MINNESOTA

LIBRARY OF CONGRESS CATALOG CARD NUMBER 66–11805

PREFACE

TROPICAL Africa in this book includes all those countries lying between the Sahara Desert and the Republic of South Africa. All of Mozambique and Bechuanaland — even parts which lie in the South Temperate Zone — are included, as are the Malagasy Republic, the Comores, Réunion, Mauritius, Seychelles, São Tomé and Príncipe, Fernando Po, and the Cape Verde Islands. (See Appendix Table 1.)

Maize is more widely grown in this area than any other major crop and probably ranks third in bulk as a supplier of calories. This study describes geographical variations in its importance as a food crop, examines the reasons for these variations, and considers the future prospects for maize in African agriculture. Maize is not yet important in tropical Africa as an animal feed, and little attention is paid there to its potential contribution to livestock production.

In purpose and approach this study is related to other investigations of major food crops in tropical economies published over the past two decades, and especially *Competition among Grains* (1940) by Naum Jasny, *The Rice Economy of Monsoon Asia* (1941) by V. D. Wickizer and M. K. Bennett, *The Staple Food Economies of Western Tropical Africa* (1958) by B. F. Johnston, and *Manioc in Africa* (1959) by W. O. Jones. Johnston examines the production, consumption, and distribution of a set of major food commodities, including maize. He considers primarily the large subgroups of staple food commodities, and does not probe deeply into the economics of any one commodity, nor does he deal with the food economies of eastern tropical Africa. The book by Jones, which focuses exclusively on one food crop, manioc, throughout tropical Africa, is closest in design and purpose to the present study; but it treats a root crop that is unlike maize in many ways and has a considerably different position in African food economies.

The initial question — the position of maize in tropical African agriculture and diets — leads to examination of the ways in which it enters into the farming systems, of its utilization as a food, and of its part in internal commerce. In addition, this inquiry requires examination of physical factors that influence yields per acre and that help to determine where maize can be grown economically, and of physical characteristics of maize that affect its processing, storage, trade, and consumption. Attention is given as well to methods of producing maize and preparing it for human consumption, to variations in its importance in diets, and to the general character of traditional African economies as it affects the competitive position of maize in production. The ways in which maize was first introduced to the people of Africa and subsequently transmitted throughout tropical areas of the continent, and alterations in its importance in recent decades are explored in order to get a better understanding of its present position and of probable changes.

The three chapters preceding the summary discuss the prospects for maize and its potential as a food in tropical Africa. Economic development presupposes increasing the productivity of agriculture, and in tropical Africa measures to increase the efficiency with which maize is produced and distributed are an important element in developing the agricultural sector. In examining this broad question problems of expanding maize production, improving techniques of storage, evoking appropriate responses from African farmers to economic development policies are discussed. Some of the methods that have already been adopted to increase production and to improve marketing are reviewed and tentative conclusions are advanced. Attention is also given to the prospective future demand for maize as suggested by estimates of the way in which maize consumption varies with income and with town or country residence.

In addition to the literature and correspondence cited in the various chapters, this study is based on a fifteen-month trip to tropical Africa during which the principal areas of maize production were visited. Partly because a good deal of the data presented was gathered through personal investigation in Africa, much more information is presented for some areas than for others.

A number of acknowledgments are due. I feel a far greater debt than I can adequately express to M. K. Bennett, who originally aroused my interest in the subject; to William O. Jones, who carefully scrutinized much of this study; and to Bruce F. Johnston, Vernon D. Wickizer, and Donald S. Barnhart, who also guided me on several matters. P. Stanley King

gave valuable help on questions of presentation; Patricia Cedarleaf contributed substantially to the organization of most of the maps, charts, and
illustrations, and put them in their final form. Parts of Chapters 1, 6, and
8 appeared as an article in *Tropical Agriculture;* some of Chapter 5 appeared as part of a chapter in Paul Bohannan and George Dalton (eds.),
Markets in Africa (Northwestern University Press, 1962); and Chapter
7 appeared in a slightly different form as an article in the *Journal of
African History.* The Ford Foundation supplied a grant, without which I
could not have adequately reinforced my background knowledge of Africa
before attempting the project or visited African countries and the colonial powers of Europe with which they are, or have been, associated. For
all opinions, conclusions, and other statements, the author alone, and not
the Ford Foundation, is responsible.

M.P.M.

Madison, Wisconsin
April, 1965

ABBREVIATIONS AND SYMBOLS

CCTA   Commission for Technical Cooperation in Africa South of the Sahara

CSA   Scientific Council for Africa South of the Sahara

FAO   Food and Agriculture Organization (UN)

IFAN   Institut Français d'Afrique Noire (French Institute for Black Africa)

ILO   International Labor Organization

INÉAC   Institut National pour l'Étude Agronomique du Congo Belge (National Institute of Agriculture in the Belgian Congo)

IRCAM   Ministère de la France d'Outre-mer, Institut de Recherches, Office de la Recherche Scientifique et Technique, Outre-mer, Territoire du Cameroun (Institute of Research, Office of Scientific and Technical Research, Territory of Cameroun)

ORSTOM   Ministère de la France d'Outre-mer, Office de la Recherche Scientifique et Technique, Outre-mer (Office of Scientific and Technical Research, Overseas)

UN   United Nations

USDA   United States Department of Agriculture

. . .   Data not available

—   None, negligible quantity, or entry not applicable

1949/50   Year beginning in 1949 and ending in 1950

1953–58   Annual average for the years 1953 through 1958

CONTENTS

ILLUSTRATIONS

TABLES

MAIZE IN TROPICAL AFRICA

1

MAIZE AS A FOOD CROP
AND COMMODITY

A S IN most economies at an early stage of development, starchy food-stuffs (starchy-staples) account for something like 70 to 90 percent of the calories produced and consumed in tropical Africa. Of the major starchy-staple food crops, maize [1] is the most widely grown. In fact it is present in every sizable area where food crops can be raised; and in a number of regions (most of Kenya, Malawi, and Rhodesia as well as considerable sections of Angola, Zambia, Tanganyika, Mozambique, Cameroun, Dahomey, Togo, and Ghana) it is the leading starchy-staple by a large margin. If the data that are available are reasonably reliable, only the millets and sorghums and manioc (cassava) bulk larger, in aggregate, as contributors of calories (see Chapter 6).

In many areas maize has been more closely linked with economic development of tropical Africa than any other starchy-staple. It commonly became of major importance where foodstuffs had to be transported considerable distances to feed laborers and populations that were not self-sufficient. In a number of such regions maize has within the past three or four decades almost completely replaced traditional starchy foodstuffs such as the millets and sorghums. It has also at one time or another been a major export of several tropical African countries.

Thus its position in diets and commerce, and its potential role in increasing productivity in agriculture, make maize of special interest in the study of tropical African economies.

THE PLANT

Maize is a tall grass with a large stalk, long arching leaves with evenly ruffled edges, and, for a grass, unusually big seed. Botanically it belongs

3

to the order *Graminae* and is customarily placed in the tribe *Maydeae*, although some current opinion holds that this may not be the best classification (*458*, p. 9); its genus is *Zea*, which has only one species, *Z. mays*. This species includes all cultivated varieties of maize; no wild or uncultivated forms are known (*227*, p. 490). When mature, the plant may have a single stalk or a central stalk with a number of stems (called tillers) which are smaller but identical in appearance with the main stalk, branching from its base; it may be as little as two or as much as 20 feet tall; and it may have from eight to 44 leaves. There is similar diversity in the number, size, shape, and color of the ear, which is the seed-bearing structure (*228*, p. 309).

THE COMMODITY

Although several commodities are obtained from the stalks, cobs, and husks of the maize plant, only the seeds are important in human nutrition. Chemically the grain is primarily carbohydrate but contains significant portions of protein and oil, and a small amount of minerals. Oil is found mainly in the germ but also in the aleurone layer of the endosperm (Figure 1-1); the carbohydrate is concentrated in the two starchy fractions of the endosperm; protein occurs throughout but is most concentrated in the aleurone layer; and minerals are found in the germ and aleurone layers (*139*, p. 10):

	Range (% of dry weight)
Protein	6–15
Fat	4.5(?)–7
Mineral	? (average 1.3)
Carbohydrate	76–88

Compared with roots, tubers, and other commodities with a high water content, the maize kernel, like all cereals, makes its nutrients available in compact form, and is therefore comparatively easy to transport. Another characteristic, unique to maize among the cereals and of considerable significance in determining its role as a food, derives from the arrangement of the seed on the seed-bearing structure and from the flavor of the roasted or boiled immature grain. Because immature maize is tasty and relatively easy to eat directly from the cob, maize may be harvested over a long period, being consumed as a vegetable at the first of the season and later as a hard grain. The formation of seed around a cob covered with a thick, tough husk facilitates harvest, the feeding of the maize to livestock,[2] and transportation; it considerably reduces losses incurred by shattering; and notably extends the range of storage techniques. The husk gives enough protection from birds and rain to make possible storage in the field (in fact, in most tropical countries, at least some storage is on the stalk) or, as in the Corn Belt of the United States, in open granaries. These characteristics make drying and indoor storage much easier, too. The husk can be stripped back, for example, and used to hang the ears on a wall or a rack. After harvest, maize is commonly so hung in the sun to dry in wet regions, and is often stored by hanging the ears from rafters or beams of the farmer's dwelling.

Use as a Food

Maize is prepared and consumed in a multitude of ways, but most of them, and all of the major ones, can be grouped as follows: ground or

FIGURE 1-1 — MAJOR STRUCTURAL COMPONENTS
OF THE MAIZE KERNEL

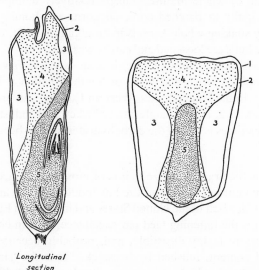

Longitudinal
section

From Paul Weatherwax and L. F. Randolph, "History and Origin of Corn," in G. F. Sprague, ed., *Corn and Corn Improvement* (New York, 1955), p. 33; and H. A. Wallace and E. N. Bressman, *Corn and Corn Growing* (New York, 1928), p. 183. These kernels are not drawn to the same scale.

[1] Bran.

[2] Aleurone layer; colorless and almost impossible to detect with the naked eye in all common varieties.

[3] "Hard" or "flint" starch.

[4] "Soft starch."

[5] Germ.

pounded and boiled; ground or pounded and baked or fried; boiled whole; roasted whole; and fermented.

In the form of roasting ears (corn-on-the-cob), a favorite vegetable wherever maize can be grown, it is eaten by most African peoples (although other forms of maize consumption are larger in total).

When maize is ground or pounded, the meal or flour obtained can be made into a starchy mush by mixing with water and cooking. Diluted to thinness, this mush is a drink or gruel; in thick soup consistency it is porridge; a still drier mush is made into the doughball, or tamale (if wrapped and steamed). For tortillas (North America) the flour is finely ground and the dough patted into thin, flat cakes which are heated until crisp. With wheat flour, eggs, and baking powder added, this technique produces cornbread, somewhat thicker than the tortilla (generally about two and a half inches) and more like bread — a typical food of the southern United States.

Consumption of whole mature grain is relatively unimportant, being confined principally to parched corn, popcorn, and hominy. The latter is produced by soaking whole kernels in an alkali solution, often lime or ashes, until the hulls are loosened and can be washed free.

Since maize is mostly carbohydrate, it is an excellent raw material for alcohol. In tropical Africa and parts of South America it is frequently made into beer; in the United States, Western Europe, and probably other temperate areas, it is made mainly into whiskey and industrial alcohol, although it sometimes is one of the carbohydrates used in beer production.

Use as Feed

As feed, it is the grain of maize that is of most importance; but stalks, leaves, and immature ears are also used as fodder in some areas, notably in parts of the Corn Belt of the United States and in Western Europe.

Maize grain is the fattening feed par excellence: high in energy; low in fiber and therefore highly digestible; and, probably because of its relatively high oil content, relished by livestock. "It is the 'standard,'" as Schneider says, "with which to compare all other grains" (*379*, p. 667).

The foremost use of maize as a feed is for fattening swine, but Jasny calls it "a good all-around feed grain. It may be not quite as good horse feed as oats, but less of it is needed by about 15 per cent. . . . As a feed for cattle, sheep, and particularly poultry, corn may probably be considered at least as good as any other grain. For some purposes, especially as part of the poultry ration, corn is even superior; . . ." (*224*, pp. 444, 445).

For forage, the stalk is cut while still green and made into silage or cured (dried in the sun). If the ear is included, it is commonly called fodder when cured, silage when not (*306*, p. 386). If the ears are removed, it is usually called stover. There is variation, too, in how much of the stalk is taken for stover. All of it may be used; but in some areas it is topped above the highest ear just before the grain is mature, the upper portion being used for stover, the lower left in the field.

Maize ranks high as a forage crop. According to F. B. Morrison, silage made from the entire maize plant gives a higher average yield of dry matter and digestible nutrients per acre than any other forage crop: it "even slightly surpasses alfalfa, the queen of legume roughages" (*306*, p. 386). However, compared to other forage crops, it is relatively low in protein (*258*, p. 488). The nutritive value of forage may vary even more than that of the grain. It depends on the variety, the cultural practices employed, the stage at which it is cut, and probably other factors (*258*, p. 487).

Industrial Uses

Maize is industrially important chiefly as starch, oil, and alcohol. These are obtained by what is called the "wet milling" method, a process of steeping the grain and then, by progressive grinding and manipulation, separating the germ and bran from the endosperm.

The main product is starch, which, when dried, can be used as such or converted into dextrins; if not dried, it can be further processed into syrups and sugars.

Oil, obtained from the germ, goes into soaps and glycerines, or may be refined for cooking and salad making.

The protein in maize, called zein, is an excellent substitute for shellac and can be made into synthetic fiber which is reportedly comparable in quality with other protein fibers.

Maize is used extensively for the production of alcohol when its price is low relative to that of other carbohydrates. Whiskey is no doubt the best known product of the fermentation industries, but industrial alcohols, ethyl and butyl, and acetone are also derived from maize.

Classification of Maize Types

Seven major kinds of maize are usually recognized: popcorn, flint corn, dent corn, flour corn, sweet corn, pod corn, and waxy corn.[3] Two of these, dent and flint, account for the bulk of world production; pop, sweet, and flour are used almost entirely for human consumption; pod and waxy are not important as foodstuffs, although waxy is used industrially in the United States.

Dent maize (*Zea mays indentata*), the leading type by volume of
world production (*311*, p. 10), is characterized by an indentation or
"dent" in the crown (Figure 1-2), caused by greater shrinkage of soft
starch between the two layers of hard starch on either side of the endosperm. Dent maize is preferred to flint as a feed because it has little "hard"
starch; since this makes it relatively easy for animals to pulverize, they
utilize it more efficiently.

FIGURE 1-2 — THE MAJOR CLASSES OF MAIZE

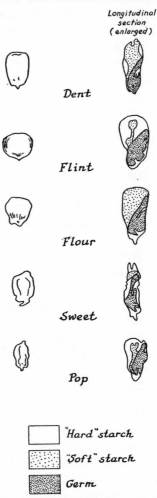

From N. P. Neal and A. M. Stommen, *Supplement to Wisconsin Corn Hybrids*,
Wisconsin Agr. Exp. Sta. Bull. No. 476, Supplement (Jan. 1956), p. 9.

Second in volume of production is *flint* maize (*Z. mays indenturata*), which has relatively little soft starch, and that only in the center of the endosperm. The relative hardness of its starch makes it more resistant than dent maize to insect attack. In tropical Africa, and other parts of the tropics where insects are a major problem, flint may for this reason sometimes rank ahead of dent maize in volume grown.

Flour, soft, or *squaw* maize (*Z. mays amalacea*) is by volume probably the third most important type grown. Complete, or almost complete, absence of "flinty" or "hard" starch is its unique characteristic. Where grinding is a chore, the ease of grinding this type may offset its vulnerability to insect attack and make it preferred to flint or dent types.

Probably next in importance is *sweet* maize (*Z. mays succharata*). Its endosperm is a glassy, sweetish starch, and upon drying the kernels show pronounced wrinkles. Sweet maize is valued for its flavor and finds a place as a vegetable or delicacy, although dent, flint, and flour types may also be eaten as a vegetable.

Popcorn (*Z. mays everta*) usually has small kernels which contain an even higher percentage of hard starch than do those of flint corn. This starch, when heated, explodes or "pops" into small fluffy white balls.

In *waxy* maize (*Z. mays ceretina*) the starch molecule differs chemically from that of other maize types, resembling a glycogen molecule (*387*, p. 6). Its starch is clear and gummy and has some of the characteristics of tapioca starch. The least important of maize types is *pod* maize (*Z. mays tunicata*), in which each individual kernel on the ear is enclosed by a hull or husk.

Nutritive Composition

Table 1-1 compares the nutritive characteristics of maize with the two most widely used cereals, wheat and rice; with sorghum, a food particularly important in some semiarid regions; with manioc, a starchy root which is a major foodstuff in tropical Africa; and with plantains, a starchy, banana-like fruit also important in tropical diets.

Compared with these crops, maize has a roughly equal yield of calories per 100 grams of dry weight. It ranks below wheat and sorghum but considerably above rice, manioc, and plantain in quantity of protein provided; however, the protein of maize is qualitatively deficient, being short of tryptophan and lysine, two of the eleven amino acids which are essential for human nutrition. Maize is especially high in fat compared with these other starchy-staples except sorghum; low in calcium; fairly high in phosphorous; exceptionally rich in vitamin A (especially the yellow varieties); high in thiamine; fairly low in niacin; and (because

TABLE 1-1 — COMPARISON OF THE NUTRITIVE COMPOSITION OF MAIZE, WHEAT, RICE, SORGHUM, MANIOC, AND PLANTAIN
(Per 100 grams)

Foodstuff	Water (%)	Food energy (calories)	Protein (grams)	Fat (grams)	Carbohydrate Total (grams)	Carbohydrate Fiber (grams)	Ash (grams)	Calcium (mg.)	Iron (mg.)	Phosphorus (mg.)	Thiamine (mg.)	Riboflavin (mg.)	Niacin (mg.)	Vitamin C (mg.)	Vitamin A (I.U.)
Maize (Zea mays), ground meal, white or yellow, E.P.[a], bolted[b]	12.0	362	9.0	3.4	74.5	1.0	1.1	6	1.8	(178)	0.30	0.08	1.9	(0)	440[c]
Wheat (Triticum aestivum), flour, E.P.[a], hard red, 80% extraction	12.0	359	12.0	1.3	74.1	0.5	0.65	24	1.3	191	0.26	0.07	2.0	0	0
Rice (Oryza sativa), E.P.[a], polished	13.0	360	6.8	0.7	78.9	0.2	0.6	6	0.8	140	0.12	0.03	1.5	0	0
Sorghum (Sorghum vulgare), whole, E.P.[a]	11.0	333	11.0	3.3	73.0	1.7	1.7	28	4.4	287	0.38	0.15	3.9	0	0
Manioc (Manihot esculenta), meal and flour, E.P.[a]	11.9	360	1.6	0.6	84.6	2.4	(1.9)	(82)	...	(132)	...	...	...	...	0
Plantain (Musa paradisiaca), E.P. [a,d]	66.4	119	1.1	0.4	31.2	0.4	0.9	7	0.7	30	0.06	0.04	0.6	14	e

Data from Woot-Tsuen Wu Leung et al., Composition of Foods Used in Far Eastern Countries, USDA, Agr. Handbook No. 34 (Mar. 1952), pp. 10–16. Parentheses indicate imputed value.

[a] E.P. stands for "edible portion."

[b] "Bolting" refers to the removal of the bran.

[c] Vitamin A based on yellow maize meal; white maize meal contains only a trace.

[d] Values are highly tentative because of the great variation in the varieties of plantains.

[e] Vitamin A values range from about 10 I.U. per 100 grams of white fleshed plantains to 1,200 I.U. per 100 grams of deep yellow fleshed varieties.

little has yet been learned about ascorbic acid in maize) in an indeterminate position with respect to vitamin C. Some vitamin C is found in immature kernels and in sweet types (*139*, p. 15; *352*, p. 8).

Perhaps the most significant feature of this pattern is the low niacin content. Deficiency of niacin and of tryptophan is associated with pellagra (described as the "disease of three D's," dermatitis, diarrhoea, and dementia). It is generally agreed among nutritionists that the niacin shortage alone would not cause pellagra if maize were rich in tryptophan, which can be converted in the human body to niacin.

Although pellagra, according to a report of the Food and Agriculture Organization, "Occurs in endemic proportions exclusively among maize-eating populations" (*139*, p. 37), there are areas — Mexico for example — where diets are based on maize and little or no pellagra is experienced. Pellagra is a major nutritional deficiency disease in the Republic of South Africa, but in tropical Africa it is of only minor importance, for reasons not well understood; possibly because of the considerable amounts of pulses consumed with maize or because of the techniques employed by peasants in processing maize.

Sorghum alone surpasses maize in a majority of nutritive components. Maize is equal or superior to manioc and plantain in all major nutritive characteristics except niacin. If thiamine also is excepted, the same can be said of the characteristics of maize vis à vis rice. Maize is excelled by wheat mainly in protein content and calcium and phosphorus.

CLIMATE AND SOIL

Soil

Since maize is a large plant with an enormous grain-producing capacity, it makes a relatively heavy drain on the fertility of the soil, taking more from it than almost any of the other cultivated plants and particularly more than the other cereals (*224*, p. 233). With its large vegetative growth, it has a notably high nitrogen requirement; in fact, this is the nutrient that usually limits yields. Maize also needs a fairly good balance among nitrogen, phosphorous, and potash. Klages (*251*, p. 396) reports that it will grow successfully over "a wide range of soil reaction, pH. 5 to 8, but yields are usually affected by degrees of acidity represented by pH. values of less than 5.5." It seems to do best on soils of neutral acid reaction of roughly pH. 7.

There seem to be no significant geographical variations in nutrient requirements; nor have notable differences been established in nutrient requirements among the major types of maize (*179*, p. 204; *183*, p. 12).

Climate

Because of the diversity of characteristics, not only those relating to physical structure and appearance but also resistance to pests, disease, cold, drought, and — probably most important — rapidity of maturation, maize can be grown in an extremely wide range of climates. It cannot grow as far poleward as several other grains, but its greater adaptability to warm and humid environments permits it to be grown over a much greater geographical area than any of the other cereals; indeed, it is grown from 58° north latitude in Canada and the USSR to 40° south in South America, from below sea level in the Caspian Plain to 12,000 feet and beyond in parts of the Andes (*228*, p. 309). Important maize-producing areas are found in 21 of Thornthwaite's 32 world climatic types.

Maize is central to the almost completely mechanized agricultural systems of the United States Corn Belt, and to systems that are exceptionally primitive, sometimes little more than the beginning of agriculture. In parts of the tropics the culture of maize may consist of nothing more than dropping a few kernels in a hole made with a sharp stick, and leaving them and the resultant plant without further attention until harvest time.

Yet, despite this adaptability to vastly different environmental conditions, there are limits to the conditions that maize will tolerate. A minimum of moisture must be available and temperatures must be above freezing during the growing season, which may vary roughly from 45 to 190 days according to variety.

Except for the United States, where the crop has attracted a great deal of attention among researchers, and possibly other temperate regions with similar climatic and soil conditions, only general, rather imprecise statements can be made about the optimum environment, and these usually relate only to minimum requirements. Very little is yet known about maximum moisture and temperature tolerances, if in fact there are maximum limits within the 21 climatic types in which maize is found. Except for the observation that excessive heat aggravates damage to maize from drought, the literature contains little reference to maximum tolerances (*228*, p. 310).[4]

Nevertheless, it is possible to give general indications of the conditions under which the crop thrives. It is a warm-weather crop, requiring considerable warmth from the time of planting until flowering (tasseling and silking), and once it is above the ground will tolerate only very brief and light frosts (*372*, p. 52; *228*, p. 314).

During the period of vegetative growth, and particularly during the three weeks preceding and following flowering, the period when the growth rate is very rapid and at its peak, temperatures should be moderately high both day and night (*463*, p. 8), and moisture and nutrient levels should also be high. Some minimum amount of sunshine is required but nothing suggests that any area meeting the minimum temperature and moisture requirements is deficient enough in hours of sunshine seriously to limit maize production.

In temperate areas, and specifically in the Corn Belt of the United States, the La Plata corn belt in Argentina, the Garonne Basin of France, Italy's Po Valley, and the Hungarian and Walachian basins, the six regions which produce roughly three-fourths of the world's maize and which are considered to have almost ideal climatic and soil conditions, fairly specific physical requirements are recognized: according to William Van Royen, "Summer temperatures should average about 75° F. (23.9° C.), with warm nights — average night temperatures of 58° F. (14.4° C.); rainfall should be fairly abundant, from 18 to 24 inches (about 460 to 600 mm.) during the growing period, and during the summer months it should be of the thundershower type, with periods of clear, warm weather in between" (372, p. 56).

CULTURE

Maize responds strongly to care. Although it may sprout and begin growth unassisted, weed competition can prevent it from reaching maturity. The slow initial growth, high heat requirement, and long growth period of maize preclude successful competition against weeds in the absence of human intervention.

In the American Corn Belt, the region where the world's highest yields are obtained, a sizable portion of total effort expended on the crop goes into preparation of the seedbed. In this operation the principal objectives are the creation of a soil texture and moisture condition favorable to seeds, seedlings, and expanding root systems by (1) breaking the surface soil into particles so fine that seed can be placed in intimate contact with moist soil; (2) loosening and fluffing the soil to improve air and water relations temporarily as well as to stimulate microbial activity and release plant nutrients; and (3) preparing the soil for easy and efficient cultivation (403, p. 365).

To achieve this rather delicate physical condition the farmer will often till his land two, three, probably even more times prior to planting. Planting itself is by machine, which permits rapid placing of seed at a uniform depth and with uniform spacing. Uneven spacing of mature plants hinders, or may make impossible, mechanical harvesting. After the crop is planted it is kept as free of weeds as possible and is frequently carefully fertilized.

It is common in the tropics for much less preparation to be given the seedbed or growing crop. For example, in tropical Mexico, the soil may be scratched once with a crude wooden plow, the seed dropped in the furrow and stepped on. Farmers who do not have draft power often pile up hills or ridges with a hoe and plant the seed in holes made with a sharpened stick or hoe. Sometimes the seedbed is not prepared at all; the farmer merely makes a hole with a pointed stick, drops in two or three seeds, and pushes the earth over them with his foot.

An even cruder method has been reported on the west coast of South America from approximately the equator to 8° north latitude: "There is no preparation of the land," writes V. M. Patiño, "the seed being broadcast over secondary growth vegetation which is then cut down. The seed remain on the surface of the ground . . ." (*343*, p. 309). In temperate zones other cereals and legumes, especially soybeans (in the United States), are often mixed or "intercropped" with maize; and in tropical areas maize is grown with practically every commonly cultivated crop, from such tree crops as coffee and cocoa to sugarcane, cotton, and, more commonly, legumes, starchy roots, and tubers.

Maize Culture in Tropical Africa

Culture practices in African farming are typically crude, and yields are correspondingly low. Although production methods vary greatly in details, it is generally true that (1) hoe culture predominates — except for parts of eastern Africa — and machinery is employed infrequently; (2) usually little care is given to the preparation of a seedbed; (3) clean cultivation is rarely attained, either because maize is grown with other crops or because the farmer is unable to keep up with the growth of weeds; (4) improved seed is not used; (5) fertilizers are not applied, except perhaps on small plots around the dwelling where maize may be grown as a garden crop; (6) maize may receive some irrigation, especially along rivers, but irrigated maize is a small fraction of the total; (7) crop "rotation" is essentially a question of crop sequences during the three or four years that land is tilled under shifting cultivation; and (8) maize may be grown at any time in the crop sequence, but is most often first and seldom last.

The outstanding features of the maize harvest are that it is usually gradual and that very little maize is harvested for feed. Harvest begins as soon as the ears are ripe enough to be used as a vegetable, and continues well past maturity. Merely a small fraction of the aggregate maize crop is harvested for feed (only non-African farmers commonly feed their livestock), and most of that appears to be as grain rather than as forage.

Insects and Diseases. Maize growers over all of tropical Africa encounter serious insect and disease problems. Of the diseases, mildews, leaf blights, smuts, and rusts are the major problems (*378*, pp. 51 and 17). The most destructive and widespread of these is probably a rust,

Puccinia polysora, which spread rapidly through Africa after its introduction in 1949, causing considerable, often catastrophic, damage, particularly in the more humid regions of western Africa. The areas of Pobé and Allada in Dahomey were so severely attacked in 1950 that a local food shortage occurred and the price of maize rose 500 percent (*85,* p. 20). That same year many areas of Togo, Ghana, and Nigeria reported a 50 percent reduction in yields. The recent development of resistant varieties of maize and the adoption of earlier planting dates have reduced losses considerably (*85,* pp. 20, 25, and 26).

Stalk borers, earworms, armyworms, the corn leaf aphid, grasshoppers, and locusts probably cause substantial yield losses everywhere; available information is too fragmentary to determine the relative importance of each of these and the extent of the damage they cause.

Yields

As one might expect, considering the techniques of production and the prevalence of insects and diseases, yields in tropical Africa are low compared with those in the major temperate production belts (Table 1-2).[5] The yield reported for Kenya, 1955–59, 16.5 quintals per hectare, while high for tropical Africa, is less than half that of Iowa, in the American Corn Belt. Chart 1-1, which shows the variation in tropical African

CHART 1-1 — TROPICAL AFRICAN MAIZE YIELDS BY ACREAGE,
ABOUT 1950

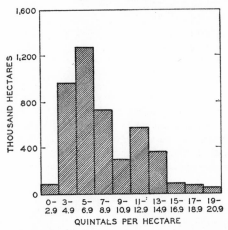

Data from the same source as Map 6-1 (see Appendix II), based on *cercle,* district, province, and major subdivision data. No yield estimates were available for Ethiopia, Liberia, Portuguese Guinea, and Zanzibar. One quintal per hectare equals 1.59 bushels of maize per acre.

TABLE 1-2 — AVERAGE MAIZE YIELDS FOR SELECTED COUNTRIES,
1945–49 AND 1955–59

(Quintals per hectare)[a]

Country	Yield 1945–49	1955–59	Country	Yield 1945–49	1955–59
Tropical Africa			Other (continued)		
Kenya	15.0[ce]	16.5[e]	Argentina	18.2	18.7
Cameroons	7.8[c]	9.3	Austria	13.0	29.6
Rwanda and Bu-			France	10.1	26.3
rundi	9.2[c]	12.0[f]	Italy	17.6	26.8
Former Italian			Spain	13.5	21.7
Somaliland	8.4[c]	6.5			
Congo (Leopold-			Guatemala	8.6[c]	7.1
ville)	8.9[cd]	10.5	Brazil	12.9	12.4
Nigeria	9.5[cd]	. . .	Mexico	6.8	7.3
Sierra Leone	10.1[cd]	5.5	Nicaragua	10.0	7.6
Ghana	4.7[cd]	9.7	Cuba	10.0	9.9
Ivory Coast	4.2[cd]	6.7[f]			
			Venezuela	8.7[b]	12.0
Togo	3.5[cd]	5.0[f]	Columbia	9.4	11.9
Senegal	10.2[cd]	9.2[g]	Philippines	6.3	6.2
Sudan	9.6[c]	9.8[f]	Ceylon	5.3[b]	5.4
Madagascar	8.4[c]	7.9	Indonesia	7.6[c]	9.3
Other			Thailand	9.1[c]	13.6
United States	22.4	30.6			
Ohio	32.2	37.3			
Iowa	30.4	37.4			
Louisiana	10.9	17.7			
Florida	9.7	14.9			
Georgia	7.0	17.0			

Data from USDA, *Agricultural Statistics,* various issues 1946–52 and 1957–61;
FAO, *Yearbook of Food and Agricultural Statistics,* Pt. 1: Production (Rome),
various issues 1953–63; and sources in Appendix II. Yield is generally equivalent
grain yield on total acres harvested for all purposes, i.e. grain equivalent computed
for acreage harvested for silage, fodder, etc.

[a] One quintal per hectare equals 1.59 bushels per acre.

[b] 1948–50.

[c] About 1950.

[d] Yields probably somewhat lower than usual because of an epidemic of maize
rust (*Puccinia polysora*).

[e] European farms only.

[f] Average of less than five years.

[g] 1959–60.

16

yields about 1950, suggests a modal yield of around 6 quintals per hectare (10 bushels per acre). The large acreage with yields around 12 quintals per hectare (19 bushels per acre) represents principally the southern parts of Ghana, the Ivory Coast, and Nigeria; the northern provinces of the Congo (Leopoldville); and northeastern Tanganyika. Yields about 15 quintals and over per hectare come from the European agriculture of Kenya, Zambia, and Rhodesia.

Data on yields are much less complete for the later years, but those for the Ivory Coast, the Western Region of Nigeria, Gambia, Eritrea, Rwanda-Burundi, and Rhodesia, if they can be trusted, suggest that there has been a shift of the modal yield in these areas from 4 to 6 quintals per hectare (Table 1-3), with a considerable increase in the amount of acreage producing more than 16.9 quintals per hectare.

Unreliable and incomplete as the data are, there can be no doubt that, as in most tropical areas, yields in tropical Africa are characteristically low. Whether they are low compared with other regions in the tropics is

TABLE 1-3 — TROPICAL AFRICAN MAIZE YIELDS, SELECTED COUNTRIES, ABOUT 1950 AND 1960

Yield (quintals per hectare)[a]	% of hectares planted	
	About 1950	About 1960
0–2.9	5.4	3.1
3–4.9	33.1	19.9
5–6.9	16.2	25.9
7–8.9	7.4	22.5
9–10.9	18.3	13.7
11–12.9	7.2	0.0
13–14.9	1.1	4.9
15–16.9	6.3	1.1
17–18.9	0.0	0.0
19–20.9	3.0	0.0
21–22.9	2.0	5.1
23–24.9	0.0	0.0
25–26.9	0.0	0.5
27–28.9	0.0	0.0
29–30.9	0.0	3.4
	100.0	100.1[b]

Data from FAO, *Yearbook of Food and Agricultural Statistics*, 1962, Pt. 1: Production (Rome, 1963), pp. 45–46, and sources in Appendix II.

[a] One quintal per hectare equals 1.59 bushels per acre.

[b] Percentages have been rounded.

not clear and cannot be until better data are available, both for Africa and other parts of the tropics.

STORAGE

Reducing the moisture content of the grain to a level that permits successful storage (10 to 15 percent, depending on temperature) is a major problem in most areas, usually but not always solved by drying the harvest in the sun. Sun-drying is unnecessary when maize is stored by hanging the ears from rafters or beams of a hut, for the open fire used for cooking helps to lower the moisture content. In addition, the smoke helps repel insects and rodents.

Simple granaries are common. They vary considerably in design but are most often cylindrical bins, raised off the ground, of bamboo, palm thatch, or a plaster of mud or cow dung applied to a framework of stakes (*389*, p. 138; *240*, p. 61; *32*, p. 6; and *1*, pp. 229–31). Pits dug in the ground are also used (*70*, p. 3; and *219*, p. 290).

In Togo maize is stored on a raised platform and is covered with a roof, but no granary is built. The mature ears are carefully stacked in a circle with the tips pointing to the center until a cylinder of ears has been constructed. The center is then filled with ears piled loosely, and a grass roof is placed on top (*285*, p. 238).

M. H. Lelong, a missionary of the Dominican Order, reports that in parts of northern Congo (Leopoldville), an area with a long dry season, maize ears still in husk are tied together in huge bunches and suspended from a high tree branch (*256*, p. 301). I have seen a similar technique employed in the same vegetation zone in the Ivory Coast, Cameroun, and the Central African Republic. This technique appears to be important only north of the equator. Although I have seen maize stored in trees in some areas of Rwanda-Burundi and Zambia, the bunches were quite small and granaries were also used; nothing in the literature suggests that tree storage is important south of the equator.

2

LEVELS OF LIVING

TROPICAL Africa is a vast and diverse belt cutting across the center of the African continent, about the same length as the continental United States and roughly twice as wide. It is generally, but not everywhere, hot and humid. Most of Rwanda and Burundi, much of Ethiopia, the Kenya Highlands, and smaller plateaus in such places as Tanganyika, Angola, and Cameroun are pleasantly mild and in many ways resemble temperate areas in climate. Rainfall is high the year round over large areas near the equator, but in general as one moves north or south the length of the rainy season (or seasons) diminishes until it is near zero in the Sahara and Kalahari deserts. More of the year is dry than wet over most of tropical Africa.

By far the greatest portion of the area is sparsely populated: typically less than 10 persons per square kilometer, i.e. 26 persons per square mile (see Appendix Table 2); but sizable areas in Nigeria, Rwanda, and Burundi, and small areas elsewhere have high population densities (the average for Rwanda and Burundi is almost 90 per square kilometer).

Tribal societies differ greatly in type, organization, institutions, and history. Colonial policies have been widely divergent. Sharp differences are found in levels of living. Within any area, towns and cities with a relatively high level of consumption, embracing many of the material luxuries of Europe and America, exist in the midst of huge expanses where consumption is basically much as it was in the days of Livingstone and Stanley.

PHYSICAL ENVIRONMENT

Since the nature of the vegetation is determined largely by precipitation, temperature, and soil characteristics, vegetation serves as a useful index of physical environment. Tropical African vegetation ranges from

19

dense equatorial (closed) rain forest to dry, treeless desert-like landscape where short, scrawny grass is the chief covering (Map 2-1); but
for general description it can be divided into two large groups roughly
equal in area: (1) humid and dry forest and (2) long- and short-grass
savanna.

In areas near the equator where rainfall is extremely high and almost
continuous, the climax vegetation is a many-specied forest of large trees,
often a hundred feet or more in height, with a relatively dense and often
interlocking canopy (398, p. 11). Where the canopy is dense, little light
gets to lower levels and undergrowth is scant (385, p. 343). If the canopy

MAP 2-1 — MAJOR VEGETATION TYPES IN TROPICAL AFRICA

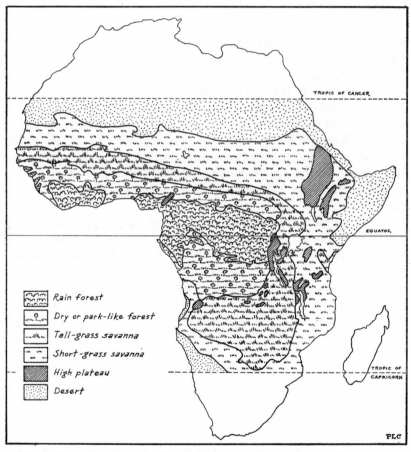

Adapted from G. Delevoy in Maurice Robert, *Le Congo physique* (3rd ed. Liége,
1946), p. 386.

is not dense, a level of smaller trees under the large ones is usual, and below them, near the ground level, a fairly dense undergrowth of vines, ferns, and the like.

Rainfall decreases in quantity and frequency as one moves away from the equator, trees become progressively shorter and smaller, and the forest less dense; no canopy exists, except perhaps along rivers and streams. When the forest becomes open and parklike with a covering of grass on the floor, it is what Shantz calls "dry forest" (385, p. 348).

With still less rain, or with a longer dry season, the trees are even smaller, few, and widely scattered. Grass is found everywhere and grows from four to six feet high during the rainy season. This is tall-grass savanna, as distinguished from the treeless, but not necessarily bushless, landscape in still drier zones that are characterized by short grass.

More than any other single factor, the amount and distribution of rainfall define these ecological zones. Temperatures vary relatively little diurnally and annually, and mean temperatures are everywhere high. Life is not limited by low temperatures except at the higher elevations of a few mountains. Large areas at an elevation high enough to alter the vegetation markedly are limited largely to parts of eastern Africa and Ethiopia (these are the high plateau zones, Map 2-1). Their total area is small.

Variations in total rainfall are important (from over 400 to scarcely more than three or four inches per year), but equally significant are regularity and distribution of rainfall. The size and density of vegetation seem to vary directly with the length of the dry season and regularity of precipitation. For example, the savanna regions are characterized both by irregular rains and by a long dry season.

Near the equator many areas have rain the year round. Up to about 10° latitude in either direction, at least two rainy seasons are usually experienced, one typically longer than the other. As one moves poleward, the rainy season becomes shorter and finally disappears. Most of the savanna region has only one season of rains, which becomes progressively shorter as one moves south or north.

Soils

Soil is also an important determinant of the vegetation, particularly of the species found. African soils vary considerably. Although much is yet to be learned about them, we know differences in texture and fertility are notable: some are extremely sandy; claylike red and yellow soils are not infrequently lateritic; and stretches of fertile volcanic soils are found in the mountainous regions.

Most common are the red and red-brown tropical soils, which dominate roughly three-fourths of tropical Africa. This vast expanse has been described by W. Fitzgerald as having "soils as a whole more uniform in character than is the case of any region of similar size, with the exception of the Sahara" (*152*, p. 23). They are light in texture (often sandy), usually low in organic matter; freely drained; and partially or wholly leached. The leaching produces the reddish color, which varies from pink to brown: the soluble minerals percolate out, leaving principally iron and aluminum hydroxides. Being largely leached of lime carbonate, the soils are of acid reaction.

Stretches of soils of volcanic origin are found around Lake Victoria (*275*, p. 71), as well as in the mountains and plateaus of the southern Cameroun. These volcanic soils, while small in total area, are important because they are relatively rich in scarce organic matter. This is attributable both to their origin — the contribution of volcanic ash — and the relatively cool temperatures (and hence relatively slow rate of oxidation) at the higher elevations where they are found.

Transportation

Transportation in tropical Africa is poorly developed. Roads are few and usually not hard surfaced. Road construction is made difficult by dense tropical forests, mountains, swamps, rivers, and heavy rains — and general lack of financial resources. Maintaining roads is hard during the rainy season. Many areas are accessible to motor vehicles only in the dry season. And the tsetse fly makes the use of draft animals impossible in much of tropical Africa.

Railroads are not so difficult to maintain, but they are few. River and lake transportation is extensive in some areas and offsets somewhat the inadequacy of other means of travel. Most extensive of internal navigable waters are the river networks of the Congo Basin and Lakes Victoria, Tanganyika, and Nyasa (*156*).

LEVELS OF LIVING

No good estimate exists of the level of living in any part of tropical Africa. Yet writers discussing economic development often present comparative data on per capita national income as though they showed exactly how far behind such less developed economies as those of Africa are. The accuracy of data on the United States economy is sufficiently questionable to make this a hazardous undertaking; and when the roughness of African estimates is taken into account, comparison of per capita national incomes has little meaning. Good statistics are expensive, a luxury that underdeveloped countries cannot afford. Not only are African data extremely rough, but they tend to understate production by excluding goods and services that are not market oriented. A smaller portion of total production of goods and services is for sale in tropical Africa than in Europe or America, but the size of the difference is not well enough known to adjust the African estimates at all accurately.

Additional bias results when national income data are converted into another currency, as all but one set of them must be if comparisons are to be made. Not only is it difficult in many countries to determine which exchange rate (or what average of rates) should be used, but whatever rate is used can, at best, reflect the rate of exchange only for items moving in international trade. It may not represent a number of important commodities. A further problem arises because the distribution of income may differ widely among countries with the same per capita income. What the distribution of income is cannot be established with any accuracy at present for any tropical African country, but it seems likely much less disparity of income exists than in most of Latin America, the United States, or Europe, if not most of the rest of the world.

Admittedly there is a great gap between the level of production per capita in African countries and much of the rest of the world. Indeed, even casual observation in any African country notes on the average far fewer material goods — of any quality — than in most of Europe, North America, and much of Asia. The point is that there is no simple index that will even approximately measure the difference.

In most tropical African villages a few bicycles may be found; no one owns a car; houses have mud walls and thatch roofs; there is neither electricity nor running water; most people have but two or three changes of clothes; only a few own shoes.

In towns and cities many houses have brick or concrete walls and tin roofs; electricity and running water are frequently available; ownership of a bicycle is more general, and a few people may own a scooter or automobile. People dress better; many homes have a considerable amount of furniture, a radio, some reading material. (Non-African groups and some of the wealthier Africans stand out in sharp contrast; they may live in neighborhoods that look almost as affluent as any in the United States or Europe. Many cities in tropical Africa have a business district with gleaming skyscrapers; wide, modern streets; and, to the surprise of most tourists, smart shops.)

Although most Africans have few durable goods, and clearly desire more and better goods and services, they are not so badly off as is often assumed. In particular, there has been much exaggeration about hunger, one of man's most dramatic ills and one that is often used to symbolize the extreme of unsatisfactory performance of an economy.

Hunger has been so played up by those who write about tropical Africa and its problems that those whose knowledge of the area extends little beyond images of big game, snakes, missionaries, and witchdoctors are apt to think of it as a place where most people do not have enough to eat.

Although apparently always popular, this concept has received special emphasis since the creation of the Food and Agriculture Organization of the United Nations (FAO) in 1946. Particularly after the early leadership of the FAO advanced the idea that two-thirds of the world — and certainly all of tropical Africa — was undernourished, numerous writers not only accepted hunger as one of the basic characteristics of African life but conducted something of a literary crusade to purge the continent of this scourge.

Few seem to have had any doubt about the evidence buttressing the FAO hypothesis; indeed, it was taken as fact, not hypothesis. This is not surprising, since FAO published, with little if any qualification, statistics purporting to show the magnitude of the gap between requirements and intake — intake based on estimated national production minus nonfood uses, and adjusted for international trade and changes in stocks — and presented a series of target levels of food consumption which it maintained must be met to alleviate hunger (*137*).

Of those who had any awareness of the paucity and unreliability of the data upon which the FAO's recommendations were based, most had scant sympathy for the idea that it might be a misallocation of resources to devote a large portion of available funds and personnel to eliminating an hypothesized hunger. Only a very few conceived of a possibility that education, medical services, transportation, or like things unquestionably below the standard desired by Africans should receive a share of what was allocated to banishing hunger. Most would have argued that hunger is so undesirable that extensive campaigns to eliminate food shortage are worthwhile, even if the existence of the shortage is highly uncertain.

In fact, little or no basis exists for the assertion that hunger is widespread in tropical Africa;[1] and this FAO later admitted (*141*, p. 34). Nevertheless, impressions about the extent of hunger will not die easily or quickly. Even though the FAO finally withdrew from its position that tropical Africa is short of calories, as a result of evidence obtained largely from consumption surveys, this idea will not spread with anything like the rapidity that the earlier statements of hunger did. It will have little appeal to the imagination or the emotions, and little if any place in the manuscripts of the journalists who generalize about the strange, far-off land most of their readers think of as the Dark Continent.

Less publicized than general hunger is the notion that much of tropical

Africa experiences a regular preharvest hunger. It is conceivable that even though a population is not hungry most of the time, and does not experience famines, it might have less food than needed for a month or two each year. There are several reports of preharvest hunger in tropical Africa, but most of the evidence either will not bear scrutiny or suggests that the phenomenon reported is not chronic (*293*).

Other exaggerations in views concerning African well-being are harder to pinpoint but are important. Basic to feelings that the African suffers for want of automobiles, bathtubs, or electrical appliances is the assumption that African needs and desires are the same as those of the traveler who reports on African conditions. Some aspirations of Africans do appear to parallel ours closely, and perhaps many of their needs do, but to expect this in general is to make an unwarranted value judgment. If a mud hut serves all the functions its owner desires and is esthetically appealing to him, there is no reason to suppose he suffers for not having a more modern home.

But despite difficulties in making interpersonal and intersocietal comparisons of utility, the African desire for rapid economic development is strongly evident. Clearly actual suffering is brought about by disease, and clearly a mandate exists for greater production and consumption of many goods and services.

GEOGRAPHICAL VARIATION IN LEVELS OF LIVING

As Table 2-1 indicates, whatever the average level of living in tropical Africa, it varies greatly from country to country. The number of telephones per 1,000 inhabitants in 1960 ranged from 18.8 on the island of Réunion to 0.6 in Ethiopia. The number of physicians per 1,000 persons stood at 0.246 in Réunion in 1958, but less than one twenty-seventh of that in Niger, the former French colony that lies north and east of Nigeria; and the majority of tropical African countries had less than 0.05 physicians per 1,000 inhabitants. The corresponding figures for the United States and the United Kingdom were 1.218 and 0.810, respectively.

The number of radio receivers per 1,000 persons in 1959 ranged from 0.2 in Sierra Leone to 71.0 in French Somaliland; only French Somaliland, Mauritius, and Liberia reported more than 40 receivers per 1,000 inhabitants, and for the majority of tropical African countries the figure was 10 or less.

The leading consumer of cement was the Federation of Rhodesia and Nyasaland, with 120 kilograms per capita in 1958; Ethiopia was the lowest with 1.9 kilograms per person.

TABLE 2-1 — INDICATORS OF RELATIVE LEVELS OF CONSUMPTION IN TROPICAL AFRICAN COUNTRIES

Country	Telephones per 1,000 persons, 1960	Physicians per 1,000 persons, 1958	Radio Receivers per 1,000 persons, 1959	Apparent Consumption of Cement per capita, 1958 (Kg.)	Length of railroads and all-weather roads per 1,000 sq. km., 1959 (Km.)	Passenger cars in use per 1,000 persons, 1958	Literacy about 1950 (% of population literate)
Réunion	18.8	.246	36.0e	...	...	33.1b	...
Mauritius	14.3	.212	54.9e	73.0h	...	13.0	...
Former Fed. of Rhodesia-Nyasaland	13.3	.121	7.5e	120.0	59.9	13.3	...
Rhodesia	...	...	...	...	...	...	20–25
Zambia	...	...	...	...	...	...	20–25
Ghana	3.5	.028	16.3e	72.0g	35.1	3.2	19–23
Ivory Coast	2.2	.031	9.1e	...	56.1	3.1	...
Liberia	...	...	42.0f	63.0g	...	...	5–10
Kenya	6.3	.094	...	...	28.7	9.2b	20–25
Rwanda-Burundi	...	.147	0.3f	...	...	...	5–10
Angola	2.0	.047	9.7e	37.0	...	5.3	1–5
Bechuanaland	...	.059	5.7f	...	...	...	20–25
Central African Republic	...	.026	4.1f	...	...	...	...
Cameroun	1.5	.035	2.4f	18.8g	10.2	2.5	5–10
Congo (Brazzaville)	5.6	.054	11.1e	...	...	...	...
Former French Equatorial Africa	...	...	...	14.5	...	1.9	1–5
Gabon	...	...	4.5e	...	...	...	...
Former French West Africa	...	...	...	22.4	...	...	1–5
Mali	...	.010	1.8e	...	...	...	...
Senegal	5.6	.014	42.0	...	...	...	1–5
Chad	...	.013	0.9e	...	...	...	...
French Somaliland	...	...	71.0f	...	...	14.7b	1–5

Kenya, Uganda, and Tanganyika	...	...	...	19.0g	...	4.5	...
Mauritania	...	...	6.9e	...	...	...	...
Malagasy	2.5	.027	10.2f	...	...	3.4	30-35
Portuguese Guinea	...	...	...	...	...	...	...
Guinea	...	...	...	...	33.8	...	...
Comoro Is.	...	...	...	...	...	...	20-25
São Tomé and Príncipe	...	.218d	0.01e	...	...	1.7	15-20
Somalia	...	...	...	3.0	...	1.0h	1-5
Upper Volta	1.2	...	3.5f	...	...	...	...
Uganda	2.1	.058	14.0f	...	25.4	4.3b	25-30
Zanzibar and Pemba	...	.118	13.0f	...	...	5.0	5-10
Mozambique	1.9	.027	4.9e	27.0h	...	3.1b	1-5
Congo (Leopoldville)	2.0a	.049	2.5e	38.0a	14.5	1.6	35-40
Sierra Leone	...	.015	0.2e	19.9h	...	1.4b	5-10
Sudan	2.1	.021	0.8e	9.6	...	1.0	5-10
Malawi	...	...	...	...	...	...	5-10
Niger	...	.009	0.8e	...	...	...	...
Togo	1.2	...	3.5f	...	...	1.0h	5-10
Nigeria	1.2c	.023	2.8cf	14.6	27.3	0.7	10-15
Tanganyika	1.5	.050	2.0f	...	7.7	2.7b	5-10
Ethiopia	0.6b	.011	4.3f	1.9	4.7	0.6	1-5

Data from UN, *Statistical Yearbook, 1961* (New York, 1961), pp. 50, 51, 398, 399, 607, 608, 609, 610, 646, 647; and from UN, *Economic Bulletin for Africa*, 1, No. 1 (Jan. 1961): xv; 2, No. 2 (June 1962): 17, 19; and W. Goldschmidt, ed., *The United States and Africa* (New York, 1958), p. 230.

a Including Rwanda-Burundi.

b 1956.

c Including British Cameroons.

d Population data for 1959; data on physicians for 1956.

e Number of radios licensed.

f Numbers of radios in use.

g 1959.

h 1957.

The length of railroads and all-weather roads per 1,000 square kilometers in 1959 ranged from 59.9 in the Rhodesias and Nyasaland to 4.7 in Ethiopia. The Ivory Coast, Ghana, and Kenya all had more than 28 kilometers of all-weather route per 1,000 square kilometers. A similar variation is found in passenger cars in use. If Réunion, which had 33.1 cars per 1,000 people in 1956, is excluded, the range is from 14.7 cars per 1,000 inhabitants in French Somaliland to 0.6 in neighboring Ethiopia. For most of the countries for which data are available, less than 6 cars per 1,000 people were in use in 1958.

The literacy rate is low throughout tropical Africa. It is estimated to have ranged in 1950 from 35–40 percent in the Congo (Leopoldville) to 1–5 percent in Ethiopia; estimates from 17 tropical African countries were 10 percent or lower.

For a number of countries data are not available on these indicators of level of living, and more indicators are needed to establish firmly the relative position of the countries for which we have data. If we bear in mind these qualifications, our data suggest that Réunion, Mauritius, Zambia, and Rhodesia are at the top of such a ranking, with Ghana, the Ivory Coast, Liberia, Kenya, and Rwanda-Burundi near the top. Angola and the Congo (Leopoldville) appear somewhere in the middle, while Sierra Leone, the Sudan, Niger, Togo, Nigeria, and Tanganyika are near the bottom, and Ethiopia is fairly clearly in last place.

A similar ranking constructed by William O. Jones and Christian Mérat for 1953–57 portrays the relative well-being of African countries somewhat differently (*239*, pp. 35–60). The Jones-Mérat index is based on per capita imports of 18 items in only 10 countries; it places Ghana first, followed by Ivory Coast; Sierra Leone; Senegal, Mali, and Mauritania; Cameroun; Uganda; the Congo (Leopoldville) and Rwanda-Burundi; Liberia; Nigeria; and Guinea, in that order. If addition of Réunion, Mauritius, Zambia, Rhodesia, and Ethiopia to the Jones-Mérat ranking would place the first three of these above Ghana, and Ethiopia at the bottom — as nonquantitative information suggests is likely — the relative position of countries in the two rankings is roughly the same, except for a reversal of the positions of Liberia and Sierra Leone.

Data on the general characteristics of tropical African economies are somewhat better — but far from as good as one would like. They too suggest that tropical Africa is a land of striking diversity, as will be seen in the next chapter.

3

GENERAL CHARACTER OF THE
TROPICAL AFRICAN ECONOMIES

IT IS fashionable to analyze underdeveloped countries in terms of a "money economy" and a "subsistence economy"; but if taken literally, these terms can be seriously misleading. Sharp differences are indeed to be found between the organization and techniques of production of small African producers and those of enterprises owned and directed by non-Africans, such as mines and plantations. But while most rural African households produce some of the goods they consume, there is great variation in the extent to which they rely on their own production.

Large and busy markets in which money was used were found in many parts of tropical Africa by the first European explorers, and evidence suggests that nonmarket trade was of considerable importance in some if not all of the areas lacking markets.[1] A more useful classification therefore is the following based on the organization of economic activity and techniques of production: (1) mines and plantations; (2) European settlers; (3) African farmers; (4) government.

African farmers and the government sector are found throughout tropical African economies; mines or plantations are found in most tropical African countries but, as Table 3-1 suggests, vary considerably in importance. European settlers are found mainly in Kenya, Tanganyika, Portuguese Africa, Malagasy, and the former Federation of Rhodesia and Nyasaland (Table 3-2).[2] The main flows among these sectors are as follows: the mines buy labor, and food to feed it, from the African agricultural sector, food from European settlers, and manufactures from developed economies; they sell industrial raw materials to developed economies. The European settlers buy labor from the African sector and manufactures from developed economies; they sell food to the mining sector and export crops (sometimes part of them as foodstuffs), mainly

29

TABLE 3-1 — MINERAL EXPORTS OF SELECTED TROPICAL
AFRICAN COUNTRIES

Country	Exports from mining 1955–59 (% of total exports by value)	Mining as % of national income	Year
Former Fed. of Rhodesia and Nyasaland	67.7	14	1958
Belgian Congo and Ruanda-Urundi	52.9	16	1958
Sierra Leone	42.2[a]	. . .	1958
Ghana	17.3	4	1958
Liberia	13.2	. . .	
Cameroun	. . .	3	1958
Angola	12.6	. . .	
Nigeria	6.0	1	1958
French Equatorial Africa	3.4[a]	. . .	
Kenya, Uganda, Tanganyika	2.5[a]	. . .	
French West Africa	0	. . .	
Sudan	0	0	1958–59
Ethiopia	0	0	1959
Somalia	0	. . .	
Madagascar	0	. . .	
Mozambique	0	. . .	

Data from UN, *Economic Bulletin for Africa*, Vol. 1, No. 1 (Jan. 1961), App. Table 4, Vol. 2, No. 2 (June 1962), 12; and UN, *Economic Survey of Africa since 1950* (New York, 1959), pp. 167–70.

[a] 1950–57.

to developed countries. The African sector sells both food and labor to the mines and plantations, and labor to European settlers; it buys manufactures from developed economies. The government buys food from both the settler and African sectors, and labor from the latter; it sells services to both these sectors and mining. Important in regulating these flows among sectors are merchants (in eastern and central tropical Africa mainly Asians) who act as middlemen, buying manufactures from developed countries and selling them to the African sector, and sometimes buying African export crops for sale overseas.

The organization of these sectors is vastly different, as might be expected. In the first two, foreign entrepreneurs have combined relatively large amounts of foreign capital with locally available factors; the scale of operation is relatively large; technology is similar to that of like industries in developed countries, and productivity is vastly greater than in the African sector. (Some of the European settlers in Portuguese Africa

TABLE 3-2 — AFRICAN AND NON-AFRICAN POPULATIONS OF TROPICAL AFRICA

Country	Year	% non-African	% of total population				
			Rural		Urban		
			African	Non-African	African		Non-African
Kenya	1957	4.2	...	1.3	...		2.9a
Former Fed. of Rhodesia and Nyasaland	1956	3.8	90.7	1.1	5.5b		2.7b
Angola	1950	1.9	...	...		6.1c	
Tanganyika	1957	1.6	95.9	0.6	2.5d		1.0d
Madagascar	1956	1.5	92.9	0.8	5.6e		0.7e
Uganda	1957	1.3	...	0.6	...		0.7f
Mozambique	1950	0.8	...	...		2.8c	
Belgian Congo	1951	0.6	...	...		8.0c	
French Cameroons	1957	0.5	94.0	0.2	5.5g		0.3g
French Equatorial Africa	1956	0.5	95.1	0.2	4.4h		0.3h
French West Africa	1956	0.4	95.4	0.1	4.1i		0.3i
Togo	1956	0.1	96.2	0.0	3.7j		0.1j
Zanzibar	1950	0.1	...	...		17.0c	
Nigeria	1952	0.0	95.0	0.0	5.0k		0.0k

Data from UN, *Economic Survey of Africa since 1950* (New York, 1959), p. 14; and UN, *Demographic Yearbook, 1951* (New York, 1951), pp. 145 and 146.

[a] Urban population of Nairobi, Mombasa, Nakuru, Kisumu, Eldoret, Kitale, Lamu, Nanyuki, and Malindi.

[b] Urban population of "twenty cities and towns."

[c] Population of towns with 5,000 or more inhabitants; no breakdown between African and non-African is given.

[d] Urban population of Dar es Salaam, Tanga, Tabora, Mwanza, Dodoma, Lindi, Moshi, Arusha, Morogoro, Mikindani, Mtwara, Mbeya, and Iringa.

[e] Urban population of Tananarive, Majunga, Tamatave, and Diégo-Suarez.

[f] Urban population of Kampala, Jinja, and Entebbe.

[g] Urban population of Douala, and Yaoundé.

[h] Urban population of Brazzaville, Bangui, Fort Lamy, and Pointe-Noire.

[i] Urban population of Dakar, Saint-Louis, Bamako, Conakry, Abidjan, and towns of 15,000 or more inhabitants.

[j] Urban population of Lomé.

[k] Urban population of Kano, Ibadan, Ile Ifé, Iwo, Lagos, Ogbomosho, and Oshogbo.

31

and the Malagasy Republic are exceptions to this since they use agricultural methods little superior to those of Africans.)

The African sector is composed of a large number of segments — the rural economies [3] — which sometimes differ considerably, and may or may not be closely linked. In Zambia and the Congo Basin, in which over 200 ethnic groups are found, each segment tends to have considerably stronger ties with non-African sectors of the national economy than with other segments within the African sector; but in much of western tropical Africa — Ghana, Dahomey, Togo, and Nigeria, for example — ethnic segments are strongly linked.

MANUFACTURING

Very little industry is found in tropical Africa, only a little light manufacturing here and there. Rarely does manufacturing contribute more than 5 percent to Gross Domestic Product,[4] and it is not over 12 percent for any of the tropical African countries for which national income estimates have been constructed (*439*, p. 12).

Appendix Table 3 gives the composition of manufacturing in all of these countries except Nigeria and Uganda.

Country	Year	Manufacturing as % of Gross Domestic Product
Former Fed. of Rhodesia and Nyasaland	1958	12
Kenya	1958	10
Congo (Leopoldville)	1958	10
Cameroun	1956	5[a]
Uganda	1956/57	4
Tanganyika	1958	4
Ghana	1958	3
Sudan	1958/59	2[b]
Nigeria	1958	2
Guinea	1956	2
Ethiopia	1959	2

[a] Includes handicrafts.
[b] Includes public utilities.

URBANIZATION

Tropical Africa is sometimes described as the "most unurbanized part of the earth" (*250*, p. 97). Yet there are a number of sizable, and economically very important, population concentrations; and the percentage of population residing in urban areas varies considerably (Table 3-3).

TABLE 3-3 — PERCENTAGE OF POPULATION LIVING IN URBAN
AREAS IN TROPICAL AFRICA

| | | % of population in | | |
Country	Year	All urban areas[a]	Urban areas of 20,000 or more	Urban areas of 100,000 or more
Gambia	1951	71.8	—	—
Mauritius	1952	34.9	—	—
Senegal	1956	22.9	10.1	9.9
Zanzibar and Pemba	1948	20.0	17.1	—
Northern Rhodesia	1951	18.4	...	...
Nigeria	1952–53	17.5	11.4	4.1
Ghana	1948	14.3	5.0	3.3
Mozambique	1954	13.9	13.9	6.6
Southern Rhodesia	1951	12.8	...	...
Ivory Coast	1956	11.1	6.8	5.1
Congo (Leopoldville)	1957	9.8	7.1	2.2
Togo	1958	9.6	4.5	—
São Tomé and Príncipe	1950	9.3	...	...
Sudan	1955–56	8.3	4.5	2.4[b]
Angola	1955	7.4	6.0	4.4
Dahomey	1955	7.1	5.5	—
Guinea	1955	6.5	5.1	—
French Cameroons	1951	5.8	...	...
French Equatorial Africa	1951	5.3	...	...
Mali	1956	5.1	1.8	—
Kenya	1948	5.0	3.8	2.2[c]
Spanish Guinea and Fernando Po	1950	4.8	...	...
Sierra Leone	1948	4.8	...	...
Mauritania	1956	4.5	1.4	—
Upper Volta	1956	4.0	2.3	1.3
Tanganyika	1957	3.3	1.9	1.5
Niger	1956	2.7	—	—
Nyasaland	1950	1.6	...	...
Portuguese Guinea	1950	1.4	...	...
Liberia	1949	1.2	...	...
Uganda	1948	0.8	...	...
Ruanda-Urundi	1949	0.7	...	...

Data from UN, *Demographic Yearbook, 1951* (New York, 1951), pp. 145–46; and UN, *Economic Bulletin for Africa*, 2, No. 2 (June 1962), 63.

[a] Areas defined as "urban" in national statistics; criteria used tend to vary from country to country.

[b] Khartoum, Khartoum North, and Omdurman taken as a single unit.

[c] Population of Nairobi only; in 1957 Nairobi had 4.2% of Kenya's population.

33

In the small country of Gambia an estimated 72 percent of the population was urban (1951), whereas for Ruanda-Urundi the figure was less than 1 percent (1949). Many of these population concentrations are about as different from their hinterlands as the hinterlands are from the rural areas of relatively developed countries. In some instances — in western Nigeria, for example, the most heavily urbanized area in tropical Africa, and a region with large cities long before colonial rule — African cities appear to be little more than enormous villages.

Several tropical African cities are growing extremely rapidly. Nine of the national capitals registered gains of over 300 percent between the decade of the 1930's and that of the 1950's; for Lusaka, Salisbury, Fort Lamy, Bangui, Brazzaville, Leopoldville, and Abidjan the increase over that period was over 400 percent. Only a few major cities witnessed less than a 100 percent increase during the same period (Table 3-4). Most of the major cities appear to continue to grow rapidly. Between the early 1950's and 1960's a majority of them grew by at least 50 percent (Table 3-4).

Throughout tropical Africa urban populations are highly mobile. In

TABLE 3-4 — PREWAR AND POSTWAR POPULATION OF SELECTED
TROPICAL AFRICAN CITIES
(1,000 persons)

City	Country or Territory	Prewar[a]	Early 1950's[a]	% increase, prewar to early 1950's	About 1960	% increase, early 1950's to about 1960
Lusaka	Northern Rhodesia	2 (1931)	33 (1956)[b]	1,550	78 (1959)[b]	136
Abidjan	Ivory Coast	10 (1931)	128 (1955)[b]	1,180	180 (1960)[b]	41
Leopoldville	Congo (Leopoldville)	36 (1938)	300 (1955)	735	402 (1959)	34
Fort Lamy	Chad	7 (1936)	44 (1955)[b]	528	88 (1962)[b]	100
Bangui	Central African Republic	14 (1937)	85 (1957)	507	80 (1959)	—6
Salisbury	Southern Rhodesia	33 (1936)	168 (1956)[b]	409	271 (1959)[b]	61
Luanda	Angola	40 (1934)	190 (1955)[b]	375	225 (1960)[b]	89
Douala	Cameroun	28 (1931)	119 (1956)[b]	325	128 (1962)[b]	8
Monrovia	Liberia	10 (1938)	41 (1956)	310	...	...
Stanleyville	Congo (Leopoldville)	10 (1938)	40 (1951)	300	127 (1959)	218

TABLE 3-4 — CONTINUED

Conakry	Guinea	7 (1931)	27 (1955)[b]	286	78 (1960)[b]	188
Bamako	Mali	20 (1931)	68 (1955)[b]	240	120 (1960)[b]	76
Nairobi	Kenya	65 (1939)	210 (1956)	223	267 (1962)	36
Dar es Salaam	Tanganyika	34 (1937)	99 (1952)	191	...	...
Addis Ababa	Ethiopia	150 (1939)	431 (1956)	187	444 (1961)	3
Lagos	Nigeria	126 (1931)	312 (1956)	148	394 (1962)	31
Brazzaville	Congo (Brazzaville)	40 (1937)	99 (1957)[b]	148	128 (1961)[b]	68
Dakar	Senegal	93 (1936)	231 (1955)[b]	148	374 (1960)[b]	62
Mogadiscio	Somalia	30 (1931)	73 (1955)	143	91 (1959)	25
Accra	Ghana	70 (1931)	165 (1954)	136	388 (1960)[b]	135
Khartoum	Sudan	45 (1938)	93 (1956)	107	131 (1962)	42
Yaoundé	Cameroun	20 (1936)	38 (1955)	90	80 (1962)	111
Kumasi	Ghana	36 (1931)	65 (1955)	81	180 (1960)[b]	122
Tananarive	Malagasy	127 (1936)	190 (1955)	50	248 (1961)	30
Kano	Nigeria	89 (1931)	130 (1952)	46	...	...
Lourenço Marques	Mozambique	68 (1940)	99 (1956)[b]	46	184 (1960)[b]	86
Port Louis	Mauritius	54 (1931)	76 (1955)	41	91 (1961)	20
Freetown	Sierra Leone	55 (1931)	77 (1956)	40	100 (1959)	30
Porto-Novo	Dahomey	24 (1936)	32 (1957)	33	65 (1961)	103
Ibadan	Nigeria	387 (1931)	459 (1952)	19	...	...
Omdurman	Sudan	111 (1938)	116 (1956)	4	162 (1962)	40
Ouagadougou	Upper Volta	...	32 (1955)[b]	...	59 (1961)[b]	84

Most of the data are from UN, *Demographic Yearbook 1957* (New York, 1957), pp. 150–51; *ibid.* (1962), pp. 316–20; and Walter Yust, ed., *Encyclopedia Britannica World Atlas* (Chicago, 1949), pp. 182–211. There are the following exceptions: Bamako, Conakry, and Douala from Ministère de la France d'Outre-mer, *Inventaire social et économique des territoires d'outre-mer 1950 à 1955* (1957), p. 27, cited in B. F. Johnston, "Changes in Agricultural Productivity and Patterns of Productivity in Tropical Africa" (unpublished manuscript, 1961). Stanleyville 1951 data from V. G. Pons, "The Growth of Stanleyville and the Composition of Its African Population," in UNESCO, *Social Implications of Industrialiaztion and Urbanization in Africa South of the Sahara* (Paris, 1956).

[a] Figures in parentheses are the year of census or estimate.

[b] Urban agglomeration.

many urban centers a fairly large portion of the population is made up of migrant laborers, and almost all urban Africans have rural kinsmen to whom they can return if they wish. Polygyny is less prevalent in urban areas than in villages but is nevertheless not uncommon. Not infrequently, urban men have wives both in an urban area and in a village in the hinterland, a practice that is encouraged by African systems of land tenure (see Chapter 4).

LABOR MIGRATION

It is impossible to measure accurately, at present, the proportion of the labor force that is migratory; but it is often estimated that over half the wage earners are migratory, although the proportion varies considerably from country to country. Elliot Berg, using the skill composition of the labor force as a guide to the degree of commitment to wage earning, argues that between half and three-fourths of the wage earners of West Africa are migratory (52, p. 472 and 51, p. 198); he cites an investigation in Kenya which concluded that one-half the wage earners there were migratory in 1953. Recorded movement of laborers in 1956 shows 41 percent of the wage earners in Southern Rhodesia to be from other countries: and the total of Rhodesian workers not permanently committed to wage labor must be considerably greater if one counts workers temporarily in towns and mines (438, p. 47). (Appendix Table 4 shows recorded labor migration in southern and eastern Africa about 1956.)

Wage labor appears to occupy no more than 12 percent of the population in any of the countries for which data are available, if published estimates are not grossly in error; and its distribution by industry appears to vary greatly (439, p. 71).

Country	Year	% of wage earners in total population	% of wage earners employed in	
			Agri- culture	Mining and manu- facturing
Uganda	1956	11.6	27.5	13.4
Kenya	1956	9.7	39.4	11.2
Congo (Leopoldville)	1956	9.2	25.1	19.8
Malagasy	1955	5.2	39.1	11.9
Ghana	1954	5.1	13.9	21.1
Cameroun	1955	4.6	27.8	9.0
Former Fed. of Rhodesia and Nyasaland	1956	3.5	34.5	20.9
French Equatorial Africa	1955	3.3	25.8	22.3

Ruanda-Urundi	1956	2.8	20.7	21.1
Tanganyika	1955	2.4	48.7	8.1
Togo	1955	2.3	10.6	2.0
French West				
Africa	1955	2.0	19.8	11.4
Nigeria[a]	1953	1.1	16.6	20.4

[a] Excluding undertakings with less than 10 employees.

EXTERNAL TRADE

Africa supplies over half the world's diamonds, columbium, cobalt, and gold, and a large share of its platinum, chromite, phosphate rock, antimony, and copper (Table 3-5). The tropical portion of the continent ac-

TABLE 3-5 — PRODUCTION OF MINERALS, 1955–57 AVERAGE

Minerals	African production (% of world)	Tropical African production (% of African exports)
Industrial diamonds	99.9	91
Gem diamonds	78.8	51
Columbium	75.5	100
Cobalt (Co content)	67.0	94
Gold	62.7	10
Platinum	47.8	0
Chromite (Cr_2O_3 content)	35.0	47
Phosphate rock	34.0	0
Antimony (Sb content)	30.8	1
Copper (Cu content)	23.9	90
Manganese (Mn content)	21.8	50
Asbestos	19.6	52
Tin concentrates (Sn content)	14.9	95
Lead ore (Pb content)	11.5	10
Zinc ore	8.9	55
Vanadium ore (V content)	8.7	0
Tungsten (WO_3 content)	5.6	83
Silver	4.3	51
Iron ore (Fe content)	3.7	37
Bauxite (crude ore)	3.5	100

Data from or derived from UN, *Economic Survey of Africa since 1950* (New York, 1959), pp. 33–34.

counts for a large proportion of African production of these, with the exception of gold, platinum, phosphate rock, and antimony. Smaller but notable amounts of asbestos, tin, zinc, tungsten, silver, and bauxite are also mined in the region, and sometimes locally are of considerable importance. Data on uranium production are not available, but tropical Africa is probably one of the important producers. It also supplies more than half the sisal, cocoa, and palm oil moving in world trade (Table 3-6), and produces a small share of the world's coffee, cotton, rubber, and tea.

External trade is principally with overseas countries. Trade with other African countries is relatively small, except for Zambia, Rhodesia, and Malawi, where imports from the Union of South Africa account for a sizable percent of total external trade. Of the tropical African countries supplying statistics on external trade the percentage of total trade with other African countries was the following for the 1950–57 period (*438*, p. 152):

Country	Trade with African countries as % of total external trade	Imports from African countries as % of total imports	Exports to African countries as % of total exports
Angola	4.7	2.0	7.0
Belgian Congo and Ruanda-Urundi	6.1	7.7	4.6
French Cameroons	3.6	3.7	3.5
Ethiopia	4.8	5.1	4.5
Former French Equatorial Africa	9.7	8.7	11.3
Former French West Africa	10.4	8.7	12.6
Ghana	4.2	6.1	2.5
Kenya, Uganda, and Tanganyika	6.0	4.2	8.0
Madagascar	7.0	4.0	10.2
Mozambique	13.1	12.7	13.7
Nigeria	1.0	0.8	1.3
Former Fed. of Rhodesia and Nyasaland[a]	26.9	36.4	18.1

Sierra Leone	2.2	3.0	1.1
Sudan	13.2	15.3	11.2

a Includes trade between members of the federation prior to 1954.

As in many underdeveloped regions, tropical African countries are heavily dependent on exports of one or two commodities for their foreign exchange. As Table 3-7 indicates, all tropical African countries derive 40 percent or more of their export earnings from two commodities, and two-thirds are about equally dependent on a single commodity. If we had more detailed data so that the former countries of French West Africa,

TABLE 3-6 — TROPICAL AFRICAN EXPORTS OF SELECTED
NON-MINERAL COMMODITIES, 1955–57

Commodity	Tropical Africa % of world exports
Palm kernels	89.2
Cocoa	68.6
Palm oil	63.0
Peanuts	62.5
Palm-kernel oil	60.0
Sisal	58.5
Peanut oil	49.0
Coffee	21.8
Rubber	15.1
Bananas	11.5
Cotton	10.6
Tobacco	8.0
Copra	4.1
Maize	4.0
Tea	3.8
Sugar	1.9

Data derived from UN, *Economic Survey of Africa since 1950* (New York, 1959), pp. 21–24; and FAO, *Yearbook of Trade 1959* (Rome, 1960), *passim*.

French Equatorial Africa, British East Africa, and the Federation of Rhodesia and Nyasaland could be shown individually, the concentration of export earnings would be even higher.

Except for the Federation of Rhodesia and Nyasaland, the Belgian Congo, and Sierra Leone, the leading export is an agricultural commodity, although for Ghana, Liberia, and Angola, the second most important export is a mineral (Tables 3-7 and 3-8). Agricultural exports range from 8 to 30 percent of Gross Domestic Product in tropical African countries for which GDP estimates have been attempted (*439*, p. 10):

Country	Year	Agricultural exports as % of Gross Domestic Product
Ivory Coast	1958	30
Uganda	1956/59	29
Tanganyika	1958	21
Ghana	1958	18
Cameroun	1958	18
Congo (Leopoldville)	1958	15
Kenya	1958	13
Sudan	1958/59	13
Nigeria	1958	12
Guinea	1956	9
Ethiopia	1959	9
Former Fed. of Rhodesia and Nyasaland	1958	8

Except for some of the export crops, agricultural commodities are produced almost entirely by the rural economies, the subject of the next two chapters.

TABLE 3-7 — CONCENTRATION OF EXPORTS IN TROPICAL AFRICA

Country	% of total value of exports represented by leading commodity	% of total value of exports represented by first two commodities	Two most important exports
Mauritius (1956–57)	97.5	. . .	Sugar
Réunion (1956–57)	81.0	. . .	Sugar
Ghana (1954–55)[a]	79.5	84.9	Cocoa, manganese ore
São Tomé and Príncipe (1954–55)	75.9	85.1	Cocoa, copra
Gambia (1954)	73.2	88.2	Peanuts, crude materials

TABLE 3-7 — CONTINUED

Liberia (1953–55)	72.7	89.6	Rubber, iron ore
Zanzibar (1954–55)	68.3	74.6	Cloves, coconut oil
Somaliland (1953–55)	63.2	75.5	Fruits, hides
Former Fed. of Rhodesia and Nyasaland (1954–55)	62.9	78.9	Copper, tobacco
Sudan (1953–55)	60.2	70.0	Cotton, gum arabic
Ethiopia and Eritrea (1953–55)	59.5	63.8	Coffee, goat skins
French Cameroons (1953–55)	52.4	67.0	Cocoa, coffee
Togo (1953–55)	49.6	66.5	Cocoa, coffee
Angola (1953–54)	49.6	60.4	Coffee, diamonds
Portuguese Guinea (1951)	49.4	75.4	Peanuts, coconuts
Bechuanaland (1957)	49.0	58.0	Meat, sorghum
Madagascar (1953–55)	44.9	52.3	Coffee, rice
British Somaliland (1953–54)	43.2	63.9	Sheep, sheepskins
Kenya-Uganda (1954–55)	37.6	67.8	Coffee, cotton
Comoro Islands (1953–55)	35.4	65.1	Vanilla, essential oils
French Equatorial Africa (1953–55)	35.4	58.8	Cotton, wood
Belgian Congo and Ruanda-Urundi (1953–55)	34.9	44.1	Copper, coffee
Mozambique (1953–54)	33.3	44.5	Cotton, copra
Sierra Leone (1953–55)	33.1	65.4	Iron ore, palm kernels
Tanganyika (1954–55)	29.5	53.4	Sisal, coffee
French West Africa (1953–54)	26.4	43.2	Coffee, peanuts
Nigeria (1954–55)	23.8	43.1	Cocoa, peanuts

Data from W. Goldschmidt, ed., *The United States and Africa* (New York, 1958), pp. 216–24; UN, *Economic Bulletin for Africa*, 1, No. 1 (Jan. 1961), 41; and G. H. T. Kimble, *Tropical Africa* (New York, 1960), 1:504.

[a] Includes British Togo.

TABLE 3-8 — MINERAL EXPORTS OF SELECTED TROPICAL AFRICAN COUNTRIES

Country	Exports from mining, 1955–59, as % of total exports by value	Mining as % of national income	Year
Former Fed. of Rhodesia and Nyasaland	67.7	14	1958
Belgian Congo and Ruanda-Urundi	52.9	16	1958

TABLE 3-8 — CONTINUED

Country	Exports from mining, 1955–59 % of total exports by value	Mining as % of national income	Year
Sierra Leone	42.2a	. . .	
Ghana	17.3	4	1958
Liberia	13.2a	. . .	
French Cameroons	. . .	3	1958
Angola	12.6	. . .	
Nigeria	6.0	1	1958
Former French Equatorial Africa	3.4a	. . .	
Kenya, Uganda, Tanganyika	2.5a	. . .	
Former French West Africa	0.0	. . .	
Sudan	0.0	0.0	1958–59
Ethiopia	0.0	0.0	1959
Somalia	0.0	. . .	
Madagascar	0.0	. . .	
Mozambique	0.0	. . .	

Data from UN, *Economic Bulletin for Africa*, Vol. 1, No. 1 (Jan. 1961), App. Table 4, and Vol. 2, No. 2 (June 1962), p. 12; and UN, *Economic Survey of Africa since 1950* (New York, 1959), pp. 167–70.

a 1950–57.

4

PRODUCTION IN THE RURAL ECONOMIES

H OW the scarce resources are used to satisfy needs in the rural economies of tropical Africa varies considerably. Almost everywhere the prime requirements for survival can be reduced to food. Temperatures are high enough in most of the region to make clothing and shelter not strictly necessary. Protection from the sun is provided by natural vegetation. In the limiting case, economic activity conceivably could consist of obtaining food and drink and deciding how they are to be distributed among the producer's family and associates.

All the rural economies for which we have data are, and probably have long been, more complex than this limiting case. Throughout tropical Africa food production has long exceeded needs enough for it to be possible to devote a good deal of energy to construction of dwellings, production of clothing and ornaments, art, and a variety of entertainments.

The major activities everywhere are production of food and drink, but there is great variation in the number and kind of products available, and in how they are derived. Some rural economies produce little for urban or international markets. Others are primarily concerned with producing commodities that can be sold to non-African sectors of national economies, or with exporting labor either to other rural economies (e.g. cocoa-producing areas) or, more typically, to mines, plantations, and European farms.

With the exception of sugar, tea, and sisal, all of tropical Africa's agricultural exports are of major importance to rural economies in one part of Africa or another as "cash" crops, and in addition many rural economies sell a number of foodstuffs to the non-African economic units.

Foodstuffs, whether for local consumption or export, come principally from agriculture. Hunting and collecting, although still present in almost every rural economy, are typically less important than agriculture, and

43

very few of the rural economies rely entirely on hunting and gathering. Some of the small ethnic groups on the middle of the Congo River produce only fish and exchange them for all other commodities they need; but groups that rely largely on hunting, fishing, and gathering often grow some crops.

No rural economy is devoted exclusively to livestock production, although some of the nomadic ethnic groups on the fringes of the Sahara and Kalahari deserts produce little else. Many other groups keep little livestock, not infrequently because the tsetse fly transmits trypanosomiasis, a form of sleeping sickness, to them.

Almost 80 percent of the tropical African countries for which data are available reported less than one head of cattle per capita for 1954–56, and for 54 percent of the countries the ratio was less than half as high (Table 4-1). The range was from 3.52 animals per person in Bechuanaland to 0.06 in Sierra Leone. Goat populations were relatively larger for some of the countries with heavy rainfall, but still were typically less than 0.5 goats per capita; and sheep populations were usually even smaller (Table 4-1).

Fishing is not of major importance as an economic activity in any national economy of tropical Africa, although in some countries — around lakes Victoria, Tanganyika, and Nyasa, for example — it is regionally of considerable importance. Data on the value of fishing are not available, but as Table 4-2 suggests, the size of the annual catch varies greatly from country to country. In 1955 and 1956 the average annual catch was only 800 metric tons in Liberia, while in Angola in 1955–57 the average yield was 368,800 metric tons.

The character of fishing varies considerably, too. French Equatorial Africa and the Belgian Congo both had relatively large freshwater catches, whereas 10 of the countries in Table 4-2 reported no freshwater catch.

Data on the value of production in the rural economies are not abundant enough to rank the major types of economic activity, but the importance of agriculture in food production for local consumption can be seen in results of food consumption surveys. Rarely is the contribution of staple food crops less than 70 percent of total caloric intake, and typically the figure is over 80 percent.[1]

The dominant foodstuffs, those contributing the bulk of the calories consumed, are cereals, roots, tubers, or starchy fruits — the starchy-staples, a group of starchy food commodities which are close substitutes. Chief among these [2] are the millets and sorghums, principally *Sorghum vulgare, Pennisetum* spp., and *Eleusine coracana; Digitaria,* spp.; maize,

TABLE 4-1 — LIVESTOCK IN SELECTED AFRICAN COUNTRIES,
AVERAGE 1954/55–1956/57

Country	Cattle per capita	Sheep per capita	Goats per capita	Trade in cattle, 1955–57	
				Exports (thousands)	Imports (thousands)
Bechuanaland	3.52[a]	0.47[a]	0.93[a]	...	...
Southern Rhodesia	1.28	0.10	0.16	...	...
Madagascar	1.24[a]	0.08[a]	0.10[a]	6.3	0.3[c]
Ethiopia	1.11[b]	0.91[b]	1.27[b]	9.3	—
Kenya	1.10	0.44	0.63	0.6	0.1
Former French Equatorial Africa	0.89[c]	0.94[c]		42.8	1.3
Tanganyika	0.82	0.32	0.48	4.4	—
Sudan	0.63[b]	0.63[b]	0.53[b]	53.4	1.6
Former Fed. of Rhodesia and Nyasaland	0.62	0.05	0.12	0.9	5.1
Uganda	0.57[b]	0.20[b]	0.48[b]	...	...
Former French West Africa	0.53[c]	1.06[c]		145.4	1.6[d]
Gambia	0.47[b]	0.21[b]	0.26[b]	...	...
Northern Rhodesia	0.46	0.01	0.05	...	...
French Cameroons	0.39[b]	0.15[b]	0.31[b]	2.9[e]	0.1[f]
Angola	0.27[a]	0.03[a]	0.11[a]	0.1[d]	0.1
Ruanda-Urundi	0.21	0.11	0.33	...	...
Nigeria	0.20	...	...	3.3	109.9
French Somaliland	0.16[a]	1.24[a]	7.22[a]	...	...
Mozambique	0.14	0.01	0.06	0.5[e]	0.1[f]
Nyasaland	0.12	0.03	0.13	...	...
Togo	0.10[b]	0.26[b]	0.22[b]	1.2	0.1[f]
Belgian Congo	0.07	0.05	0.14	0.4	0.2
Mauritius	0.07	...	...	—	5.9
Sierra Leone	0.06	0.01	0.01	—	0.2
Réunion	...	...	...	—	0.9
British Somaliland	...	...	...	4.1	—
Zanzibar	...	...	...	—	4.5

Data from UN, *Economic Survey of Africa since 1950* (New York, 1959), pp. 27 and 28; population data are mainly for 1956.

[a] 1954/55.
[b] 1954/55–1955/56.
[c] 1955 and 1957.
[d] 1957.
[e] 1955 and 1956.
[f] 1955.

TABLE 4-2 — RECORDED FISH CATCH, 1955–57
(1,000 metric tons)

Country	Total	Fresh water	Marine
Angola	368.8	—	368.8
Former French Equatorial Africa	100.0[a]	100.0[a]	—
Belgian Congo	99.2	96.5	2.7
Former French West Africa	62.4	—	62.4
Tanganyika	54.1	49.1	5.0
French Cameroons	45.8	38.0	7.8
Uganda	42.5	42.5	—
Ghana	20.0	—	20.0
Ethiopia	18.1[b]	—	18.1[b]
Italian Somaliland	13.3[a]	—	13.3[a]
Kenya	12.9	8.7	4.2
Sudan	12.3	11.3	1.0
Former Fed. of Rhodesia and Nyasaland	9.3[a]	9.3[a]	—
Zanzibar and Pemba	8.8	—	8.8
Ruanda-Urundi	6.8	6.8	—
Sierra Leone	5.0[c]	—	5.0[c]
Mozambique	3.3[b]	—	3.3[b]
Mauritius	1.7	—	1.7
Réunion	0.8	—	0.8
Liberia	0.8[a]	—	0.8[a]

Data from UN, *Economic Survey of Africa since 1950* (New York, 1959), p. 30.
[a] 1955–56.
[b] 1955.
[c] Includes British Togoland.

Zea mays; rice, *Oryza sativa* and *O. glaberrima*; wheat, *Triticum vulgare;* manioc (or cassava), *Manihot utilissima;* yams, *Dioscorea* spp.; taro (or cocoyams), *Colcasia* spp., malanga (also called cocoyams), and *Xanthosoma sagittifolium*; sweet potatoes, *Ipomoea batatas;* and bananas and plantains, principally *Musa sapentium* and *M. paradisiaca*. The preeminence of these starchy crops in diets is not surprising; the same phenomenon is observed in nearly all, if not all, of the low income countries the world over (*50*, p. 218). The reason is economic: in the production of the starchy-staples less land and labor per thousand calories are required than for animal products, vegetables, or fruits.

In most of the driest areas the starchy-staple is a millet or sorghum; in the wetter zones manioc, rice, banana-plantain, taro, sweet potatoes, or yams may be important. Both maize and manioc are found fairly widely, and maize assumes its greatest importance in the moderately moist zones between the extremes of rainfall.

No matter which starchy-staple, or combination of starchy-staples, rules in any particular area, the principal product made is a bland cooked doughy paste or mush that is broken into chunks with the fingers and dipped into a tasty stew or relish of such things as meat, fish, insects, and vegetables.

Studies by colonial research officers in both the French and Belgian Congo suggest that fish are the leading source of protein there, followed by meat from wild game, with insects — mostly caterpillars and termites — in third place, and domestic livestock last (see *298*). Detailed data are not available for areas of similar size elsewhere, but fishing is clearly a major source of protein in most areas; while in many the importance of wild game is considerably less, and that of domestic livestock greater, than in the Congo Basin. Although consumption of insects is reported widely, it is not clear whether they are generally a significant part of the diet.

A good portion of the production of starchy-staple foodstuffs is converted into alcoholic drinks that range from very weak beers to distilled beverages. Alcoholic beverages are also made from the sap of palm trees, from sugarcane, from honey, and in a few areas from such exotic sources as bamboo sap and cashew fruit.

After food, the major categories of consumption goods are clothing and shelter. Huts with mud, wattle, or thatched walls and thatched roofs are found everywhere; they may be elaborate affairs which are maintained a generation or more, or hastily built structures used only a year or two. Traditionally, bark cloth trees and raffia palms were cultivated in many areas to provide raw materials for clothing or fabric. Cloth was also sometimes made on local looms or obtained in trade. Now imported cloth dominates in most, if not all, areas.

TRADITIONAL PROPERTY RIGHTS

Before examining production techniques, it is helpful to consider the general system of traditional property rights and obligations. Knowledge of these is still relevant, for although the social change that followed colonial rule has, in some instances, markedly altered the traditional system, much of it still remains in the rural economies.

Traditional property rights differ greatly in detail, but communal ownership of the land used to be found everywhere. Individuals were given use of the land by the chief, a group of elders, or some similar authority,

and were entitled to whatever it yielded. Once a plot was left uncultivated, it was usually available for reallocation. (In a few areas — parts of
the Ivory Coast, Dahomey, Zambia, and Kenya, for example — land
is now beginning to be bought by African farmers. In parts of Uganda
individual ownership of land by Africans dates from the turn of the century.) Trees, unlike land, were often owned by individuals and usually
could be inherited, even though the land on which they grew could not be.
Livestock and objects of manufacture were likewise generally private
property.

Precolonial governments were maintained by tribute, sometimes a
portion of the yield of each type of economic activity. Thus a pot of beer
from each brew, one of the tusks from a slain elephant, or a few baskets
of grain from each harvest might be given the chief or some village authority, or both. Sometimes labor was supplied for the chief's enterprises. Although tribute not infrequently was forced on the commoners,
in some instances there was a feeling of mutual obligation — obligation
to support the governing authorities, and expectation that the prevailing
government would provide protection and assistance when needed. In
some societies individuals shared a general obligation to supply communal labor for maintaining roads and paths, or for similar tasks.

Most, if not all, rural economies traditionally had slavery, although it
was not necessarily a major institution. In some instances slavery and the
slave trade were of great importance, but in others slaves were few and
of little significance. Slaves were usually captured or bought, though in
some instances individuals enslaved themselves to pay debts.

Within the household, rights and obligations were generally well defined. In polygynous families each wife usually had her own hut, her own
allocation of land to work, and obligations to contribute to feeding and
clothing her husband. However, wealth remaining after such obligations
were met was commonly her own. In many areas this sort of arrangement is still found and sometimes gives rise to sale of commodities or loan
of money by wives to their husband, who, because of business ventures,
requires more than is due him under marriage obligations.

Both husband and wife have extensive obligations to care for any kinsmen in need, and sometimes special obligations to particular kinsmen.
For example, in some ethnic groups maternal uncles are responsible for
helping men obtain whatever training and capital they need upon reaching manhood.

All individuals in the rural economies are generally obligated to respect the property of others and to honor agreements. Disagreements

can usually be dealt with by traditional courts. Cases that are won are typically settled by payment of damages by the defendant to the plaintiff.

THE ORGANIZATION OF PRODUCTION

Such activities as smelting, iron working, weaving, and pot making were often done by specialists; and in some of the economies of which we have record, production was traditionally highly specialized. In the Lozi area of the Zambezi Valley, for instance, not only were warriors, smelters, weavers, and other craftsmen specialists, but there was specialization in the production of all the major crops. In the old Cazembe kingdom, located in or somewhere near what is now lower Katanga, each clan was assigned to different work. Viscount Mountmorres, who toured parts of the Congo Basin in 1904 to investigate allegations of maladministration of the Congo Free State, says of the Bonjo on the Ubangi River (*308*, pp. 18–19):

> Their towns are all divided into three sections devoted respectively to the warriors; the manufacturers; and the food producers. This last class is, on the river, composed of the fisher folk; inland, it consists of the agriculturalists. There is little or no admixture betwen the castes . . . . In any given town the castes of necessity trade with one another — the fisherman or the farmer buying his canoe or his hoe from the manufacturer in return for foodstuffs, and the warrior levying on both in return for the protection he affords the community . . . the fisherman on the river can effect an exchange with the farmer inland, but cannot deal direct with the smith or cloth-beater of any town but his own.

Descriptions of western Nigerian towns by early travelers suggest that production has long been fairly highly specialized there, and almost certainly other examples exist of which there is no record or which we have missed.

In some instances there is clearly much less specialization that the above examples suggest. Nevertheless considerable specialization is found in most of the rural economies of Tropical Africa.

In every ethnic group a strict sex division of labor is found. Some activities that are considered men's work in one group are women's work elsewhere; but generally men hunt and fish, clear the land, build huts and canoes, and care for livestock, while the women carry out agricultural operations once the field is cleared, carry water, process foodstuffs, cook, and brew. Neither sex dares do tasks assigned the other for fear of open ridicule.

Some tasks, such as hut building, hoeing, harvesting, fishing, and hunting, may be done communally. Labor is hired in some instances, and may also be enlisted by promise to pay in food commodities or with beer. Use of beer to pay for labor is usually through a beer work party: an individual with work to do announces a beer party for all those who will first help him with a particular task.

TECHNIQUES OF PRODUCTION

Techniques of production are crude even when compared with a number of underdeveloped countries elsewhere. As a rule, little or no mechanization is found. Forest or grassland is cleared with fire, ax, and knife. Hoes and knives are used in tillage and harvest operations, and pestle and mortar or grindstones operated by hand are the most common tools in postharvest tasks.

The major forms of investment, beyond hoes and other simple tools, are grain-grinding mills, bicycles, goats, chickens, and tree crops. Where cattle are of some importance ox-drawn equipment may be used, but in general beasts of burden are not known; transportation is almost entirely by foot or bicycle in most areas, although villages near roads, rivers, and lakes also have use of motor vehicles or canoes. A few tractors are to be found in some of the more prosperous areas, of which portions of Uganda and Zambia are conspicuous examples. In most areas wives are also a form of investment, for they can be obtained only if the wife's kinsmen are given a sizable gift (often called "bride price"), and taking a wife increases the household's labor supply and its rights to land, hence its production.

Agricultural Methods

In most of tropical Africa the method of growing crops can be described as unirrigated hoe culture. Only in the Malagasy Republic is more than 18 percent of all arable land irrigated, and the portion irrigated by African farmers would be much less yet, in most areas (143, 1961, pp. 7–9):

Country	% of total arable land and permanent crops irrigated about 1960
Malagasy Republic	51
Somaliland	18
Zanzibar	13
Sudan	11
Réunion	4
Kenya	2

Mauritius	2
Bechuanaland	1
Southern Rhodesia	1

Plowing is common only in the Malagasy Republic, Ethiopia, Somaliland, and relatively small areas elsewhere, e.g. in parts of Zambia, Rhodesia, Uganda, Kenya, and Tanganyika.

Almost everywhere in tropical Africa methods of growing crops are variants of "shifting cultivation" or "slash-and-burn agriculture," general terms commonly applied to agricultural systems based on cultivating land only a few years, then returning it to natural vegetation for several years — usually more than twice as long as it is cropped, and not infrequently much longer — in order to restore soil fertility depleted by cropping. Under this system, some fields are cleared and some are abandoned each year.

Fields are made as near the homestead as possible,[3] but after a few years the only new land left may be quite a walk from the hearth. Unless some other consideration such as superstition or fear of sorcery prompts a move sooner, the homesite is deserted when the distance to the field has become intolerable; a new homesite nearer uncleared land is chosen. Land around the old homestead, especially plots that have been enriched by accumulations of household wastes, may continue to be cultivated for several seasons. Not all ethnic groups in tropical Africa shift their homesites, but all shift fields from crops for a short period to bush or grass fallow for a long period. How frequently the homesite is shifted depends on the fertility of the soil, the crops grown, the production techniques employed, and the density of population. In Rwanda and Burundi and parts of Nigeria, for example, homesites are not shifted; the Bemba and Lala of Zambia were moving their homesteads every five years or so in the 1930's; and the Azande of the southern Sudan shifted their homesites every ten years, roughly, in the 1950's.

Field production is supplemented by gardens in which cultivation is more intensive and the soil is usually not rested until the homesite is shifted; gardens that are rested are usually given only a short fallow. Garden plots near the homesite usually receive household refuse and sometimes compost or animal manures. Other gardens may be made at a distance in relatively fertile valleys.

Information is not available on the agricultural techniques of a number of tropical African ethnic groups, but enough is known to demonstrate that terms like "slash-and-burn agriculture" suggest a uniformity of agricultural techniques unsupported by fact. In the Congo Basin alone at least 18 different methods are used to prepare uncleared land for crops (see *298*). All of these techniques employ fire either to help remove vegetation so there will be room for crops, or to reduce vegetation to ash, which is everywhere employed as a fertilizer. Hatchets or fire are used to kill or fell undesirable trees, while useful trees, such as the oil palm and trees which bear edible fruit, are left standing. Large trees or trees of exceptionally hard wood are usually killed by ringing with a band cut in the bark, or they may be killed by burning debris piled around their trunks. Small trees, bushes, and vines may be cut with either a long-bladed knife or a hatchet. Hoes, long-bladed knives, or fire are used to remove grass. Once the soil cover has been reduced to manageable proportions, the soil may be hoed or, in a few areas, plowed, but not infrequently crops are planted without working the soil.

In general, a number of crops are grown together because of the need to keep the soil covered at all times to prevent erosion, because of differences in the timing of labor requirements, in order to stagger harvesting and thereby reduce the amount of storage required, and undoubtedly for yet other reasons.

The combinations of crops grown together vary widely, as do the sequences of crop combinations followed. Most of the ethnic groups whose agricultural systems have been carefully studied have a set of rules they hand down from generation to generation which specifies the kind of soil each combination of crops should be grown on,[4] when planting should be done, and what sequence of crop associations should be followed.

Animal Husbandry

Where cattle are kept they are typically herded; pastures are usually burned when they become coarse, to make grazing easier; animals are given salt regularly; calves are often provided supplementary feed; and in some places quite a number of treatments are practiced for animal maladies. Sterilization of animals appears to be widely known and practiced. Animals kept for breeding purposes may be carefully chosen.

Cattle were traditionally kept for products that could be derived from their milk; for their blood (in some areas), drunk raw or cooked with other foodstuffs; and for their meat and hides. Drawing blood is rarely done now, and the main livestock product is butter, sometimes used mainly as a skin lubricant, and the curd jointly produced with it, which is eaten. Consumption of fresh milk appears not to be common.

Except for swine, small livestock seem generally to receive less care than cattle. Swine are not widely of any importance; when kept, they are often penned part of the time and fed. Goats, sheep, dogs,[5] and poultry are found almost everywhere. They are often given access to the owner's hut at night, or are provided with their own shelters; otherwise they receive little care.

Storage

The amount of foodstuffs stored appears to be sizable only outside the zone of wet forest, and the amount of storage probably increases with the length of the dry season. In the wet forest zone, which is a relatively small portion of tropical Africa, not only can crops with a relatively long harvest period, like plantains, yams, taro, sweet potatoes, be grown, but, because the dry season is short, planting can be extended over a much longer period, making is possible to extend the harvest period by staggering the planting of any particular crop. In addition, a larger number of staple crops can be raised, which gives scope for staggering the various crops.[6]

Five major types of storage techniques are found: storage in the farmer's hut, in granaries, in hermetically sealed pots, in pits, and in packages suspended in trees. When foodstuffs are stored in the farmer's hut, they are usually placed on a platform located over the hearth. Heat keeps their moisture content low, and insects are largely repelled by smoke. If granaries are built, they are usually raised off the ground so that small fires can be lit under them from time to time.

Processing Foodstuffs

The flour or meal needed for the staple dishes is produced by various methods. Plantains, manioc, and yams are peeled, sliced, and dried in the sun before the processing begins. Perhaps the most common of the processing methods is pounding the grain or dried chunks of roots or tubers or the plantain fruit in a fairly large wooden mortar with a pestle of heavy wood. Grain may also be ground between stones, by placing it on a large stone and grinding it with a smaller one. In a number of areas hand mills are now available, and villages near urban areas usually have access to motorized mills (231, chap. 8; and 32, p. 12).

Alcoholic beverages are made by widely varying methods. The simplest is that for making palm wine: some sap is drawn from a palm tree and allowed to sit a few hours. A great variety of beers is made from starchy foodstuffs; banana wine is drunk in several areas; and occasionally crude stills are used to produce stronger drinks.

5

DISTRIBUTION IN THE
RURAL ECONOMIES

THE first part of this chapter indicates some of the more important ways in which knowledge of trade and traders is relevant to an analysis of tropical Africa's problems. The remaining sections briefly summarize what is now known about the characteristics of trade and African traders within tropical Africa.

The "traders" discussed in this chapter are, in tropical Africa, called African traders — those belonging to one of the African ethnic groups. In numbers this category is by far the largest, although perhaps in some areas it does not yet dominate commerce. In terms of value, either Asians or Europeans possibly now control the largest share of trade in most, if not all, of Portuguese Africa, Zambia, Rhodesia, and Kenya, at least; but there is every indication that African nationalist groups will not tolerate this long. While non-African traders may have a significant role to play in solving tropical African problems in some areas, this is by no means certain, whereas there is almost no doubt that the part played by African traders will be of major significance in the years ahead.

What can be learned from the economic history of the relatively developed countries of Western Europe and North America suggests that traders were often largely responsible for accumulation of capital during periods of rapid economic development, and often led the way in replacing traditional techniques and forms of organization of production and distribution with more efficient ones. Evidence now available supports the hypothesis that this can be expected in tropical Africa.

Also relevant to problems of economic growth is the fact that data now available on the characteristics of African trade and traders greatly augment the growing evidence that, contrary to notions long prevalent, African response to economic incentives is normal. This is of considerable significance. It is of paramount importance in executing a development program to evoke from producers, consumers, savers, and investors responses which will favor rapid and continuous economic development. Particularly because of the scarcity of capital and the impatience of relatively backward peoples for economic advancement, one would like to identify and avoid policies which would fail to achieve the response needed in any development project or would achieve it only at a cost considerably higher than that of a feasible alternative. Therefore, kinds of analysis which can give us information about the response of Africans to economic stimuli are of special interest.

CHARACTERISTICS OF TRADITIONAL AFRICAN TRADE IN TROPICAL AFRICA

Only the barest outlines of historical trade can be sketched, but there is sufficient information to refute the notions that in large areas of tropical Africa very little or no trade existed before European colonization of the continent, or that the use of money in exchange was rare until fairly recently.

One of the things one can establish through a careful reading of the writings of early observers, such as explorers, travelers, administrators, and missionaries, is that commerce varied among regions in complexity of organization, regularity, and the institutions through which it was conducted.

Along most of the western African coast which runs parallel to the equator — particularly along what were called the Gold and Slave coasts in the days of the slave trade and which now constitute portions of Ivory Coast, Ghana, Togo, Dahomey, and Nigeria — markets appear to have existed long before these areas were made known to Western Europe by Portuguese navigators and others.

Evidence recorded by the first white man known to have penetrated the upper portions of the Congo Basin, the amazingly extensive observations of Livingstone preserved through his journals, shows that long before this region was controlled by non-Africans markets existed that were large both in number of people attending (Livingstone estimated over a thousand persons in several of the markets he visited) and in the range of goods and services exchanged.

But neither Livingstone nor other early non-African travelers in the portions of the extreme northern and southern Congo Basin, and the areas adjacent to the south in what is now Zambia and Rhodesia, reported having encountered markets there. In fact, anthropologists have gone so far as to assert that there were no marketplaces in tropical Africa east of the Congo Basin prior to European rule, a generalization that stands in need of qualification. How much of eastern tropical Africa clearly belongs in the nonmarket category cannot yet be established, but there were marketplaces in some areas. Livingstone describes marketplaces he found when he visited Nyasaland, and it is not unlikely that they were common in some of the other areas of eastern Africa.

The notion sometimes advanced by anthropologists that little or no trade took place in these areas can be still more easily refuted. Zambia and Katanga, for example, seem to have traditionally had no marketplaces yet an extensive system of nonmarketplace trade. The evidence is strong that all the major ethnic groups of this area were active in trade, and that traders not infrequently traveled a hundred miles or more for purposes of exchange.

Few attempts have been made to establish what the historical trade of any Zambian or Katangan ethnic group was, and much of the information we have was recorded only because it was directly related to some aspect of political or social structure; hence the data almost certainly err in underestimating the range of commodities traded and the distances involved. Nevertheless, the evidence we have suggests that three of the larger ethnic groups, and three that were at least two hundred miles apart — the Plateau Tonga, the Lozi, and the Yeke — each had a system of trade that involved twenty or more commodities, and that each of these groups traded with at least ten other ethnic groups (79, p. 223; 22, p. 235; 167, pp. 72–81; and 291, pp. 39–42).

Other large ethnic groups of the area, such as the Lovale, Lamba, Soli, Nsenga, and Senga, appear to have had at least ten commodities in their commerce, and to have had commercial intercourse with five or more other ethnic groups (460, pp. 37–42; 294, pp. 212–22; and 295, pp. 700–5).

These eight ethnic groups were well dispersed over the area which is said to have had little or no trade before European rule; the Lovale, Lozi, Plateau Tonga, Nsenga, Senga, and Yeke in fact roughly outline its perimeter. The trade they conducted in itself involved enough societies and commodities to suggest that trade was considerable throughout the area. Sketchy accounts of trade by some of the other ethnic groups inside the perimeter lend further support to this view.

It is my hypothesis that the reason for this rather striking difference in the organization of historical trade between Katanga, Zambia, and Rhodesia, and the marketplace areas of the middle portions of the Congo

Basin and western tropical Africa is the relationship of environment and technology to the structure of trade, through their influence on the density of population and the range of material goods available.

The greater the density of population, the easier it is for an individual with something he would like to exchange to dispose of it; and what is particularly significant is that after some fairly high density of population is reached, he will not need to travel far to find a spot which is passed by several people during their daily activities. It then becomes fairly obvious that sitting and waiting at a location people frequently pass on their way to fields, or to a source of water, for example, is as effective — and not as tiring — as traveling about in search of buyers. This encourages regular use of a particular location for exchange — i.e. creation of a marketplace.

As the density of population increases, so does the diversity of human abilities and tastes, both of which increase the possibility of exchange and encourage specialization of economic activity. There is also probably greater incentive to organize the activities of individuals, including exchange, because proximity increases awareness of the effect behavior of an individual or a group has on others.

In general, the more favorable the environment to plant and animal life, the greater the range of useful products that man can derive from his environment; and the greater the range of products available, the greater the chance that an individual will have control of some commodities much less useful to him than others he can obtain from a person with a different order of preferences. The chance of such individuals being easy to contact increases with the density of population, which, in turn, is a function of how favorable the environment is to human life.

In terms of tropical Africa my argument is that the forest areas — mainly because their rainfall is greater, is distributed over a greater proportion of the year, and is more reliable — can, given a fairly simple technology, support a much denser human population and provide a far wider range of goods than the savanna areas.

What data we have support this hypothesis: the marketplace areas are found in regions of relatively high rainfall with considerably fewer dry months, and some of them have very high man-land ratios. The non-marketplace areas have relatively low and irregular rainfall and long dry seasons. As a rule they are, and appear always to have been, sparsely populated. Where marketplaces were found in savanna — such as parts of western tropical Africa — their existence may well be accounted for by presence of different production techniques (such as irrigation) or political structure than that found in most of the savanna zone. (In such areas marketplaces may not have arisen spontaneously, but for political reasons, for example to serve the needs of a distant but powerful people.)

No satisfactory notion of the volume of trade in times past can be established, other than that it was not necessarily small; in fact, from the number, size, and regularity of markets there is good reason to think that in some areas commerce may have been large relative to other economic activities.

Of the composition of trade somewhat more can be said. Probably best known are the slave and ivory trades. Slaves were, in all probability, a major commodity in many of the tropical African economies long before non-Africans began buying them for sale in other continents; but undoubtedly the significance of the slave trade greatly increased once they could be sold overseas.

Ivory appears to have been a second major item of traditional commerce in a number of areas; demand for this too probably expanded after extensive contact with traders from other continents. The peak of this trade appears to have come considerably after the slave trade began to decline [1] — perhaps even after it was suppressed.

Commerce in gold, copper, and iron was important in a few areas; and salt and livestock were items fairly widely traded. Other major commodities were foodstuffs, of which the starchy foodstuffs and their derivatives were, in the market areas, at least, probably of major importance in terms of volume, if not value. Part of the demand for these goods was based on the needs of those dealing in, or transporting slaves; hence in a number of areas the trade in foodstuffs probably increased sharply with expansion of the slave trade.

In Zambia, Rhodesia, and the northern Congo Basin, the only areas of marketless aboriginal trade which we have so far studied in detail, commerce in starchy commodities appears to have been relatively unimportant.

Throughout tropical Africa many of the other prominent items in commerce were things requiring special skill in production, special knowledge of sources of supply, or so much time or effort to produce that they were something of a luxury; for example, animal products; various non-starchy foods and foodstuffs from fields or forest; spears, hoes, and other metal objects; cloth, baskets, and other items requiring weaving; beer; fiber; various ornaments; and sometimes medicines and charms.

The commodities used as money varied greatly. For tropical Africa as a whole, the kinds of money used in historical trade form a list almost as long as the one of commodities; however at any particular point in time the number of things serving as medium of exchange within a given ethnic group were usually few. The commodities most commonly serving as money were such things as seashells, salt, hoes, cloth, and in some areas gold, copper, or cattle.

In some areas these commodities served merely as a standard of value, not as the medium of exchange. Among the Lovale and Lamba of Zambia, for instance, cloth served only as the standard of value; that is, price is said always to have been stated in terms of units of cloth even though payment was not necessarily made in cloth. Cloth was easy to measure and could be readily divided into extremely small units, if bargaining so dictated. The units commonly used — fingertip to elbow, to shoulder, to center of chest, to opposite shoulder, etc. — were easily visualized and did not give much latitude for cheating. Moreover, in this area cloth was one of the major items of trade, if not the most common one.

Throughout tropical Africa prices varied according to skill in bargaining, among other things. It is impossible to establish what typical rates were, despite a common tendency of explorers to give long price lists in their journals and to comment on apparent price relationships they found interesting: e.g. that the price of a cow was twice that of a woman slave in a certain area.

TRENDS IN HISTORICAL TRADE

For the first four centuries after the Portuguese navigators made tropical Africa known to Western Europe, commerce tended to expand. As mentioned earlier, the slave and ivory trades expanded, and to some extent the demand for food expanded with the slave trade, to feed slaves between capture and shipment and to meet the needs of ships and trading stations.

Indirectly, new technology that was introduced, and sometimes spread, by foreigners tended to expand trade. Use of more productive techniques can increase the population that an area can support, and moreover it can, and usually does, considerably extend the range of useful products a given environment will yield.

A further indirect stimulus to trade was introduction of a number of plants and animals not previously known: examples are manioc, sweet potatoes, peanuts, several tropical fruits, and possibly maize.

Toward the end of the nineteenth century European powers limited one of the important categories of commerce, the slave trade; and from roughly the beginning of the twentieth century the form contacts with Europe took served further to limit trade, although in some ways they provided stimuli at the same time.

Limitations came from increased competition from non-African trad-ers. In Zambia and the Ivory Coast, for instance, European hunter-traders began to tour the country, living off the land and trading such items as hoes, salt, blankets, cloth, beads and other ornaments, and the meat of the game they shot. For these they got grain, other foodstuffs, and when they could be found, elephant tusks, cattle, and hides. African traders could not withstand the new competition. European traders sup-plied, at reasonable terms, the mainstays of traditional commerce, or a substitute (and often one of superior quality).

Administrators sometimes discouraged trade by regulating it; by re-stricting the movements of Africans; or by forcing them to work for the government or for Europeans needing labor. Sometimes the will of the administration was enforced indirectly through taxes, but the effect on traditional trade was little, if any, different.

At the same time, importation of new technology which improved communications and transportation stimulated trade. Similarly, the intro-duction of production on a larger scale requiring bigger concentrations than before of populations which were mostly not self-sufficient encour-aged commerce. Greater productivity added to the factors which en-couraged trade, for reasons already discussed.

Settlers and hunters had an additional indirect influence through al-tering the environment in a way that encouraged trade. In a number of areas settlers relied heavily on the herds of game to supply meat for labor gangs, and for themselves as well. They were often mainly responsible for destruction of the meat source which had traditionally been the major source of protein. Thus they indirectly encouraged substitution of fish for meat, which was significant as a stimulant to trade. Since in tropical Africa fish were not nearly as evenly distributed geographically as game, a smaller proportion of the population could easily supply their own protein needs from fish — assuming population concentrations are not clustered mainly along streams, lakes, and seacoasts rich in fish. A large proportion of contemporary African traders in the Ivory Coast, Uganda, the Congo Basin, Malawi, Zambia, and Rhodesia, at least, are fish traders, and most seem to have become so fairly recently.[2]

To restate briefly the major forces underlying trends in trade: Ad-ministrative regulations and restrictions, and increased competition from non-African traders, have acted to depress tropical African trade. The introduction and dissemination of new products however have probably considerably more than offset this. And new technology, from which other new products could be derived, has increased productivity, a develop-ment that was, in turn, an additional, separate stimulus. Another major indirect technological effect came from improvements in transportation and communications. A marked stimulus to trade was created in many areas through increase in the demand for food that was generated by the entry of non-African administrators, settlers, soldiers, and the like, and also because the activities of these non-Africans required large numbers of African laborers. Such laborers were too busy with their assigned tasks to produce foodstuffs, or were forced to live in communities where the population density left too little land for everyone to be self-sufficient in food production, even if there were members of the family who had time to tend crops. Moreover, the wages these laborers received gave them a relatively great purchasing power, so that they could buy larger amounts of food and other desired commodities than formerly. Rises in real incomes were also realized by those not employed by non-Africans; wages were quickly distributed to nonwage earners through trade, obligations, and gifts. In many areas nonwage earners also benefited directly from colonization through increased productivity of agriculture and the development of an overseas market for their crops, or introduction of crops for which there was already a foreign market. Increments in income, from whatever source, allowed expression of desires for an increased variety of consumption goods, and in almost every instance the additional goods demanded could be obtained only through trade. Finally, colonization was accompanied by changes in the availability of traditional commodities, and on balance possibly caused substitution of commodities unevenly distributed geographically (such as fish) for those more widely distributed (such as game); this, other things being equal, would encourage trade.

PRESENT TRADE

The only sizable area for which reasonably accurate estimates of the volume of commerce exist are Ghana and Katanga. Data we have for the former cover twelve months, October 1957 to September 1958, and for the latter the calendar years 1957 and 1958. Estimates of food trade in northern Nigeria have been published for 1957, but the techniques of estimation were so rough that the data are of little value. Elsewhere a rough idea can sometimes be obtained of the commerce in particular commodities, but in general there is little or no reliable information. Therefore little can be said about the importance of trade relative to other economic activities or of one category of trade compared to others. Even for Ghana and Katanga what we have are quantities of commodities moving between certain points, not value; and quantities alone are not meaningful for most economic analysis because usually there is no way of comparing the significance of unlike things. About the composi-

TABLE 5-1 — COMPOSITION OF INTERNAL TRADE, GHANA, 1957–58 (% of total internal trade, by weight)

Item	Northern Ghana to Ashanti and Brong-Ahafo	Brong-Ahafo and Ashanti to Northern Ghana	Northern Ghana to Volta	Volta to Northern Ghana	Volta to Eastern Region	Eastern Region to Volta	Ashanti and Brong-Ahafo to Western Region	Western Region to Ashanti and Brong-Ahafo	Ashanti and Brong-Ahafo to Eastern Region	Eastern Region to Ashanti and Brong-Ahafo	Western Region to Eastern Region	Eastern Region to Accra	Accra to Eastern Region
Maize	—	5.7	9.8	13.2	1.2	21.8	—	6.4	3.6	14.5	0.6	5.8	2.6
Other cereals	4.0	—	0.1	2.3	0.5	—	0.6	1.7	2.2	0.2	0.5	2.9	0.4
Manioc	—	4.3	5.8	12.4	0.2	—	—	0.6	2.9	6.3	0.1	13.1	1.6
Yams	7.8	—	—	8.6	—	4.8	—	15.2	—	—	—	1.7	0.6
Other roots and tubers	—	4.4	2.3	0.1	—	—	—	0.4	—	—	—	1.5	0.1
Plantain	—	6.3	8.5	0.2	2.9	23.6	0.3	29.0	—	7.5	0.2	10.9	1.5
Pulses and vegetables	3.0	—	—	2.8	—	—	1.1	2.6	7.0	3.5	0.4	2.5	1.0
Nuts	4.0	0.3	0.4	4.8	—	—	—	0.7	1.6	0.5	—	1.6	0.1
Fruits	—	6.6	14.7	0.1	2.1	0.3	—	—	2.8	3.3	—	3.6	0.2
Meat	0.5	—	0.1	—	—	—	—	—	—	—	—	—	—
Fish	8.2	—	2.1	2.8	1.0	0.2	4.1	4.2	1.9	0.3	6.6	2.9	4.0
Oils	0.8	—	—	4.5	0.8	—	0.7	—	2.3	0.8	0.5	0.2	0.2
Other local produce	—	13.7	18.2	22.8	10.6	1.9	6.1	1.0	14.3	4.3	2.1	6.5	2.6
Imported food	—	4.7	—	—	11.9	0.5	12.4	4.0	13.2	2.5	11.7	0.6	18.9
Livestock[a]	66.5	—	—	8.0	—	1.5	—	6.5	—	0.5	—	6.1	1.8
Other goods	5.1	53.5	37.3	17.1	67.9	45.0	74.3	29.4	47.5	55.6	77.0	39.6	63.6
Total	99.9[b]	99.5[b]	99.3[b]	99.7[b]	99.1[b]	99.6[b]	99.6[b]	101.7[b]	99.3[b]	99.8[b]	99.7[b]	99.5[b]	99.2[b]
Volume of trade (long tons)	48,630	61,990	10,020	96,250	56,890	56,850	65,430	43,970	42,530	28,710	32,910	486,600	300,160

Data from Ghana, Central Bureau of Statistics, *Field Survey Work in the Ghana Statistics Office, Statistical and Economic Papers No. 8* (Jan. 1961), pp. 89–90, which defines the above sectors as follows (p. 91): "Northern Ghana corresponds approximately to the northern savannah area, Ashanti and Brong-Ahafo comprise the Ashanti survey area and Kumasi municipality, while Volta, Eastern and Western Regions and Accra cover the same area as the coastal plain and southern forest." All goods transported in government or special vehicles — e.g., cocoa and timber — are excluded.
a Excludes animals driven on foot.
b Percentages have been rounded.

tion of trade a little more can be established, but again the relative signifi-cance of commodities exchanged cannot be assessed without data on prices.

The Ghana data are from a traffic census in which all traffic was stopped day and night at 22 checkpoints; and all cargo passing these points was recorded. Checkpoints were located in such a manner that the country was divided into sectors. Only rail and canoe traffic, believed by local authorities to be relatively small (59), and goods such as logs, trans-ported in government carriers, are excluded. The returns from this census show the composition of trade to vary greatly from region to region. Livestock accounted for 66.5 percent of total shipments from Northern Ghana south, but were never more than 8.0 percent of the total elsewhere (Table 5-1). Plantains were 29.0 and 23.6 percent of shipments from Ashanti and Brong-Ahafo to the Eastern and Western Regions, respec-tively, but in no other instance did a single starchy-staple account for more than 15.2 percent of trade. Nonfood items ranged from 5.1 to 74.3 percent of trade. The total volume of trade ranged from 10,020 long tons passing from Volta to Northern Ghana to 486,600 long tons in flow into Accra from the Eastern Region; the median was 56,850 long tons.

In 1957 and 1958 the major items in the trade between Katanga and other tropical African regions were considerably different, although edi-ble products predominated. Starchy-staples were more important than in Ghana, and were principally manioc and maize; there was no record of trade in cola (not listed separately in Table 5-1 but known to be im-portant), salt, sheep, goats, or cattle (Table 5-2). If we had data for more areas we would find still different patterns of trade, but almost cer-tainly edible products, stimulants, fibers, building materials, and clothing would be the outstanding categories.

Yet another approach, but still one which gives no precise idea of the relative importance of commodities, is to list things found in markets. In September 1959 when I visited the major marketplaces of the copper-mining region in Africa called the Copperbelt, an area partly in Katanga and partly in Zambia, I found the following commodities:

Manioc roots

Manioc *cossettes* — leached, dried
  chunks of manioc roots

Manioc flour

Fermented manioc wrapped in wild
  leaves

Manioc paste — cooked, mashed
  manioc

Boiled manioc roots

Maize, dry grains

Maize meal

Maize fritters

Maize-manioc fritters

Kaffir corn (sorghum), whole
Kaffir corn meal

Bulrush millet, whole
Finger millet, whole
Rice, whole
Cooked rice (boiled)

TABLE 5-2 — RECORDED INTERREGIONAL NON-EUROPEAN TRADE
AND ESTIMATED PRODUCTION OF THE MAJOR AGRICULTURAL COM-
MODITIES, KATANGA PROVINCE, BELGIAN CONGO, AVERAGE OF
1957 AND 1958

Commodity	Trade as % of estimated production	Recorded trade (metric tons)	% of total
Tobacco	681	444	0.1
Palm oil	600	7,748	2.6
Rice	520	4,695	1.6
Manioc products	170	69,805	24.2
Wheat	161	1,093	0.3
Maize and maize meal	110	56,903	19.6
Beans and peas	88	3,635	1.2
Irish potatoes	71	642	0.2
Groundnuts	64	12,970	4.5
Vegetables	59	1,714	0.6
Banana-plantain	48	5,996	2.1
Fruits	29	728	0.2
Sweet potatoes	28	2,650	0.9
Millet and sorghum	13	900	0.3
Manioc roots	1	10,731	3.7
Palm nuts	. . .	4,716	1.6
Dry fish	. . .	570	0.1
Rough timber	. . .	22,076	7.6
Sawn timber	. . .	7,896	2.7
Cotton	. . .	2,690	0.9
Other	. . .	71,010	24.8
Total		289,612	99.8[a]

Data derived from Belgium, Ministère des Colonies, Province du Katanga, Affaires Économiques, *Rapport économique* (Elisabethville, 1957), pp. 170, 171, 193, and 194; and ibid. (1958), pp. 158, 159, 175, and 176. Trade is defined as movements by rail to the Elisabethville-Kolwezi area from other provinces and recorded sales within Katanga. Not all transactions are reported; especially lacking are records of transactions between African individuals. Commerce by road and air with other provinces is also missing, but local authorities think this is negligible. Production estimates were kindly provided by the Katanga Department of Agriculture.

[a] Percentages have been rounded.

Irish potatoes (whole tubers)
Sweet potato roots
Cooked sweet potatoes (boiled)

Bread (wheat loaves and buns)
Wheat fritters — doughballs deep
    fried in vegetable oil
Plantain, fresh bunches

Raw beef
Fresh fish (large)
Fresh fish (small, sardine-like fish)
Smoked fish
Salted fish

Chickens (live)
Ducks
Pigeons

Fresh hen's eggs
Boiled hen's eggs

Dried caterpillars
Dried locusts
Dried termites

Tomatoes
Onions
Cabbage
Manioc leaves
Lettuce
Mushrooms
Pumpkins
Pumpkin leaves
Asparagus
Wild greens — at least 6 kinds,
    some of which are buds or leaves
    of trees, either fresh or dried
Bean leaves
Cowpea leaves

Raw roasting ears
Boiled roasting ears
Peanuts (fresh)
Roasted peanuts
Dry, whole cowpeas
Dry, whole beans — many sizes
and colors

Chillies — small, hot, red peppers
Salt
Curry
Palm oil
Oil palm fruit
Peanut oil
Apples
Oranges
Lemons
Bananas
Mangoes
Pineapple
Paw paw

Sugar
Sugarcane stalks
Sweet sorghum stalks
Honey

Sprouted maize
Sprouted Kaffir corn
Sprouted Bulrush millet
Sprouted Finger millet

Munkoyo — several kinds of wild
    roots and tubers used in making
    light beer
Munkoyo, or "African tea"; the
    light beer made from the mun-
    koyo root and maize, manioc, or
    some other cheap carbohydrate

Coffee

Chikanda — a spongy, cakelike preparation made from a wild, starchy tuber

Pumpkin seed (roasted)
Lump tobacco (for pipes)
Leaf tobacco (for cigarettes)
Snuff

Firewood
Charcoal
Kerosene

Sponge—a wild spongelike growth used in washing pots and pans, in bathing, and for other cleaning purposes
Broom — bundles of palm-frond ribs used for sweeping

African Manufacture

Baskets
Charcoal braziers (tin)
Combs (carved of wood)
Furniture

Mortars (wooden; for grinding grain)
Pots (clay)
Shoes
Sieves (wire; for sifting meal)
Spoons (wooden; for cooking, not eating)

Services
Bicycle repairing
Hair cutting
Tailoring

European Manufacture
Bottled soft drinks
Combs (plastic)
Drinking glasses
Hair oils
Jewelry
Matches
Mirrors
Pans (metal)
Perfumes
Pots (metal)
Rubber strips (cut from tire tubes; for tying bundles on bicycles)
Sewing thread

The Organization of Trade

A good deal is known about how African commerce is organized in some areas, but for a number of regions data are scant and little can be established as yet.

Markets are currently found throughout tropical Africa in the larger towns and in cities, but in many of the rural areas of southern and eastern tropical Africa, at least, they are rare. In most of these areas, however — even those that are extremely isolated — one finds stores, usually owned, and/or operated by non-Africans, particularly Asians.

In much of western Africa large open-air marketplaces are characteristic. In western Nigeria and parts of southern Dahomey and Ghana which I have visited, goods seem typically to flow from small markets to larger ones. Other studies suggest this is characteristic of much of the Ivory Coast, and I suspect it is true of much of the rest of western Africa.

The Organization of Food Trade in Western Nigeria.[3] The economy of Western Nigeria is particularly interesting because, although production is largely agricultural (see Table 5-3), something like half the population is in towns and cities of over 5,000 inhabitants.[4] The marketing system which supports this highly urban population is one of the most complex ones found in tropical Africa.

Trade in foods and foodstuffs is conducted through several channels. In addition to the hawking of prepared foods in the streets by children,

TABLE 5-3 — ESTIMATED GROSS PRODUCT OF THE WESTERN
REGION OF NIGERIA, 1950–51

Productive activity	% of total value	Value (million £)
Farm crops, ex-cocoa[a]	35	70.2
Cocoa	7	13.1
Livestock	2	4.5
Forest products[b]	16	33.0
Fishing	1	2.3
Transportation and distribution	21	41.3
Manufacturers and public utilities	1	1.4
Craft industries	2	3.3
Building and civil engineering	6	12.2
Other	9	19.2
	100	200.5

Data from A. R. Prest and I. G. Stewart, *The National Income of Nigeria, 1950–51*, Great Britain, Colonial Office, Col. Res. Stud. No. 11 (London, 1953), p. 61. Heroic and arbitrary assumptions were liberally employed in deriving these estimates, so they almost certainly contain a large margin of error. My research suggests that they badly underestimate long-distance truck trade, for example; and the estimates of agricultural production and yield are based mainly on a 1.5% sample. The authors reckon that their gross product estimates have a standard error of 9%, on the whole, but this is largely conjecture, for there is no basis for checking many of the data. Careful study of the techniques employed, and particularly of the assumptions made, suggests that 9% is extremely conservative. However, for showing the low level of nonagricultural output, the faults are less serious. Industrial production is relatively easily measured and is not likely to be much larger than the data indicate; moreover, even if it is twice as large (or if agricultural production is actually twice as small as shown), agriculture still predominates by a considerable margin.

[a] Mainly cassava (manioc), yams, cocoyams (taro), sweet potatoes, maize, millet-sorghum, rice, groundnuts (peanuts), peas and beans, and sugarcane.

[b] Oil palm products, rubber, cola nuts, bananas and plantains, citrus fruit, coffee, timber, and firewood are the principal items.

or at roadside stands, and the sale of prepared food in the housewife's home, trade is conducted through an intricate network of markets.

Larger towns and the cities have daily markets, but these are also part of a network of four-day markets (markets with a four-day interval) or eight-day markets, which differ from the four-day markets in that they usually are larger and offer a wider variety of goods and services. The days on which markets are held rotate in such a manner that for almost any community there is a market each day within walking distance. (Often people walk as much as five miles to the marketplace, and considerably longer distances are not unknown). To state it another way, a small trader who is engaged solely in trade will usually trade in his (or her) home market one day and in a neighboring market each of the four or eight days following.

There are at least twelve, but probably more, categories of intermediaries and agents active in one phase or another of marketing; among sellers are producers, collectors, local traders, long-distance traders, wholesalers, retailers, brokers, buying agents for wholesalers, truck drivers, and processors (housewives). In addition, the services of informants and measurers are employed in some transactions.

Producers usually sell on the way to market or in the four-day markets; they are often restricted from selling in larger ones.

Collectors commonly meet the farmer or his wife on the way to market early in the morning; buy the produce on the path; and transport it — usually by foot — to the nearest road, or maybe to a market, where they sell their headloads to larger traders. Collectors are also found in long-distance trade, in this case buying small quantities in the four- or eight-day markets and selling to large traders who transport the produce to bigger markets.

Local traders usually travel to a different four- or eight-day market each day, buying from farmers or collectors and selling to long-distance traders or processors. They may do some retailing too, but transactions with a larger trader seem to account for most of their sales.

Long-distance traders appear to buy mainly from large daily markets for sale in other large markets (often 150 to 200 miles distant). They also buy from collectors or small traders in smaller markets, however, as has been noted, and they may buy an unprocessed commodity like maize or manioc roots directly from the larger farmers who can supply them with the quantities they need.

Wholesalers may also be long-distance traders; they may employ buying agents; and they seem often to sell on commission for those without enough produce to justify, or enough capital to afford, a stall in the marketplace. They also sell for large producers. Thus they are often brokers.

Truck drivers seem frequently to be engaged in petty trade, buying a commodity en route for sale at a point where it is dearer; but it is not known how significant transactions of this sort are. Produce buyers, however, typically do not invest in trucks, even when they regularly travel two or three hundred miles for supplies. Instead, what typically happens, it seems, is that they are "sent a message" from an informant as to where supplies can be obtained and what prices and market conditions are; or they have a traditional supplier, who not infrequently will have pledged part or all of his crop to the trader as payment for a loan. Following receipt of the message, a visit is made or an agent sent, and when the transaction is completed a truck is hired on the spot. Such a trader may alternatively merely visit a large market, buy what he needs, and then search for a means of transporting it. No account has been found of enlisting the services of a truck before supplies were actually in hand.

Processors are housewives. The majority of women engaged in trade but not full-time specialize in one or more dishes which are popular in the community, buying the ingredients and selling much of the product — perhaps all of it, if it is a dish not well liked in their own household.[5] Most housewives seem to produce an excess of some item and rely on other specialists for other dishes. (Only with the recent trend toward purchase of preprocessed food and preprepared meals have Western countries approached this degree of specialization in food production.)

Processors often rely on local markets for raw materials, and may use them for selling the finished product, but, as has been noted earlier, they also sell in their homes and peddle their wares.

Informants and measurers are employed mostly by the large traders. The function of the informants is to locate supplies and furnish information on market conditions; the measurers are employed to reduce the disagreement that almost always arises between buyers and sellers as to the size of the "standard" unit of measure.

Marketing seems generally competitive but in fact probably is not because of product differentiation and restrictive arrangements. In markets meeting with a four- or eight-day interval there are typically many sellers in total, but perhaps only a few of each commodity, and some sellers may work for others. Probably nothing more competitive than monopolistic competition is found and oligopoly is common.

From merely casual observation of the markets one might think that prices are fixed, for most bargaining takes place over the method of measuring — the seller believing the proper amount of heaping to be something less than the buyer has in mind — and there may also be disagreement over whether the buyer is allowed to take part of an extra unit after the measuring is finished. This last practice possibly results partly from the fact that most transactions involve only a few pence, and the final adjustment in bargaining over price involves a fraction of a penny, a monetary unit which does not exist in Nigeria. When the price per unit is relatively high — transactions involving meat or fish, for example — bargaining over price in terms of the amount of money for a given quantity, rather than the quantity for a given amount of money, seems more common.

At any point in time, then, stated prices tend to be the same for all sellers of a commodity, providing their goods approximate the average quality, while actual prices vary among sellers because of bargaining over quantity to be received. The stated price per unit varies, too, with the passing of the day: prices tend to be lower toward the end of the trading day, as sellers attempt to dispose of unsold stocks before trading ends.

In daily markets it would appear there is considerably less competition. Farmers often say they have no choice but to sell to a middleman [6] if they take their produce to a daily market; that if they attempt to sell in the market themselves, traders refuse to buy, except at a discount from the prevailing price, and that it may be necessary to waste a day or two waiting for enough processors to absorb their produce. There is also hint that middlemen might resort to cutthroat competition to drive farmers out of the market, but this is seldom emphasized by informants.

Prices appear to be fixed and regulated in the daily markets by traders, who often belong to a guild or a trade association.[7] Thus with some exceptions the producer seems typically to face a monopsony and the processor a monopoly.

Nonprice competition seems common, and often takes the form of packaging a customer's purchases (e.g. supplying him free sacks or baskets) or helping him to find transportation. To create goodwill some traders also advance credit to suppliers at less than the going rate of interest.

The Organization of Trade in Other Areas. There are conspicuous differences in the organization of African commerce in Katanga, Zambia, and Rhodesia, the only other region for which we have detailed information.[8] Links between markets appear to be rare; large urban markets and small rural markets alike attract producers or middlemen who have come directly from the scene of production. Moreover, the number of middlemen between the producer and consumer is typically less; credit is used less; and there is much less buying and selling of information about supply and market conditions.

Marketplaces in the Copperbelt of Katanga and Zambia vary greatly in size and shape. Some accommodate fewer than fifty sellers, others as many as 2,000. All are "open air," for when shelters exist they are always without walls, although the bounds of the marketplace are often marked off by a fence, and sometimes a wall. In Zambia most sellers are provided with a roof. In the Congo only fish, meat and sometimes charcoal sellers have shelter, though some Congolese provide their own umbrellas, often of a bright red.

All sellers pay a daily fee for use of the market; usually the charge is 3 or 6 pence, or 2.5 Congolese francs, depending on the area.

As in other parts of tropical Africa, sellers tend to locate near others selling the same item. One finds a row of meal sellers, a cluster of vegetable vendors, the meat and fish section, the charcoal area, etc. A number of vendors display three or four commodities, sometimes more; others have only one or two.[9] In general, the number of items a vendor sells seems to vary inversely with the volume of sales. Sellers of things for which there is a steady stream of customers — e.g. meat, fish, poultry, starchy-staples and their derivatives, pulses, sugarcane, or tobacco — usually specialize in one or two items. Those with wild greens, vegetables, condiments, and the like often deal in small quantities of several items.

A few sellers use scales, but despite efforts by both the Katangan and Zambian governments selling by weight has been strongly resisted. Each seller arranges his wares in small heaps before him, or in one large heap, with a spoon, tin cup, bowl, or something similar, for measuring, if the commodity lends itself to scooping.

Usually the price can be ascertained only by query, although in the Congo a few vendors, especially those with scales, have prices displayed on a scrap of paper or piece of slate. There is little haggling over the price quoted, but actual prices sometimes can be altered through bargaining over quantity, as in Nigeria.

Most sellers try to divide their merchandise into units worth the lowest monetary unit people commonly have (three pence in Zambia or one franc in Katanga);[10] with fluctuations in supply or demand, stated prices tend to remain fixed but the size of the measure or heap varies.

The major part of the explanation for this is that the quantity sold is, for most commodities, so large relative to the smallest monetary unit, and changes in the market value of the commodity are usually sufficiently gradual, for price changes dictated by economic conditions to be achieved only through altering the quantity offered, since consumers do not usually buy more than their needs for one or two days.

As an illustration, suppose that at a time when one franc will buy a half-gallon can of grain there is a change in supply or demand calling for a 10 percent reduction in price. To change price when there is nothing smaller than the one-franc coin would require selling ten half-gallon units for nine one-franc coins instead of the original ten. But nine half-gallons is considerably more grain than most consumers can afford, or want, at a time. The alternative is to increase the size of one's measure by about 10 percent.

Another reason for adjustment of price through the measure of the commodity rather than through the number of monetary units asked may be the greater scope it gives for raising prices without consumers noticing. A small reduction in the size of a heap of beans, for example, is hard to detect. Even in the United States, where manufacturers are required by law to state on food and drink containers the measure inside, this method of price adjustment has been common; processors in recent years have frequently made the unit of sale smaller rather than charge more for it.

Besides direct adjustment of the unit of measure, quantities offered can also be altered through varying the amount of gift (called *basela* in most of Zambia and *matabiche* in Katanga) that is given by the seller at the end of the transaction. The primary function of basela, however, seems to be to provide scope for bargaining, or to make possible hidden price reductions in situations where selling is oligopolistic and an overt price reduction risks causing action by one's competitors which would erase the advantages it creates.[11]

Selling is characterized by both pure monopoly and atomistic competition, and by almost all the species of competition that lie between these two. In Zambia maize, millets, sorghums, grain meals, salt, sugar, coffee, and tea (and possibly a few other items) cannot legally be sold in most marketplaces or hawked by Africans. For the grains and grain products, such prohibitions support a statutory government marketing monopoly which appears to have been designed to disguise a subsidy to European farmers producing these commodities. Restriction of the sale of other products is designed to protect storekeepers who commonly assert that unless competition is limited some of them would go bankrupt. Government officials say they must cater to the demands of the store owners because they pay a disproportionately large share of municipal taxes.

There appear to be no official restrictions in the Congo sector of the Copperbelt, but the development of cartels is permitted, if not encouraged.

Perhaps a few commodities found in marketplaces are sold competitively, often approaching the classical pure competition. But anything more competitive than monopolistic competition is rare and the degree of competition varies considerably with the commodity; for fruit, condiments, and sugarcane, for example, there are often only a few sellers, and collusion is relatively easy. Attempts to corner the market for some commodities are not unknown; I saw the sugar market cornered for a day in one market of the Elisabethville area. At Ndola an association of African charcoal producers seems to exist mainly to regulate price and restrict competition.[12] An African hawkers' association near Kitwe appears to have a similar raison d'être.

Markets appear to have no barriers to entry, other than the official limitations of commodities that can be sold, and the small market fees which have already been mentioned; and evidence on market attendance suggests that for most commodities the number of sellers fluctuates widely from month to month (Chart 5-1).

Markets are held daily on the Congo side of the Copperbelt, but in Zambia they usually close one or two days a week.

Market activity fluctuates within the year, month, week, and day. Markets are most active toward the end of the dry season, when supplies are plentiful and farm labor is light; they are least active near the end of rains, when fields must be prepared and crops planted.

During the dry season, following harvest, there are few agricultural tasks to be done, and many farmers try their hand at marketing. A seasonal abundance of produce strengthens this movement; from July to November not only is the new harvest in but fish — probably the most important commodity marketed, quantitatively and in terms of number of sellers — are the most plentiful.

Within the month it is buyers who account for the major fluctuations. The greatest number is found toward the month's end, reportedly because this is when monthly wages are paid. The end of the week, too, is a time of notably increased activity, as consumers buy for weekend entertaining and feasting (and in parts of Zambia, at least, to tide them over Sunday when markets are closed). Monday, too, is a day of greater-than-average attendance: people are possibly replenishing stocks depleted over the weekend.

Within the day, fluctuations are less marked in the Zambian portion of the Copperbelt than in the Congo. Selling begins as early as 7:00 A.M., and attains a mid-morning peak, after which activity gradually diminishes until about 5:00 P.M., when the market closes. There are no sudden changes in the pace of selling during the hours when marketing is allowed.

Fluctuations are more pronounced in the Congo. There selling begins about an hour earlier with a few individuals; activity gradually increases as the main body of sellers arrives, and the market is often in full swing

CHART 5-1 — SEASONAL VARIATION IN THE NUMBER OF MARKET VENDORS, SELECTED MAJOR MALAWI AND ZAMBIA MARKETS

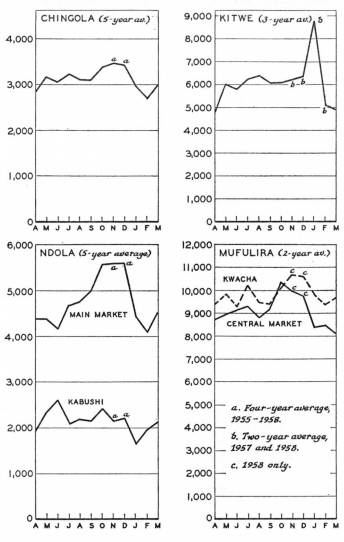

CHART 5-1 — CONTINUED

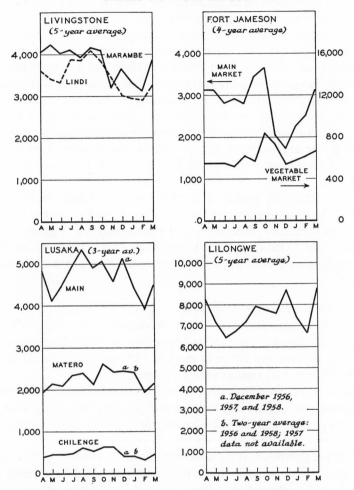

Data from the files of the respective municipal administrations.

by 8:00 A.M. About 11:00 A.M. activity begins to diminish as both buyers and sellers go home to prepare, or eat, midday meals. By noon only fish and meat sellers and a handful of specialists and people with manufactured goods remain; the cleaning crew has already begun to dispose of rubbish left behind by departed vendors. In the early afternoon a number of sellers return, but the morning peak is not regained.

The reason for this contrast between Zambia and the Congo seems to lie partly in the character of the vendors. Congolese sellers appear more frequently to be housewives who buy from a wholesaler and combine a morning's shopping with an attempt to do some selling. Zambian vendors seem more typically to be people who rely on market sales as a major source of income. But there are important geographical variations.

Sales outside the marketplace are of considerable importance, too. Near most marketplaces, often adjacent to them, are establishments selling alcoholic beverages (bars in the Congo; much larger and less elegant beer halls in Zambia), tea rooms (Zambia), coffee bars, and stores. In the Congo especially one frequently sees goods displayed in front of homes, and the front rooms of many houses seem to serve as stores. In addition, one sees vendors, mainly women, sitting under a tree near a road or a place of employment with food for sale. This is rarely permitted in Zambia.

Common to both western and central tropical Africa, including the Copperbelt — and apparently to other regions as well — are hawkers who deal in used clothing, ornaments, and various things of high value relative to weight. Often these traders operate in areas several hundred miles from their homes, even when this involves crossing international bounaries.

Characteristics of Traders in Zambia

The information given here on the characteristics of traders is from a survey I conducted in the Zambia Copperbelt in 1959, using a questionnaire and interviewing sellers in markets (African assistants did the actual interviewing); 473 sellers were interviewed.[13]

Well over half the sellers (59 percent) were male; almost three-fourths (71 percent) were married; and the typical seller was fairly young — about 40 percent said they were under thirty. Nearly three-quarters had no education, but 18 percent reported three or more years of schooling.

By ethnic group the sellers were well mixed. Thirty-four ethnic groups were represented, and only five of them each accounted for as much as 5 percent of the sellers; the majority of vendors (75 percent) were from ethnic groups located in the part of Zambia which lies to the north and east and due west of the Copperbelt; 8 percent came from Zambia to the south; 4 percent came from Katanga or other parts of the Congo Basin; 2 percent were from Malawi.

Only 28 of Zambia's 80-odd ethnic groups were encountered in marketplaces; some of the larger ethnic groups — the Plateau Tonga, Chewa, Ngoni, Lozi, and Senga, for instance — were infrequently represented among sellers.

A likely reason for this uneven representation is, I think, the different economic alternatives available to each ethnic group. The Zambian ethnic groups northeast and due west of the Copperbelt (which together account for three-fourths of the vendors interviewed) have a relatively unfavorable environment for agriculture; and the little physical yield that can be obtained with present techniques is greatly reduced when translated into economic yield (i.e. money value), because of the high transportation costs. Most of these ethnic groups find agriculture relatively unattractive; for them, marketing or working in the mines is the major option open.

Most of the African vendors interviewed did not consider the question why they had selected their chosen occupation worth asking; they assumed it to be as obvious to others as to themselves that there is no alternative way of earning a comparable income. But since the quest for leisure and the desire to gossip have been stressed as motives for becoming vendors in some of the scant literature on African trade in this region, the question is perhaps worth examining.

Both Nyirenda and Brelsford (*333* and *67*) slight the question of income, and the latter takes an extreme position: "It is not undesirable for an African to make money, but the danger lies in the second fascination of marketeering, for added to the financial reward is the attraction of a leisurely way of life . . . . In a great many cases this desire for the lesiurely life has developed into loafing, paid loafing, for there are a few shillings profit to be made. . . . Such profits are not deserved, and they are earned by a lazy man or unemployed worker at the expense of the consumer" (*67*, pp. 34–35). Brelsford seems to be suffering from the falacious assumption, not uncommon among British colonial administrators, that middlemen are nothing more than parasites who exploit both producers and consumers. But if they did not provide a service demanded, as is evidenced by the fact that people are willing to pay for it, they could not earn enough to make their profession worth while; consumers would seek out producers or vice versa, and the middleman would be circumvented. Only when selling or buying is not competitive — a situation fostered by administrative orders limiting the number of middlemen — can there be consumer exploitation.

As for the hypothesized laziness of market vendors, if Brelsford's hypothesis stems directly from a general assumption that Zambian and Rhodesian whites have about African traits, I am certain it can be demonstrated false by a brief sojourn in any Zambian or Rhodesian village during the agricultural season. In any event, my survey suggests that greater reward for effort was the magnet in markets rather than less work for the same reward.

The reasons given by vendors for selling in the market also furnish some indication of motivation. Only 1 percent (mostly women) reported non-

economic motives, such as boredom, loneliness, etc.; 31 percent express-
ly stated they were dependent on trade for their livelihood; 7 percent
said they were trying to accumulate capital to start another business; 4
percent were working to defray the expenses of schooling of a relative;
3 percent said they were trying to supplement the family income; 1 percent reported they were in quest of a little pocket money; and nearly half
(49 percent) gave no reason (most of these seemed to be professional
traders and thought it was a silly question).

Experience of Traders

Approximately two-fifths — the women — of the traders surveyed, because of their illiteracy and unfamiliarity with spoken English, had no
other way of earning income — except possibly through prostitution. Less
than 1 percent of the women vendors surveyed had previously been employed, but a little over 40 percent of the men had. Twelve percent of
the male vendors had worked in the mines; 9 percent had been employed
either as teachers, tailors, policemen, clerks, storekeepers, carpenters,
painters, bricklayers, or drivers; 8 percent reported employment as unskilled laborers; 5 percent had previously been servants; and 4 percent
had served as professional assistants; the remainder did not answer this
question.

There appears to be a distinct dichotomy between professionals and
people with a specific goal or target for which they are trying to accumulate money. Professionals, defined as people regularly in the market, can
be further divided into relatively large-scale operators, most of them men
trading in fish, and housewives who ply their trade fairly continuously
but on a much smaller scale.

It was not possible to determine market attendance accurately; a majority of vendors were so vague on this point that their answers could
not be trusted. Another indicator, the number of years of market experience, is somewhat more reliable, although many may not have reported
all of their experience. Almost a third (29 percent) claimed to be new at
selling in the market. At the other extreme, a fifth reported over five years
of experience; and probably most of another 14 percent, the "no information" category, should be grouped in the over-five-years category, for it
represents mainly people who had been selling several years but could not
remember how many.

A sample survey of 208 traders in the principal Accra markets during
August and September 1959, by Astrid Nypan, provides a basis for a re-
gional comparison of some characteristics of trading. In the Accra survey, a much smaller proportion of traders was men (Table 5-4); there

TABLE 5-4 — COMPARISON OF ZAMBIAN COPPERBELT
AND ACCRA MARKETS, 1959

Item	Zambian Copperbelt (% of sellers)	Accra (% of sellers)
Male sellers	59	15
Largest ethnic group	24.6	52.3
Years of market experience		
0–2 years	29	18
Over 5 years	20–34[a]	65
Types of Vendors		
Fish	40	10
Vegetable	39	20
Fuel	8	3
Pulses	21	. . .
Fruit	7	. . .
Tobacco	5	. . .
Wild roots	4	. . .
Insects	4	. . .
Poultry	3	. . .
Condiments	1	. . .
Cloth	. . .	8
Meat	. . .	5
Grains	. . .	10
Prepared food	. . .	5
Oil	. . .	3
Hardware	. . .	5
African medicine	. . .	5
Tailoring	. . .	15
Material	. . .	5
Sellers with employees		
One employee	73	67.5
Two employees	7	25.7
Three employees	. . .	5.8
Four employees	. . .	1.0
No information	20	0.0
Number of sellers	473	208

Data from M. P. Miracle, "African Markets and Trade in the Copperbelt," in
P. Bohannan and G. Dalton, eds., *Markets in Africa* (Evanston, Ill., 1962), pp.
712–17 and 738; and A. Nypan, *Market Trade*, University College of Ghana, African Bus. Ser. No. 2 (Accra, 1960), pp. 11–19.

[a] The higher figure if all vendors not supplying information had over five years'
experience, the lower figure if none of them had.

79

were possibly many fewer ethnic groups (eight compared with 34 in the Zambian Copperbelt),[14] and greater disparity in the importance of ethnic groups; traders appeared far more experienced; and the relative importance of commodities differed strikingly from the Zambian markets surveyed: fish and vegetable trading seems to attract a much larger proportion of traders in the Zambian Copperbelt, while grain trading, tailoring, and hardware vending are clearly relatively more important in Accra.

Kinsmen and Business

Most traders are partly responsible for the support of younger brothers, nephews, and possibly other kinsmen who are less prosperous. Hence dependents are often put to work as assistants, more from necessity than choice, and sometimes with unfortunate results. A number of the more articulate traders have pointed out that assistants who are relatives are difficult to control, and sometimes help themselves to stock or money as if it were their own. (Another observer confirms this for Lovale traders: see *460*, p. 42.)

There is a further drain on profits by kinsmen not involved in the trade, which perhaps explains why Copperbelt African storekeepers seem on the whole more successful than their counterparts in the African reserves: in the Copperbelt a merchant is less accessible to most of his relatives. The possibility of regularly supplementing the working capital needed for a store by mine employment or other jobs is probably of equal importance, however.

But if affinal obligations hinder the African's success in commerce, at the same time they also make a vital contribution. The trader who must support a younger brother or nephew can call on an older brother or uncle for capital and usually get it without interest.

A relatively small proportion of traders rely on nonrelatives for working capital and shun their kin as employees or partners.[15]

In conclusion, the characteristics of African trade and traders outlined above provide a strikingly different image of the African from that long held in some quarters. Africans emerge not as indolent, poor but happy savages, but as acquisitive, often dynamic individuals limited much more by ignorance, lack of capital, and institutional restrictions than by insufficient economic motivation.

6

THE IMPORTANCE OF MAIZE
IN TROPICAL AFRICA

ALTHOUGH maize ranks behind manioc and the millets and sorghums as a supplier of calories in tropical Africa (Chart 6-1), it has been more closely linked there than any other foodstuff with economic growth, and in many areas is much more important in African economies than aggregate data suggest.

CHART 6-1 — PRODUCTION OF THE MAJOR TROPICAL AFRICAN
STARCHY-STAPLES, ABOUT 1950

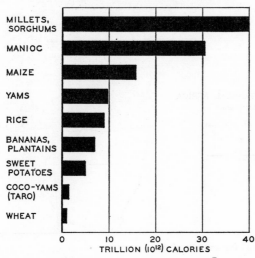

Data from sources in Appendix II.

GEOGRAPHICAL DISTRIBUTION OF MAIZE IN
TROPICAL AFRICA ABOUT 1950

In general, maize production is fairly evenly distributed over tropical Africa (Map 6-1). There are, however, a few distinctly heavy concentrations. One is Malawi and a relatively small region on its periphery. Zambia and parts of Rhodesia are areas where maize is especially important, and the Bié Plateau of Angola is probably another, although data are not yet at hand to confirm the impression one gets from qualitative sources. The Kenya Highlands and the lake regions of Uganda stand out, as does Rwanda-Burundi. On the other side of the continent, the eastern Guinea coast has two conspicuous pockets of production: one is in the Bamenda Highlands of Cameroun, while the other has its center about the city of Ibadan, near Nigeria's western border. About one hundred miles south and west, in lower Dahomey, is found tropical Africa's greatest concentration of maize production. Here the map would have to be three dimensional to make room for all the dots.

MAP 6-1 — MAIZE IN TROPICAL AFRICA ABOUT 1950

See Appendix II for sources of data.

At the other extreme there are a few areas, in some instances sizable ones, in which very little maize is grown. The largest of these is in the wet tropics characterized by heavy rainfall and dense tropical forests. It extends through the center of the Congo Basin. Almost none of the provinces of this region from about 1° north to 2° south latitude, extending at least a thousand miles from the Atlantic Ocean almost to Rwanda-Burundi, reported as much as 2,000 metric tons of maize production in 1950. Other areas where very little maize is grown are dry savanna regions, like those bordering the Sahara and Kalahari deserts, where millets and sorghums, which are better able to withstand drought, predominate.

A number of the newly independent African countries have failed to publish maize production statistics broken down by administrative division, and it is impossible to construct a dot map of maize production for recent years. Table 6-1 gives aggregate data available for about 1960.

MAIZE TRADE

Maize is not a major export of any tropical African country, although it is important in Angola and Kenya; nor is it a notable import except in

TABLE 6-1 — MAIZE PRODUCTION IN TROPICAL AFRICA,
ABOUT 1950 AND 1960

Country	Production (1,000 metric tons)	
	About 1950	1958/59–1961/62 average
Angola	320	326
Bechuanaland	1	3[a]
Cameroon	98	177
Central African Republic	16	. . .
Chad	2	9[a]
Congo (Brazzaville)	3	1[f]
Congo (Leopoldville)	313	276
Dahomey	155	193
Ethiopia	160	167[a]
Gabon	1	1[f]
Gambia	7	. . .
Ghana	200	205
Guinea	62	58
Ivory Coast	63	132
Kenya	574[d]	1,074[b]

TABLE 6-1 — CONTINUED

Country	Production (1,000 metric tons)	
	About 1950	1958/59– 1961/62 average
Liberia	20	11
Malagasy	48	78
Malawi	274	. . .
Mali	65	60
Mauritania	5	3[b]
Mauritius	4	1[b]
Mozambique	262	. . .
Niger	2	3
Nigeria	543	963
Northern Rhodesia	180	. . .
Portuguese Guinea	8	6[b]
Réunion	8	16[a]
Ruanda-Urundi	101	169
Senegal	14	29
Sierra Leone	8	8
Somalia	13	50[c]
Southern Rhodesia	250	1,014[e]
Sudan	15	35[c]
Tanganyika	393	538
Togo	62	52
Uganda	139	225
Upper Volta	86	55
Zanzibar	. . .	1[b]

Data from FAO, *Production Yearbook 1962* (Rome, 1963), pp. 45–46; USDA, Economic Research Service, *The 1964 Africa and West Asia Agricultural Situation* (Washington, D.C., Mar. 1964), pp. 67–68; letter to author from R. D. Narain, Chief FAO Production Branch, Aug. 5, 1964; letter to author from Paul J. Bennett, U.S. Embassy, Nigeria, Aug. 7, 1964; and sources in App. II.

[a] 1956/60–1961/62.
[b] 1959/60.
[c] Average of two years.
[d] 1948.
[e] 1960/61.
[f] 1958/59.

Zambia and Rhodesia (Table 6-2). Internal maize trade is poorly known for most areas, but is probably considerable wherever there are sizable towns and cities. For areas where we do have data, amounts of maize marketed are often on the order of 20–30 percent of estimated production (Table 6-2). Where the trade is important, it appears that maize is not uncommonly transported a hundred miles or more from producer to do-

TABLE 6-2 — NET MAIZE EXPORTS, AND MAIZE MOVING INTO COMMERCIAL CHANNELS, SELECTED COUNTRIES, TROPICAL AFRICA, 1948/49–1950/51

Country	Net exports (1,000 metric tons)	Maize moving into commercial channels (metric tons)	Known marketings as % of production
French West Africa	−2.6	?	?
Dahomey	a	50?	33?
Nigeria	a	?	?
Ghana	a	60?	33?
Angola	113.6	?	30?
Belgian Congo	19.5	65.5[b]	20
Northern Rhodesia	−11.1	57.2[c]	31
Southern Rhodesia	−25.6	147.5	59
Kenya	13.8	133.5[b]	23
Nyasaland	4.5	7.9[e]	3
Mozambique	−3.7	30?	10?
Tanganyika	1.3[b]	46.3[bd]	12
Uganda	9.7[bf]	42.0[b]	30

Data from FAO, *Yearbook of Food and Agricultural Statistics 1952*, Pt. 2: Commerce (Rome, 1953), pp. 50–51; the files of the Ghana Government Statistician; Belgium, Ministére des Colonies, *L'Agriculture au Congo Belge et Ruanda-Urundi de 1948 à 1952* (Brussels, 1954), p. 51; Uganda, Department of Agriculture, *Annual Report . . . 1949*, p. 29; ibid., *1950*, p. 44; ibid., *1951*, pp. 39–48; Colony and Protectorate of Kenya, Ministry of Commerce and Industry, *Notes on Commerce and Industry in Kenya, Annual Report 1948* (Dar es Salaam), passim; ibid., *1950*, p. 14; Sir Alexander Gibb and partners, Great Britain, Colonial Office, *Report on Central African Rail Link Development*, 1 (London, 1952), p. 49; Southern Rhodesia, *Seventh Report on the Agricultural and Pastoral Production of European Farmers, 1952–53* (Salisbury, 1954), p. 7; and Nyasaland, Central African Statistical Office, *Statistical Handbook of Nyasaland, 1952* (1952), p. 27. Data are for crop-years (July–June), except as indicated. Net imports are indicated by negative values.

[a] In 1952–56 Ghana averaged net imports of 6,657 metric tons from Togo, Dahomey, and Nigeria.

[b] Calendar years.

[c] 1949–50.

[d] Average 1948 and 1950.

[e] 1948.

[f] 1950.

mestic consumers, and in a few instances three to five times that far (Table 6-3). Where maize is not an important crop it would appear to be rare to ship it more than about twenty or thirty miles. The organization of its marketing is the subject of Chapter 13.

TABLE 6-3 — AVERAGE DISTANCE MAIZE IS TRANSPORTED FROM PRODUCER TO DOMESTIC CONSUMER, SELECTED TROPICAL AFRICAN COUNTRIES, 1954–59

Country or area	Estimated distance transported (miles)	Date
Southern Belgian Congo	500	1954–58
Northern Rhodesia	300	1959
Kenya	150	1959
Western Region, Nigeria	100	1958
Ghana	100	1958
Nyasaland	50	1959
British Cameroons	20	1958
Ruanda-Urundi	20	1959
Uganda	20	1959
Dahomey	20	1958

Data for the Belgian Congo are from Province du Katanga, Affaires Économiques, *Rapport économique* (Elisabethville), various issues, and are a five-year average of shipments by rail to the Congo Copperbelt — Elisabethville and nearby mining centers. Most of the hinterland supplying this mining complex is too far away to be economically tapped by road, under Congo conditions, hence the statistics used — amounts shipped by rail — should be a close approximation to trade of the Copperbelt with the areas supplying it; and this clearly seems to account for the bulk of maize trade in the southern part of the Belgian Congo. Of net imports to the Congo Copperbelt, 1954–58, 27% came from about 200, 48% from about 500, and 20% from 800 miles away.

The data for Ghana are derived from an unpublished census of trade in 1957–58 in which all carriers were stopped 24 hours a day for 12 months at selected stations, and their cargoes recorded.

Estimates of the average producer-consumer distance maize moves in southern Nigeria and Bamenda Province of British Cameroons are based on my impressions during a survey of markets in those areas conducted late in 1958.

Other estimates are, at best, very rough first approximations based on the opinion of observers I contacted in Africa, and published information on the main maize-producing and maize-consuming areas of the respective countries.

7

THE INTRODUCTION AND
SPREAD OF MAIZE IN AFRICA

A LTHOUGH maize is often listed as one of many food crops introduced in Africa by the Portuguese, how and when it was brought to
the continent cannot yet be established with certainty. This chapter examines, with respect to African territory south of the Sahara, such evidence as may be found, chiefly in early travel accounts, of its introduction
and spread.

Two important aspects of the problem, however, are not scrutinized
here. One is the view that maize is a plant of New World origin; the
other is the view that, whether or not there was pre-Columbian contact
between Africa and the Americas, maize was unknown outside the New
World prior to Columbus' return to Spain with ears of maize in 1493. Although both views have been challenged, they have been widely accepted
by competent scholars and are accepted here pending the appearance of
additional convincing evidence to the contrary.

More is known about the time when maize began to be important in
parts of Africa than about the precise points of introduction or the responsible agents. At best only a rough history of the introduction and
spread can be sketched at present, and because of the size of the area it
probably varies from region to region. Here we look first at western tropical Africa, next at areas farther inland and south, and last at the eastern
tropical coast.

WESTERN AFRICA[1]

The earliest reference to what may have been maize is for western
Africa. *Milho zaburro* is mentioned in a description of the West African
coast by the Portuguese writer Valentim Fernandes in 1502 (*303*), but

it is not certain whether his reference is to maize or a millet or sorghum. There is fairly good evidence that the term meant maize about 1550. A reference by the Italian historian Gian Battista Ramusio to *miglio zaburro* in his *Del navigatione e viaggi* (1554) is illustrated with a drawing of an ear of maize (*226*), unmistakably indicating the plant to which he was referring — unless someone else added the illustration.[2] Furthermore, Ramusio, in his reference to maize on the island of Santiago, Cape Verde Islands, used the description of an anonymous Portuguese pilot who sometime between 1535 and 1550 wrote an account of the West African ports he had visited. The unknown pilot was more precise in identifying this crop than many later writers: he explains that milho zaburro is known as *mehiz* in the West Indies, and that it has grain the size of a chickpea — which clearly suggests that it was too large to have been one of the millets or sorghums. But an earlier documentation of the term has not been made, and meanings could have changed in the 48 years since the first mention, even if there were no notable differences in usage from one locale to another.[3]

Changes in the meaning of crop names with time are usually a source of difficulty and confusion to students of crop origins and dispersals. Other than "Indian corn" and "Turkish wheat" there are few common names for maize in Africa that one can be fairly certain have not changed. The English term "corn" refers to food grains generally, not necessarily to maize alone. The Portuguese term *milho* now means maize, but in earlier centuries embraced other cereals.[4]

R. Portères argues that maize was introduced from the north, across the Sahara, by Arab traders, as well as along the coasts by the Portuguese (*355*). Much of Portères' reasoning about the Portuguese introduction into western tropical Africa is based on the belief that maize with soft starch, the "flour types," which are found more along the coast, came from Brazil whereas the "flint types," with harder starch, came from the Caribbean. Portères suggests that these flint types came by way of Spain through the Mediterranean to Egypt, and thence to inland areas of western Africa. It is possible, of course, that the distribution of maize types has changed considerably during the intervening centuries.

W. R. Stanton cites the diversity of maize types along the north-south trade routes of the interior of western Africa as evidence of the trans-Saharan route of introduction (*399*, p. 4). But this also does not necessarily tell us anything about when or how maize was introduced; it may have no more value than to suggest the direction from which varieties now found in West Africa came. The types of maize in Africa may have been changed several times by introduction of new varieties since maize first made its appearance.

Teixeira da Mota reports that *milho basil*, the name by which maize is known in Portuguese Guinea, may be a corruption of *milho brasil*, Brazilian grain (*307*). On the whole, however, linguistic evidence supporting the introduction of maize by the Portuguese is meager compared with that suggesting entrance from the Mediterranean (*355; 277*, p. 106; and *225*).

The only archeological evidence on the introduction of maize to western Africa is pottery with an imprint resembling an ear of maize, found at Ifé, Nigeria (Map 7-1), which is thought by some to have been manufactured in 1100 A.D. (*170*), a date estimated from the depth at which it was found. This is certainly contrary to the hypothesis of Portuguese introduction, but it has not been definitely established that the date of manufacture is pre-Columbian.

MAP 7-1 — AFRICA: SELECTED LOCATIONS

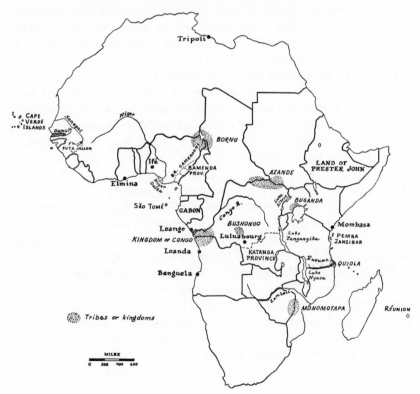

Possibly the earliest references attributing the introduction of maize to the Portuguese are statements by Olfert Dapper, a Dutch writer of the seventeenth century who compiled information from 68 works on Africa available at that time, and by William Bosman, a factor for the Dutch at Elmina in the latter part of the same century. Dapper, speaking of the Gold Coast, noted: "First of all rice grows there and Turkish wheat, which the Indians call *Mays*, and which was first brought from the West Indies where it is plentiful by the Portuguese to the island of Saint Thomas and which was distributed thence along the Gold Coast for consumption by the blacks . . ." (*117*, p. 463).[5] Bosman reports: "It is told me as the truth that before the Portuguese came to this coast, the negroes . . . were utterly ignorant of milho" (*60*, p. 300).

Unfortunately the source of Dapper's information is not known; his statement may have been a surmise based on theories of the origin of maize that prevailed in his day and the importance of São Tomé in the maize trade of the seventeenth century.

It is not possible to learn much about how common maize was in western Africa during the sixteenth century; Fernandes and the anonymous pilot indicate that it was widely grown along the coast from the Gambia River to São Tomé, if we take *milho zaburro* to mean maize in the first third of the century as it did later.

Nor do we know much about how widely it was grown in the interior in the sixteenth and seventeenth centuries. William Bosman and John Barbot both visited the Guinea coast in the latter part of the seventeenth century and tell us something of maize, but neither of them got far inland.

Bosman's position as a factor for the Dutch gave him occasion to travel along the coast; Barbot's account is based on a voyage he made in 1682, and, to a large extent, apparently, also on Bosman's writings. Both authors list maize as an important foodstuff between Liberia and the Niger Delta, but mainly between the Gold Coast (Ghana) and Dahomey.[6] Barbot suggests it was not nearly so prominent in other areas, probably the interior: "it is well known, that to this day there are several countries in *Guinea*, which have little or no *Indian* corn . . ." (*30*, p. 231).

The first documented report of maize deep in the interior of western Africa dates from almost a century later. In 1788 the Association for Promoting the Discovery of the Interior Parts of Africa obtained from a man of Tripoli, referred to simply as Imhammed, a description of the Bornu Empire (located near Lake Chad) and Cashna, southwest of it (apparently in Northern Nigeria), which he had visited some years earlier. He listed maize as the principal grain cultivated in the first of these kingdoms and as an important crop in the second (*23*, p. 202). Imhammed's report was verified by Ben Alli, who independently gave the association an account of the same countries.

Mungo Park noted maize along much of the route of his journey up the river Gambia to the Niger and thence back to the mouth of the Gambia in 1795–97, but gave no indication that it was a staple food (*342*). A similar report was made in 1818 for the same area and for the Futa Jallon by G. Mallien (*271*).

Agents of Introduction in Western Africa

Although the evidence is not sufficient to support the hypothesis that the Portuguese were the first or sole agents to introduce maize to western Africa, there is good reason to think they would have tried, at least in some areas. Aside from curiosity about whether maize would grow in this new land they had discovered, there was at least one economic motive for attempting it:[7] the need for a cheap staple food for slaves, which became particularly pressing after 1517 when the development of the New World market greatly swelled the volume of slaves sold and increased considerably the average distance they were transported.

Barbot emphasizes the importance of maize in the slave trade: "Tis generally observ'd, that *Indian* corn rises from a crown to twenty shillings betwixt February and harvest [August according to Bosman], which I suppose is chiefly occasion'd by the great number of *European* slave ships yearly resorting to the coast. . . ." He also refers to the vast profits maize farmers made "by selling it [maize] to the *European* forts, and slave ships; as also to all the other nations about them" (*30*, p. 197).

In 1721 John Atkins observed that vegetables, horsebeans, rice, maize, and manioc meal were the "common, cheapest, and most commodious Diet" (*24*, p. 171) for slave ships, but he does not indicate which commodities the slaves received, or the relative importance of each in slave rations.

Jean Baptiste Labat, in a narrative published in 1728, states that maize was the staple for slaves along the Senegal River (*253*, p. 166; and 167).

It is difficult to get an idea of the magnitude of production required to support the slave trade, but at most it is not likely to have been more than 10,000 metric tons in the peak year. Assuming (1) that slaves were fed a kilogram of maize per day; (2) that the period between capture and delivery to the New World was three months (four months for slaves that survived the voyage and two months as the average period in captivity for slaves who died en route, taking the mortality rate as 50 percent); and (3) that at the peak of the trade 100,000 slaves were taken from West Africa yearly, only a little more than 9,000 metric tons of maize would have been required.

Minimization of costs dictated (1) that the staple foodstuff for slaves be storable and cheaply transportable; and (2) that it be grown near the source of slaves, at least in western Africa. Slave ships coming from Europe were laden with merchandise to be traded for slaves and other cargo; they probably did not have room for slave rations, and it is unlikely that European cereals could have been purchased at prices competitive with West African grains.

The roots, tubers, and plantains that were among the starchy-staples of western Africa could not compete with the cereals in satisfying the first requisite unless they could be cheaply converted into flour or meal. Perhaps manioc could have qualified on this score, but there is no indication that it was widely cultivated along the Guinea coast in the sixteenth century (although it was grown in Angola then), and efficient techniques of processing the roots into meal appear to have been learned in this part of Africa only after 1700 (236, p. 110).

The only important cereals which will thrive in most of tropical Africa are rice, the millets and sorghums, and maize. Of these, the first was in demand for European consumption, and since it was grown along only a short portion of the coast, a sizable surplus over the needs of garrisons and ships was probably difficult to obtain. With the millets and sorghums it was more likely a question of costs. Their yields were probably greatly inferior to those of maize in the wet tropics — and most of the West African coastal areas are included in this vegetation zone — while growing provisions for slaves in the inland savanna regions would have been prohibited by transportation costs, if for no other reason. Hence there is good reason to think that the Portuguese early tested maize as an economic crop and found it remunerative.

In support of this thesis is (1) the fact that the Cape Verde Islands were probably uninhabited when the Portuguese discovered them in 1456 (263, p. 29); (2) on at least one of these islands, Santiago, maize production was reported by the anonymous Portuguese pilot, mentioned earlier, who visited the islands sometime between 1535 and 1550; (3) Santiago was a principal West African entrepôt at the time (54, p. 21); and (4) as John W. Blake states, at this period slave ships "were allowed royal ordinances to the ports of northern Guinea for the purpose of buying quantities of maize to feed the slaves they were bringing home" (54, p. 148).

However, this evidence, if trustworthy, implies nothing about where the Portuguese obtained the maize they established in the Cape Verde Islands. It could have come from the African coast, if it was available there. What the evidence does suggest is that the Portuguese had good reason to initiate the growing of maize, if it was not already a common crop when the slave trade became lucrative; or if it was a common crop, they had ample reason to introduce American varieties in hope of finding one with superior yields.

SUDAN, THE CONGO BASIN, AND ANGOLA

Only linguistic evidence is available on the introduction of maize into the Sudan, the Congo Basin, and Angola. Two routes are suggested: one across the Sahara to the Sudan and northern French Equatorial Africa, and the other from the Atlantic coast. Reference has been made previously to the route across the Sahara to tropical Africa; introduction from the coast is suggested by Duarte Lopez' note in 1591 that maize was known in the Kingdom of Congo as *Mazza Manputo*, which Filipo Pigafetta explains means grain of Portugal, Manputo being the local adjective for Portuguese.[8]

Additional evidence of a similar nature comes from northern Angola, where it is reported that in 1600 maize was called *Masimporto* (*192*, p. 312), which could be an indication of the Portuguese introduction. There is written record of at least one Portuguese attempt to introduce useful plants to this area. C. R. Boxer reports that Paulo Dias de Novais, a grandson of the discoverer of the Cape of Good Hope, was given a charter in 1571 for colonization of a part of Angola, which provided that the peasants from Portugal sailing with him were to be given "all the seeds and plants which they can take from this kingdom and from the island of São Tomé" (*64*, p. 669).

There is additional early evidence of maize in these three areas in a bit of Bushong oral tradition that can be dated by an eclipse of the sun on March 30, 1680, the only eclipse visible in the area in the seventeenth and eighteenth centuries (*418*, p. 142). Using this as the base for calculations, E. Torday estimates that the Bushong, who are found in the south-central Congo Basin, were not acquainted with manioc until about 1600; according to their tradition, maize and millets had been their staples until that time (*418*, p. 143). Jan Vansina's analysis of Bushong oral tradition suggests that maize was not introduced to the Bushong before the rule of Shyaam A Mbul A Ngoong, which began about 1630 (*445*, p. 261).

In any event, Bushong tradition seems to suggest that maize not only had made its way into the heart of Africa fairly rapidly, if introduced by the Portuguese, but was recognized as a valuable food. This is not un-likely: being easy to transport, it would have been a convenient object of trade or means of provision for travelers, warring parties, and the like; and little technique needs to be learned in order to grow it or convert the harvest into edible form.

There is an additional reason to think maize may have spread quickly through the Congo Basin: if these people had a narrow range of staple foodstuffs prior to maize, say mostly millets and sorghums, as seems likely, they may have welcomed variety and therefore readily adopted maize. Moreover, the similarity between these crops could have hastened the adoption because they not only are alike in appearance but require simi-lar care and processing. It is quite possible that maize gave a higher yield than millets or sorghums then as it does now, under the rainfall conditions of most of the Congo Basin. Thus it may well be that maize was brought by the Portuguese to the Congo sometime after 1493 and spread so rapidly that by 1600 it had become established as a staple six hundred miles or so inland.

That maize was known along the Angola coast and near the mouth of the Congo River during the seventeenth century is affirmed by an anony-mous writer who mentioned it in Benguela about 1617 (12, p. 17); by Garcia Mendes Castello Branco, who described it as a crop of Angola and Loango in 1621 (66, p. 21); by Jean-François de Rome in 1648, who suggests it was then the principal food crop in the Kingdom of Congo (58, p. 89); by Michael Angelo and Denis de Carli, who visited Loanda and Congo in 1666–67 (8, p. 157); and by Jerome Merolla who was in Con-go in 1682 (390, p. 696). Judging from Angelo's and de Carli's ac-count of how it was used, it was in all probability still a major foodstuff in Loanda at least as late as 1667: "instead of bread they [the people of Loanda] use the root of manjoza, as they do in Brazil, and Indian Wheat, of which they make little cakes . . ." (8, p. 157). Manioc has long since replaced maize as the staple food in this area. Barbot too men-tions maize in this region, in his account published in 1725, but it is almost certain that he was merely repeating what he had read in the ac-count of Angelo and de Carli (30, p. 515). Abbé Proyart provides about the same sketch for Loango in his account written in 1776 (358, p. 552).

Evidence of the importance of maize elsewhere in these countries is not available until the nineteenth century. Monteiro lists maize as second only to manioc in Northern Angola in 1878 (304, p. 162); and Du Chaillu mentions maize along the coast of Gabon in 1856, but complains bitterly that 200 miles in the interior there was none, and therefore no roasting ears (94, pp. 46 and 338).

In northern Gabon, the Bulu maintain they had no maize until the latter part of the nineteenth century, when they obtained it from Hausa traders who came from the northwest (*207*).

Livingstone was much impressed with the extent to which maize was grown on the eastern edge of the Congo Basin, in the country bordering Lake Tanganyika on the east, which he visited in 1871. He leaves little doubt that it was a staple in some areas of that region (*262*, p. 42). By 1885 it is reported to have been replaced by manioc among at least one ethnic group of the southern Congo Basin (*446*, pp. 232 and 307).

Two fragments of evidence suggest that maize reached parts of the northern Congo Basin sometime after 1830. Belgian agricultural officers in the early part of the present century say that, according to oral tradition, the Azande introduced maize to peoples now adjacent to them in the south (*254*, p. 105); and the Azande are said to have invaded northern Congo about 1830 (*282*, p. 379). George Schweinfurth found maize grown only as a garden crop in northern Belgian Congo in 1870; but in the extreme north and extending into southern Sudan, in Azande country, it was depicted as the most important crop thirty-five years later by A. de Calonne-Beaufaict (*83*, p. 210; and *382*, p. 87). Today, however, it is said to be only a secondary crop in Azande agriculture (*378*, p. 228).

Among the Logo, a group adjacent to the Azande to the southeast, maize is said to have replaced millets and sorghums sometime prior to the present century, but to have lost its place as the primary staple to manioc and sweet potatoes after advent of European rule (*256*, p. 300). M. H. Lelong reports that manioc was unknown in precolonial times and that sweet potatoes, although known, were little cultivated. How and when these crops assumed importance is not clear, but a severe invasion of locusts in 1930 probably accelerated the shift away from maize. Because neither sweet potatoes nor manioc is nearly so vulnerable to locust attack, for a number of years following 1930 the Belgian administration forced the Logo to grow relatively large acreages of these crops to ensure a reserve in case of famine (*256*, p. 300).

Frans Pauwels notes that among the Congo Alur, who inhabit an area adjacent to the northwestern corner of Lake Albert, maize is today the second most important food in the diet; maize and manioc, the major starchy-staple of the area, have almost completely replaced sorghum, which was originally the most important cereal. Unfortunately he does not give information on the timing of the shift to maize, but it seems likely that its expansion has been limited by recent introduction of manioc, which was brought in in 1948 and by 1960 had become the principal starchy-staple in the diet (*345*, p. 236).

EASTERN AFRICA

Documentation of a Portuguese introduction of maize to the coast of eastern Africa is no better than for other regions. The linguistic evidence is perhaps better than for western Africa, but other evidence is not as persuasive as that for Angola and the Congo Basin. A. C. W. Wright argues (1) that peoples of the Nyika group have the root name *pemba* for maize, hence they probably got it from the island of that name; and (2) that the Cisena of Malawi call maize "sorghum of the sea coast" (*471*, pp. 66–67).

The earliest reference to maize in eastern Africa is possibly one made by João de Barros. If M. D. W. Jeffreys, who attempts to prove that maize had a pre-Columbian introduction to Africa, is correct, this early Portuguese writer mentions maize in the land of Prester John (Ethiopia) for a date that can be established as 1516 (*226*, p. 116).

There is no record of maize in southeastern Africa in the first part of the sixteenth century. The chronicles of Cabral's voyage in 1501 contain no mention to it. Duarte Barbosa's description of the towns he visited in 1501–16 mentions milho several times along the coast and in Madagascar, but he does not specify milho zaburro, and so seems to have been referring to the millets or sorghums (*265*). Perhaps the first clear reference to maize in this region is found in an early Portuguese account of Monomotapa, an ancient kingdom in western Mozambique or the eastern part of Rhodesia. The entry notes that in 1561 a priest there lived mainly on milho zaburro (*411*, p. 127). Sir Harry Johnston categorically states that it was introduced into Mozambique about 1570 (*233*, p. 426), but provides no documentation.

Regardless of how long maize may have been established in eastern Africa, it was little observed before the end of the sixteenth century. At least it did not attract the attention of travelers, and they rather consistently discussed foods of the strange lands they had visited. Therefore maize seems unlikely to have been a common staple. I have found two references to it in eastern Africa during the next century, but neither suggests that it was important. For 1643 there is an account of Portuguese settlers on Zanzibar and Pemba growing maize among other crops to supply the Portuguese garrison at Mombasa, which at that time had difficulty obtaining provisions from the peoples of the mainland.[9] The second reference is contained in Dapper's description of Africa published in 1668, which mentions maize at Quiola, a former Arab kingdom near the mouth of the Ruvuma River (*117*, p. 675).

The record during the next century is a little more substantial, but not notably so until the last few years. According to one account, maize seems to have been found in Madagascar in 1717 (*173*, p. 25). However, Perrier de la Bathie claims that maize was introduced to Réunion in 1735 by the French and speculates that it spread from there to Madagascar (*36*, p. 836). This speculation is based on the fact that Governor-General de la Bourdonnais, who was the first governor of the island and began his administration in 1735, appears to have introduced manioc to feed slaves working on the island's sugar plantations. According to the memoirs of Baron Grant, who lived on Mauritius as early as 1740 and spent twenty years there, Governor de la Bourdonnais "introduced, though not without considerable difficulty, the cultivation of *manioc*, which he at length obtained from the island of St. Jago [São Tiago, Cape Verde Islands] and Brazils.[10] He was, indeed, obliged to employ his authority to compel the people to cultivate this plant . . . . He published an ordinance, by which every inhabitant was obliged to plant five hundred feet of manioc for every slave he possessed . . ." (*174*, pp. 199–200). Gilbert Cours adds that manioc was brought to Réunion in a ship named *Le Griffon*, that it arrived in 1738, and that the first Africans to eat it were fatally poisoned because they did not know correct processing methods (*109*, p. 1).

An extract from a 1690 narrative by M. du Quesne published by Charles Grant, son of the baron, along with his father's memoirs, clearly indicates that maize was known in Réunion in 1690, almost half a century before 1735; but the statement suggests that it may have been recently introduced there, for it is listed with crops that were "experimentally known to flourish"[11] (*174*, p. 154). Moreover, whatever the date that maize was introduced to Réunion, there seems to be no clear evidence that it spread thence to Madagascar.

Francisco de Melo de Castro, governor of Mozambique in 1750, in a report on that colony gave *milho grosso* as one of the crops grown there (*64*, pp. 178 and 179). He probably meant maize, since during the eighteenth century, and even until recently, *milho grosso* was one of the Portuguese designations for maize (*64*, pp. 178 and 179; *62*, p. 196; and *448*, p. 12). In 1798 maize was described as the staple of Mozambique (*462*, p. 35); and in the same year Lacerda is recorded as having encountered it deep in the interior, in what is now eastern Zambia. According to R. F. Burton, the translator of Lacerda's account, Lacerda purchased a small basket of millet heads, but in parenthesis Burton notes that they were "corn-cobs," a term now commonly used in the area for ears of maize; moreover, in an earlier note Burton comments that "The greater Millet (milho grosso) is the Jowarri, Durrah, Ta'am, Mtam, or *Holcus Sorghum*. Monteiro and Gamitto, however, translate Milho Grosso by 'Zea maiz' " (79, p. 17). Thus there is good chance that it was milho grosso (maize) that Lacerda purchased. In any event, there is verifiable mention of maize in the same area thirteen years later (37, p. 223).

By the end of the next century, during which the interior of eastern Africa was fairly thoroughly explored, maize was found nearly everywhere.[12] The one major exception was Uganda.

Captain J. A. Grant, a member of John H. Speke's party which explored Uganda in 1861 and 1862, took copious notes of the plants found, and commented that maize was "very rare as the equator is approached [from the south]; and quite unknown beyond it northwards to 5° N" (396, p. 651). After Grant's note there is no further reference to maize in Uganda until the early 1880's, when C. T. Wilson and R. W. Felkin, in a book published in 1882, listed it as one of the minor crops grown (468, p. 159). Thus it appears to have been introduced into Uganda between 1863 and about 1880. By 1900 maize was apparently widely grown. Sir Harry Johnston, then governor, reported to the Foreign Office concerning the potential of the Protectorate: "Wheat, oats and barley, grow well in some districts, Indian corn everywhere . . ." (234).[13]

Who introduced maize and how is a mystery. Linguistic evidence suggests that it came from the east, and we know that soon after 1850 Arab traders began to visit the Kingdom of Buganda (132, p. 20). These merchants typically reached Buganda from the coastal areas opposite Zanzibar, with caravans composed mostly of African porters, and required as a staple foodstuff a commodity that was storable and cheaply transportable. Maize, millets and sorghums, and rice satisfy these requirements and clearly seem to have been grown along the East African coast, the point of origin for these caravans, long before 1850. But was maize the staple, or one of the staples, taken by these voyagers?

Cyril Ehrlich, speaking of the activities of these and other entrepreneurs of the same period, writes: "There was Andrew Dick, ex-chief accountant of The Imperial British East Africa Company, who by 1895 had a complete chain of 12 stores established from the coast to the Lake [Victoria], principally to facilitate transport work. 'I am in a position therefore to "posho" [sc. supply with maize flour] caravans right through,' he wrote to Entebbe . . ." (132, p. 21). This is helpful but not so conclusive as it may appear. The current meaning of "posho" in Swahili, the lingua franca of this part of eastern Africa, is maize meal, but it had a wider meaning something more than half a century ago.

Mrs. Stuart Watt, who in 1855 began her labors as a missionary in a region of Kenya traversed by the caravan routes, finished a description of the heavy loads porters carried with: "To this, however, must be added the men's own 'posho,' which consists of grain or beans for food" (455, p. 25). J. H. Patterson, one of the explorers in eastern Africa in the first decade of the present century, commenting on the personality of a typical porter, observed: "Be his life ever so hard, his load ever so heavy, the moment it is off his back and he has disposed of his *posho* (food),[14] he straight away forgets his troubles . . ." (344, p. 19).

The change in the meaning of "posho" from a general term for food of porters (and possibly others) to maize meal (68) suggests that maize or maize meal was possibly the principal staple of caravans. One must bear in mind, however, the possibility that it is only in the past fifty-five years — since the advent of European settlers in British East Africa, especially Kenya — that there has been a sufficient surplus of maize to permit it to be so universally the African laborer's ration that "ration" and "maize" in Swahili could become synonymous. To maximize cargo loads, caravans obtained food supplies en route (414, p. 117, cited in 31, p. 801); and over at least three-quarters of their route (all but perhaps the coastal area of Kenya), maize, if grown, appears to have been important only as a garden vegetable prior to European settlement. Millets and sorghums, or beans, are likely to have made up the bulk of trading surpluses of these peoples; therefore it is probably mainly these crops that caravans would have carried as rations.

In sum, then, maize was probably not logistically important for the early Arab caravans, although they may have introduced it to Uganda, as to other parts of Africa. Linguistic evidence suggesting that maize was introduced from the coast also supports this hypothesis. It may, of course, have been introduced simultaneously, or earlier, by other means and from other directions; or it may have been introduced to one part of Uganda by one means and to other areas by another. There could also be considerable differences in the date at which it reached various areas within what is now Uganda.

Although maize was probably known throughout Kenya by the 1880's (205, p. 352), it seems to have been important as a staple food only along the coast and in the southeastern corner of the country,[15] where it was described as the principal starchy-staple as early as 1848 by J. L. Krapf: "The food of the Wakamba consists chiefly of milk and meat, and of a thick porridge which they make out of Indian corn-flour by boiling it in water" (252, p. 356). It was not until the present century that maize became a widely accepted staple.

SUMMARY

Linguistic evidence strongly suggests that maize penetrated the interior of tropical Africa from the coastal regions, but the timing and mode of its introduction cannot be established. The commonly repeated assertion that the Portuguese brought maize to tropical Africa from the New World cannot be documented at this juncture, although they seem clearly to have had economic motives for doing so.

Maize probably was introduced to tropical Africa at more than one point and at different times. Even though the Portuguese may have been the first to introduce it to the African continent, it is unlikely that they were the responsible agents at all points of its introduction. Linguistic evidence suggests that many areas of northern tropical Africa received maize across the Sahara, and Arab traders may also have introduced it to other areas.

Very little can be established about how maize spread from one ethnic group to another in the interior, although a little more can be learned about when it became an important crop.

The first mention of maize in tropical Africa is probably by Valentim Fernandes in his description of the western African coast he explored in 1502, but he may have been referring to some other grain. Other data suggest that maize was widely grown along the coast from the Gambia River to São Tomé around the mouth of the Congo River, and possibly in Ethiopia, later in the sixteenth century. There is reference to it in all these places, in Zanzibar, and around the mouth of the Ruvuma River in the seventeenth century; and it was not only mentioned but described as an important foodstuff and a major provision for slave ships between Liberia and the Niger Delta during the same century.

Much less information is available for the interior, but some evidence indicates that maize reached the northern Congo Basin after 1830; it clearly seems to have been unknown in most if not all of Uganda as late as 1861. Until well within the present century, it was neither a major export nor a mainstay of the diet in most of eastern and central tropical Africa, the bulk of the areas where it is now of major importance.

8

MAIZE IN AFRICAN DIETS

IN tropical Africa virtually all the maize grown is utilized as food. Relatively insignificant quantities are used for feed by African farmers, and most of that seems to go to poultry. About all that is fed are the bran and grinding offal (*32*, p. 12; and *1*, p. 237). Most Africans are too poor to feed their maize to domestic animals; 1,000 calories of maize fed to animals can ultimately result, at best, in no more than about 250 calories of livestock products (*50*, p. 76), and probably much less in tropical Africa because of the poor quality of most African livestock and the backward state of animal husbandry. Maize is fed to livestock by European farmers in some areas. The practice appears to be fairly widespread in Zambia, Rhodesia (*140*, pp. 291–92), and Kenya, but the total amount fed is quite small.

PREPARATIONS MADE FROM MAIZE

The major preparations made from maize in tropical Africa can be classified as follows:

I. Immature maize
  1.0 Food
    1.1 Roasting ears
      1.11 Boiled whole ears
        1.111 Eaten fresh
        1.112 Sun-dried, stored, and reboiled at time of consumption
      1.12 Parched whole ears eaten fresh
    1.2 Juice from immature kernels that has been flavored, cooked, and allowed to jell

II. Mature maize
  1.0 Food

1.1 Cooked paste
    1.11 Fermented
    1.12 Unfermented
    1.13 Mixed with sour milk
    1.14 Cooked in milk
1.2 Cooked dough
    1.21 Unleavened bread
    1.22 Doughballs cooked in hot oil
        1.221 Maize dough mixed with dough of other starchy-staples
        1.222 Dough made from maize only
1.3 Cooked starch
    1.31 Fermented
    1.32 Unfermented
1.4 Flavored flour
1.5 Whole kernels
    1.51 Boiled
        1.511 Eaten whole
        1.512 Beaten until like boiled rice in appearance
    1.52 Parched
    1.53 Popped
2.0 Drink
    2.1 Gruel
        2.11 Sour
        2.12 Sweet
    2.2 Light beer
    2.3 Beer
    2.4 Distilled beverages
3.0 Other
    3.1 Substitute for tobacco

REGIONAL VARIATION IN FORMS OF CONSUMPTION

Precisely how maize is consumed varies considerably from one area to the next. Details on food consumption are not available for a number of areas, but fortunately data are relatively good for most of the areas where maize is of major importance in the diet.

Dahomey

The best account of processing techniques and maize preparations is provided by Adandé (*1*) in his study of maize in Dahomey. The summary here is based on his work.

Immature maize may be prepared as follows: The green ears, with or without the shucks, may be placed directly on embers or on a grill above embers; when they have cooked a little, they are soaked in salt water and eaten. Or the ears may simply be boiled in salt water. Cooked either way, they may be eaten with coconut or roasted peanuts.

An alternative method is to cut the immature grains from the ear, pile them in a cloth, and press them to extract the white liquid they contain — or the ear may be grated to obtain it. A little water and sugar are added and the mixture poured into a cooking pot and placed on a fire. A sack of cloves is introduced to give additional flavor. To make it light the mixture is stirred with a wooden paddle. After it has come to a boil it is poured into shallow plates which serve as molds, and as it cools it thickens to the consistency of gelatin.

Whole mature grain may be prepared by boiling in salt water until the grains burst, or it may be parched before boiling. Alternatively, fresh or parched grain may be pounded in a wooden mortar and ground between two stones, or it may be ground directly without prior pounding. The product obtained is sifted, and the bran is given to poultry. By a third method, maize may be soaked in water for 24 hours, then pounded; when the pericarp has been removed in this way, the broken grain is subjected to further pounding until it attains the fineness desired. Flour or meal so obtained is slightly fermented.

To make paste, grains are soaked thus for a day, and when they are swollen with water are taken out for a light pounding in the mortar to remove the pericarp. They are soaked for a second 24-hour period to ferment, before being ground between stones. The resulting product is poured into water to float off the bran; the remaining solid is separated from the liquid with a calabash sieve. This solid, called *ogi*, is used in a number of preparations.

The same procedure is used to make fermented paste, but the fermented liquid is exposed to the air after straining the paste from it. It is then poured back into the paste, the two are kneaded together, and the mixture is left to ferment another 12 hours. Hot water is then added to stop the fermentation.

For a cooked paste, a little flour is mixed with cold water in a bowl; a pot of water is heated, and when it begins to boil the flour-water mixture is stirred into it with a wooden paddle. This gruel is simmered for 10 to 15 minutes; then a small quantity of it is dipped out with a bowl and left to cool. Handfuls of flour are added to the remainder until the mixture is doughlike. Gruel reserved in the bowl can be added from time to time to help get the desired consistency. When the paste is quite stiff, it is ready to eat, and is consumed with a sauce or relish of vegetables, meat, or fish.

Other preparations from maize paste appear identical to those described in somewhat greater detail for southwestern Nigeria (below).

Fritters may be made of the cooked paste by dividing the mixture into balls about the size of a hen's egg and deep frying them in palm oil. Another product is made by kneading and rolling a mixture of unroasted flour, ground chillies, salt, and water·into small balls which are wrapped in banana leaves and steamed. For *zakpiti*, beans are boiled about three-quarters of an hour; salt, tomato, pimento, onion, chillies, and ground ginger are added; and the mixture is abundantly sprinkled with maize flour. With a wooden pallet, the preparation is turned and then left to cook another 15 to 20 minutes before it is consumed. To make a simple griddle cake gruel is added to ordinary maize flour and sugar. Small handfuls of this mixture are given various shapes and fried in coconut oil.

Gruel goes into another dish. Fermented sweet gruel is combined with a mixture of maize and wheat flour to make small balls, which are wrapped in leaves, fermented about 12 hours, and steamed. Alternatively, the gruel may be added to maize flour only, and the dough steamed before it can ferment. There are a number of variations according to the technique of obtaining steam and the ingredients that go into the gruel-flour dough.

There are two flavored flour preparations: roasted maize flour may simply be mixed with sugar and eaten that way; or palm oil, salt, and ground chilies may be added instead of sugar.

A major use of maize is in beer production. Malt is obtained by germinating maize grain about five days; then the malt is exposed to the sun to stop germination, and the grains are broken coarsely in a mortar or on the grinding stone. The malt is cooked in a pot about 12 hours; the liquid strained off, cooled rapidly and let stand until it is well covered with mold. It is then transferred to another container which is sealed with clay. At the end of three more days of fermenting in these pots, it is beer. Beer may be further processed into alcohol with a rudimentary still.

Adandé describes a number of medicines made from maize and discusses several other nonfood uses, as in hut or fence construction, for smoking fish, etc.

Nigeria

In southwestern Nigeria, maize processors account for nearly all the purchases of maize in the market. These processors may be called the *ogi* and *agidi* makers, for these two products appear to comprise the bulk of consumption.

To make ogi, dry maize is soaked from one to several days, depending on the variety of maize and the urgency of need for the product. A minimum period seems to be three days with the flour types of maize (types of harder starch take longer); if hot water is used, 24 hours may suffice. After soaking, the grains are washed and ground. (Many areas have mechanized milling, but lacking this, grinding is between stones.) The product from the mill or grindstone is put into clean water and passed through two sieves, one finer than the other, to remove bits of pericarp. This by-product of the operation is usually fed to poultry or livestock. The primary product, which is almost pure starch at this stage, is placed in pots of water to settle; it can be stored this way for several days if the water is changed every day or two.

The product in this state is ogi; boiled and eaten hot, it is *eko* or *pap*; wrapped in banana or similar leaves and cooked, it is agidi.[1] One finds great specialization in production of these dishes. For example, in the Benin area Yoruba and Hausa women are the ogi and agidi specialists; but even in a predominantly Yoruba community some may not have mastered the skill. In addition economies of scale make unit costs of a large preparation less than if a small amount is prepared more frequently.

Ogi and agidi makers sell their produce at home to callers, send their children to hawk it in the streets, or take it to the market. At the same time they will probably buy from other specialists the pounded yam and manioc products which their family eats.

In addition to products made from ogi, a great variety of maize dishes can be found in the markets. Those most frequently noted are boiled or roasted green ears; parched grains; popcorn; boiled whole grains; roasted grains ground and mixed with palm oil and made into balls; roasted grains ground with peanuts and pepper, rolled into balls or made into sticks and fried; boiled grains beaten fluffy until they resemble rice; maize flour made into a hot porridge; maize flour fermented (*kenkey*); maize flour mixed with plantain flour, rolled into balls, and fried; and maize beer (in the savanna areas). (See *33* and *34* for detailed descriptions of some of these.)

Ghana

Kenkey, the principal dish made from maize in Ghana, is prepared as follows: whole grain is washed and soaked one to two days, ground and made into dough and let stand another day or two. The dough is divided into two parts, one of which is cooked and then combined with the uncooked portion. This mixture is divided into balls of a pound or so each, which are wrapped in dried corn husk or plantain leaves and steamed about two hours, until ready to eat. Sometimes a similar product — called *banku* — is made by boiling dough, then stirring and shaping but not wrapping it (*26*, p. 20).

As in Nigeria, there are local variations in the timing of operations and the amount of water used — which result in quality differences consumers are quick to notice. In the eastern coastal region kenkey is usually more sour in taste, while in the western coastal region it is whiter and less acid and coarse (*26*, p. 20). In the western coastal area, especially, a sour gruel is prepared by adding hot water to the fermented dough used in preparing kenkey (*26*, p. 20).

Cameroun

Schwab describes some of the maize preparations in central Cameroun:

Corn (*mbaha*) when in milk, is known as *biyede*. In this state it is scored on the cob, or cut from the cob and crushed on a grinding stone, and added to *basm* or *mintja* greens which have been cooked tender and to which palm oil has been added. *Hisan* grass, with its resinous taste, is sometimes used to flavor it . . . . *Koga* — fresh, ripe corn, is ground, palm oil, salt and ground Capsicum pepper added and the mixture rolled and steamed in a plantain leaf. Green corn is also roasted on the cob or boiled in its husks. Ripe dry corn . . . is sometimes eaten with roasted *sa*-tree fruit, or the kernels are ground, salt and ground Capsicum pepper added and eaten as a relish with makabo when other relishes are scarce (*380*, p. 19).

Masseyeff and Cambon give a supplementary account:

Maize is a popular food and is consumed in several ways. Above all, the "corn on the cob" of the Americans. One uses it as a staple eaten with manioc-leaf sauce, and several kinds of dough-balls are made . . . . The consumption of maize beer has spread greatly (*278*, p. 11).

Southern Congo Basin

Among the Baluba of Kasai Province, Congo (Leopoldville), the staple food is an admixture of maize and manioc flour cooked into a stiff dough-porridge in a manner similar to that described above for Dahomey. Other major maize dishes are (a) dough-porridge from maize alone; (b) boiled, roasted, or parched immature maize ears; (c) immature maize grain cooked with peanuts, sweet potatoes, milk, or sugar; (d) mature maize grain boiled with beans, peanuts, or simply salt; and (e) maize (or maize-manioc) beer and alcohol made by processes basically the same as those described for Dahomey (*357*).

Southern Sudan

The Balanda of extreme southern Sudan boil or roast immature ears.

Mature grain is consumed whole, boiled with cowpeas or alone; ground into flour and made into beer, thick or thin porridge, stiff steamed dough-cakes, and occasionally into a thin, flat bread (*111*, p. 94).

Flour is most commonly made by pounding or grinding grain which has been soaked 12 to 24 hours, but either of two more complex methods involving sieving may also be employed.

With the first of the complex techniques the grain is soaked overnight (sometimes the water is heated to about 40° C. first), and the swollen grain is rubbed through a sieve in order to separate the flour into two fractions. The fraction passing through the mesh (about 47 percent of the original grain by weight) is used for making porridge or steamed cakes. The coarser fraction, after being ground and dried in the sun, is used in making beer.[2]

The second method is used in producing flour for a flat, thin cake called *kisra*, reportedly introduced from northern Sudan, that is eaten mainly in the more sophisticated homes and is usually made from sorghum flour; maize is used only when sorghum is not available. For kisra maize is not soaked; water is added to dry grain during pounding. The grain is lightly pounded, winnowed, and left in water overnight; then it is ground and sieved. Enough cold water is added to make a mixture of thick cream consistency, and this is left to stand a day. This slightly sour batter is finally mixed with a little boiling water, and the batter is poured wafer thin on a greased iron sheet.

Porridge is made by mixing flour into boiling water and cooking and stirring until the desired consistency is obtained. For steamed cakes, stiff dough (plain or mixed with honey or mashed ripe bananas) is shaped into long rolls, wrapped in banana leaves, placed in warm water, covered with additional banana leaves, and boiled about an hour.

There are four methods of beer production (*111*, p. 59):

1. Maize is sprouted, ground wet, soaked two more days, dried in the sun, and the lumps are ground down and boiled several hours; then malted millet is added and the brew is set to stand overnight.

2. Mixed maize and sorghum grain is sprouted, ground wet, put in a basket two days, and then dried and stored. To brew, the dried lumps are ground, boiled, and left to stand 24 hours. (No malted grain is added.)

3. Maize is soaked 48 hours, ground wet, mixed with malted millet, and the mush is put in a pot and left three days to sour, then dried. To brew, the dried lumps are ground, added to malted millet and boiled, and let stand one or two days.

4. Maize and sorghum are mixed and sprouted, ground wet, soaked for two days, dried, and ground. The flour is then mixed with just enough

water to keep it from burning, cooked from 15 to 30 minutes, added to boiling water, and cooked and stirred for a few minutes. Finally, cold water and either sorghum or millet malt is added, and the brew stands until the next day.

Ethiopia

In Ethiopia, important maize preparations are an unleavened bread, mush, roasted and boiled immature ears, parched mature grain, and beer (222).

The Plateau Tonga of Zambia

Among the Plateau Tonga of Zambia one finds, in addition to boiled or roasted immature ears, dough-porridge, and maize beer — all dishes that are common throughout tropical Africa — boiled mature grain, and immature ears that are boiled, sun-dried, and then, at a later date, soaked and boiled again just before eating.

The Plateau Tonga also have a drink, munkoyo, commonly found in Zambia and Malawi but not mentioned elsewhere. After the first cooking of the mash in the production of beer, juice of the root of the munkoyo bush (the Plateau Tonga distinguish at least four kinds of this bush, none of which is yet botanically identified) is added. This drink has a very low alcohol content (probably less than 1 percent) and seems to be prized as a thirst quencher.

A food of the Plateau Tonga not usually mentioned in accounts of diet in tropical Africa, although it is in all likelihood widely known, is green stalks of maize. These are sucked raw for their slightly sweet juice.

An interesting nonfood use of maize among the Plateau Tonga and the neighboring Ila is as tobacco: dry kernels are sometimes mixed with tobacco for pipe smoking when tobacco is scarce.

The Nsenga of Zambia and possibly several other Zambian ethnic groups distill maize beer in rudimentary stills. This beer also appears to be a common maize product in Mozambique and Angola.

Malawi

In an exceptionally complete account of maize processing in Malawi, Williamson gives the following outline of the stages in the preparation of maize flour (467, p. 128):

(a) The grain is stripped from the cob by rubbing against a second cob. Any badly weevilled grain is removed.

(b) The bran is removed in the first heavy pounding, kukonola.

(c) The grain is soaked in hot water for several days, kubviika.

(d) The softened grain is pounded for flour, *kutibula.*
(e) The flour is spread on a mat to dry.

The principal foods derived from maize in this area are dough-porridge; gruel; boiled maize bran, eaten alone; roasted or parched whole mature kernels; roasted, parched, or boiled immature ears; dried immature ears (as described for the Plateau Tonga above); and four types of beer.

The Kikuyu of Kenya

The Kikuyu, one of the principal maize-eating groups of Kenya, roast or boil immature ears, or crush the unripe grain, sieve the pulp, and add cold water to the liquid obtained, to produce a gruel. Mature grain is cooked whole with beans, or made into flour by grinding between stones — sometimes with the aid of water power (269) — or mechanically. Stone-ground flour is sieved, and a doughlike porridge called *posho* or gruel, consumed either hot or cold, is made from the finer fraction. The coarser fraction may be boiled to produce a fluffy product, *chenga*, that resembles boiled rice and is substituted for it when rice is not available.

Muchopes-Chibuto Area of Mozambique

A monograph published in 1960 by J. Montalvão Marques on the agriculture of Muchopes and Chibuto *circunscrições* (political divisions) gives some information about part of the southern maize belt of Mozambique (273). Together these two adjacent administrative divisions roughly cover a rectangle extending from the mouth of the Limpopo River 50 miles east along the coast and 100 miles inland. Maize is the base of the diet in the valleys, but in the hill areas it is usually second to either manioc, rice, or beans (273, p. 69).

In the valley areas there are three methods of grinding maize: *cucila, tinzoho,* and *tiove*; in the hills only one technique, a variation of the second named, is practiced. In the first method maize is pounded, sieved, soaked 48 hours, drained, and ground in a jar with a pestle until a flour is obtained. The second method is the same but requires only two to three hours of soaking in the valley areas, 24 hours of soaking in the hill area variation. The third method is like the first except that, after soaking, the preparation is boiled two hours and combined with pounded peanuts. The maize-peanut mixture is then boiled lightly before serving.

Doughlike mush and a sort of cornbread not described in Marques' study are made from ground maize produced by the first two techniques, and sometimes ground sorghum grain is added to the maize in preparing dishes. Marques does not list other food preparations, but his commentary on the agricultural calendar implies that one of the two maize crops grown annually in valley areas is planted mainly to supply roasting ears. Both maize beer and a distilled maize brew, "maize brandy," are listed among drinks, but no description of how they are manufactured is given (273, p. 75).

Central Mozambique

Oscar Reis Cunha, a Portuguese agronomist, gives a brief account of maize processing a little farther north, roughly from Beira to the Zambezi River. Maize is first soaked, then pounded in a mortar and screened twice, then ground between two flat stones (112, pp. 139–40).

Northern Huila District, Angola

In northern Huila District of southern Angola, the staple dish is maize porridge mixed with sour milk. Dry maize is made into flour by pounding the grain in a wooden mortar with a long wooden pestle, by pounding it on a rock with an elbow-shaped wooden pounder (see 441, fig. 64, p. 95), or by grinding it on a flat stone with another stone held in the hands (44, pp. 94–95). The resulting flour is boiled in water until a porridge is obtained. The porridge is then "mixed with sour cow's milk, and possibly greens, meat, or condiments" (441, p. 95).

Southern Malagasy Republic

In the extreme southern end of the Malagasy Republic, the region of the island where maize is of greatest importance in the diet although not generally the dominant starchy-staple, roasting ears are boiled and roasted; whole mature grain is boiled; and mature grain is crushed and cooked in cow's milk (120, pp. 48–49). Neither dough-porridge, beer, nor other beverages are made from maize, although it is the dominant cereal grown (120, p. 53).[3]

AMOUNTS OF MAIZE CONSUMED

Measurement of maize consumption in Africa is fraught with difficulties, the outstanding ones being how to include everything eaten away from the hearth and to record seasonal variations in consumption. These problems have rarely been handled adequately in tropical African diet surveys. Added to them are the difficulties of getting a representative sample when the size and location of the population to be sampled are often only vaguely known, and problems of measuring and recording consumption without altering consumption behavior by the very act of observation. For most rural areas, only indirect estimates — "quantities available for consumption" — can be obtained. These, shown in Map 8-1, were calculated on the basis of production plus net imports (or minus

net exports), less allowances for seed and waste (stocks carried from one
year to the next are insignificant in most areas). International trade in
maize is of substantial importance only for Angola, whose annual maize
exports ranged from 31,000 to 149,000 — and averaged 109,000 —
metric tons between 1950 and 1960 (*144*, various issues). Internal trade
data are not generally available, and no attempt is made here to take account of trade within countries. Hence, for districts which export and
import a considerable volume of maize, such as the area around Elisabethville, the estimates presented in Map 8-1 are not a good indicator of
actual consumption. Moreover, errors in the underlying estimates of
maize production and population, which may, indeed, be large and not
offsetting, introduce a further qualification. On the other hand, waste in
preparation of maize is never large in tropical Africa, nor would one ex-

MAP 8-1 — TROPICAL AFRICA: PER CAPITA MAIZE PRODUCTION AND CONSUMPTION ABOUT 1950

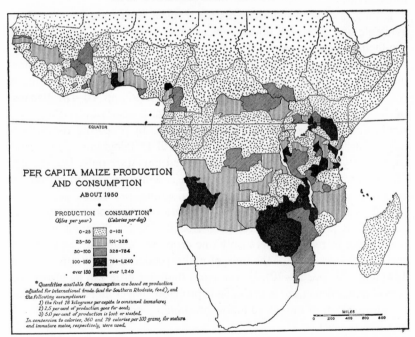

Population data are from official sources, in the main; where these were not used,
information was usually obtained from G. T. Trewartha and W. Zelinsky, "Population Patterns in Tropical Africa," *Ann. Ass. Amer. Geog.*, June 1954, or UN,
Demographic Yearbook, 1952 (New York, 1952). See App. II for discussion of
production data.

pect that much food would be prepared but not consumed. In general Map 8-1 may be a fairly good indicator of consumption. The relative importance of maize that it portrays checks fairly well with nonstatistical information and with consumption surveys where they have been made.

In carrying through the calculations on which Map 8-1 is based, it has been assumed that waste and storage losses are everywhere 5 percent, and that 2.5 percent of the crop was saved for seed.

Very little information is available about storage losses in tropical Africa. "Some believe that the natives usually suffer very small losses in store," says T. A. Oxley, who spent three months investigating grain storage facilities in East and Central Africa, "while others believe that losses at the end of the season are very large indeed. My own observation shed little light on this" (*340*, p. 6). The loss figure of 5 percent is in line with recent investigations in the tall-grass savanna of Nigeria and the Congo Basin (see Chapter 12), but it is possibly low for the humid forest areas.

Estimates of seed requirements for tropical Africa are few, but those available and those for other tropical areas suggest that 2.5 percent of production is not unreasonable (*138*; and *146*, p. 34).

Another difficulty is estimating the size of the crop harvested immature, an important matter because the calorie content of immature maize is a little less than one-third that of mature grain (*97*, pp. 10–18). Because of the popularity of roasting ears, some maize is nearly everywhere consumed immature as soon as ripening begins. In preparing the map of maize consumption it was assumed that until 18 kilograms of maize per capita per year is eaten, maize is consumed immature only, i.e., the first 18 kilograms of consumption per capita is converted at the conversion factor for immature maize. Eighteen kilograms per capita per year is roughly eight half-pound ears or 630 calories per person per day for 21 days; this is probably the average period during which immature maize is available in regions where only one crop can be grown per year, and such regions account for the bulk of maize production (*389*, pp. 141 and 144; and *272*, pp. 19–20). Where more than one crop can be grown, the period immature maize is available is probably longer and therefore yearly consumption of immature maize presumably greater (*240*, pp. 60–61; and *129*, p. 166).

In Rhodesia, Malawi, Kenya, and west-central Angola, qualitative information suggests, as do the aggregate data, that maize is the dominant staple for the majority of the population, usually accounting for half or more of the calories contributed by starchy-staples.[4] These countries, plus the lower part of Zambia, form the largest continuous maize areas, but

pockets of maize dominance are found in Tanganyika, the Bamenda Highlands of western Cameroun, and the southern portion of Dahomey and
Togoland.

Areas shown in the map where maize may be the dominant staple, or
at least a close second (areas of 328–783 calories per capita per day) are
southern Mozambique; portions of Tanganyika, Uganda, and parts of
the savannas of the Congo (Leopoldville); Zande District of the Sudan;
southern Cameroun; and a sizable area extending from the northern portion of the Ivory Coast into the southern districts of Upper Volta. In
most areas adjoining these — northern Mozambique, scattered areas in
Tanganyika, Uganda, and the Congo (Leopoldville), much of Angola,
southwestern Cameroun, western Nigeria, southern Ghana, and a zone
extending from northwestern Ivory Coast to Gambia — maize is of
modest importance (101–327 calories per capita per day). Over the rest
of tropical Africa it is a negligible item in the total diet, although it may
be an important component seasonally.

Data from sample surveys of food consumption give some idea of the
relative importance of maize in diets and the income elasticity of demand
for it (Map 8-2). (Surveys reviewed here are those available from which
reasonably reliable estimates of the contribution of the major foodstuffs

MAP 8-2 — MAIZE AS A PERCENTAGE OF STARCHY-STAPLE CALORIES
IN SELECTED FOOD CONSUMPTION SURVEYS

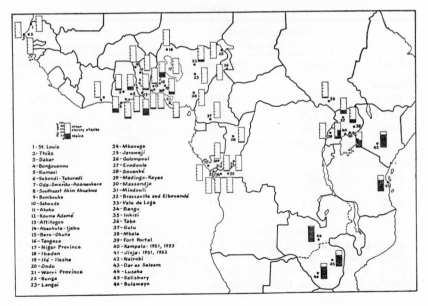

1 - St. Louis	24 - Mbanaga
2 - Thiès	25 - Jarawaji
3 - Dakar	26 - Golompoui
4 - Bongousnou	27 - Evodoula
5 - Kumasi	28 - Souanké
6 - Sekondi - Takoradi	29 - Madingo - Kayes
7 - Oda - Swerdu - Asamankere	30 - Massandjo
8 - Southeast Akim Abuakwa	31 - Mindouli
9 - Bombouka	32 - Brazzaville and Kibouandé
10 - Sahoude	33 - Vala de Loga
11 - Akaba	34 - Bangu
12 - Kouma Adamé	35 - Inkisi
13 - Attitogon	36 - Tabe
14 - Abaokuta - Ijebu	37 - Gulu
15 - Boro - Okuta	38 - Mbala
16 - Tangaza	39 - Fort Portal
17 - Niger Province	40 - Kampala: 1951, 1953
18 - Ibadan	41 - Jinja: 1951, 1952
19 - Ifé - Ilesha	42 - Nairobi
20 - Ondo	43 - Dar es Salaam
21 - Warri Province	44 - Lusaka
22 - Bunga	45 - Salisbury
23 - Langai	46 - Bulawayo

could be calculated.) In nearly all of the surveys that have been made
south and east of the Congo Basin — all surveys of a sample of Africans
in towns and cities — maize was found to be of major importance. Surveys of food purchases by 1,200 Africans in Salisbury, Southern Rhodesia, in July and November 1957 and in March 1958, and of 922 consumers in Bulawayo, Southern Rhodesia, in June and October 1958 and
in February 1959, are summarized in Table 8-1. Maize, bread, and rice
were the only starchy-staples of importance, and maize was two to three
times as important as the second most important starchy food, bread.

Less reliable, but helpful, are data from Betty Preston Thomson's survey in Lusaka, Zambia. In this study the sample was not random, "but
had to be selected from those who were willing to cooperate" (*415a*,
p. 3). The women of 23 African households were questioned about food
consumption during four weeks extending from January to February
1946. Each family was visited every day and the woman of the household
was asked about quantities coming into the cooking place over the past
24 hours. Foodstuffs were weighed when possible, "but frequently it was
necessary to rely on estimating the weight from a description of the quantity in a basket or a pan or from price" (*415a*, p. 2). Of the starchy-
staple commodities, only maize meal, rice, and bread were reported, and

TABLE 8-1 — SOUTHERN RHODESIA: STARCHY-STAPLE FOOD PUR-
CHASES BY AFRICANS IN SALISBURY (1957/58) AND BULAWAYO
(1958/59)

Food	Calories per person per day		% of starchy-staple calories	
	Families	Single men	Families	Single men
Salisbury				
Maize	1,176	2,059	68.2	74.2
Bread	526	696	30.5	25.1
Rice	22	21	1.3	0.7
			100.0	100.0
Bulawayo				
Maize	1,632	2,350	78.4	77.8
Bread	435	646	20.9	21.4
Rice	14	22	0.7	0.8
			100.0	100.0

Derived from Southern Rhodesia, Central African Statistical Office, *Second
Report on Urban African Budget Survey in Salisbury 1957/58* (Salisbury, June
1959), pp. 49–51; and *Second Report on Urban African Budget in Bulawayo,
1958/59* (Salisbury, Jan. 1960), pp. 44–46.

maize meal accounted for from 93 to 95 percent of daily consumption
of starchy-staple calories (*415a*, p. 18):

Foodstuff	% consumed in African sector of Lusaka	
	Main location (*10 households*)	Chilenge (*13 households*)
Maize meal	95.3	93.1
Bread	4.7	6.3
Rice	. . .	0.6
	100.0	100.0

Budget surveys in other Zambian towns from May to August 1960 do
not give information on quantities consumed but do show expenditures
on starchy-staple foodstuffs to be almost entirely on maize. In all the
towns surveyed — five Copperbelt towns (Ndola, Luanshya, Kitwe, Mu-
fulira, and Chingola), Broken Hill, Lusaka, and Livingstone — maize
purchases were estimated to account for 28 to 29.4 percent of expenditures on food and foodstuffs (*148*, p. 14). Bread was the second most
important starchy-staple purchased (4.4–4.7 percent), and all other
starchy-staples were insignificant, accounting for less than 1 percent as a
group.

According to a survey of 95 laborers in Dar es Salaam, Tanganyika,
made in 1950, maize represented a little more than two-thirds of the daily
purchases of starchy-staple foodstuffs in terms of calories; manioc, bread,
and rice were the only other important starchy-staples, but none of them
accounted for more than 11.4 percent of the total (*405*, p. 24):

Foodstuff	% of starchy-staple calories purchased
Maize	68.9
Manioc	11.4
Bread	9.2
Rice	9.1
Sweet potatoes	1.3
	99.9[a]

[a] Percentages have been rounded.

In Nairobi, maize accounted for some 80 percent of purchases of
starchy foods by 349 families surveyed for the entire month in Novem-

ber 1957, and February, June, and August 1958. Wheat and wheat products were the only other starchy-staples of importance (*249*, pp. 18–19):

Foodstuff	% of starchy-staple calories purchased
Maize	79.8
Wheat flour	9.1
Bread	8.6
Rice	2.5
	100.0

Surveys in Uganda show considerable variation in the importance of maize geographically and from year to year. Estimated per capita daily purchases of 96 laborers in Jinja during November 1951, of 104 during the same month the following year, and of 130 laborers in Mbale in February 1958 showed maize to be more important than bananas and plantains in Jinja in 1951, but less important the following year, although firmly in second place (cf. *237*, p. 230). In Mbale (Map 8-2) maize was a weak second and only slightly ahead of finger millet, which was third (*425*, Tables 2 and 4; *427*, p. 10, cited in *237*, p. 230; and *430*, pp. 26–27):

	% of starchy-staple calories purchased		
Foodstuff	Jinja (Nov. 1951)	Jinja (Nov. 1952)	Mbale (Feb. 1958)
Maize	56.3	45.7	18.7
Bananas and plantains	33.8	48.1	59.6
Finger millet	. . .	. . .	15.0
Manioc	7.4	6.2	2.6
Sweet potatoes	. . .	. . .	2.8
Rice	. . .	. . .	0.9
Bread	. . .	. . .	0.4
	97.5[a]	100.0	100.0

[a] Because of incomplete data percentages do not add up to 100.

A survey of 200 laborers in Gulu, located in north-central Uganda, during February 1961 shows maize to be considerably less important than sweet potatoes but only slightly behind millets, while substantially more important than manioc or plantain (*433*, App. VI):

Foodstuff	% of starchy-staple calories purchased
Sweet potatoes	39.5
Millet	26.1
Maize meal	22.3
Manioc	9.6
Plantain	2.5
	100.0

In a similar study conducted during February 1960 in Fort Portal, located in extreme western Uganda, purchases of maize by 180 laborers accounted for less than 1 percent of starchy-staple foodstuff purchases (*432*, pp. 22–23):

Foodstuff	% of starchy-staple calories purchased
Plantain	44.0
Finger millet	37.7
Sweet potatoes	9.8
Manioc	7.5
Maize	0.5
Bread	0.5
	100.0

Maize had a vastly different position in the 1951 and 1953 surveys of Kampala, a result which appears to be explained by changes in relative prices of maize and manioc between the two surveys. In the purchases of 110 workers in September 1951 maize accounted for only 13.7 percent of starchy-staple calories, whereas among 175 workers surveyed in September 1953 it represented 55.8 percent, and was almost twice as important as manioc, the foodstuff in second place (*424*, Tables 3 and 5; and *428*, Tables 3, 4, and 7):

Foodstuff	% of starchy-staple calories purchased	
	1951	1953
Maize	13.7	55.8
Manioc	50.8	28.9
Plantain	23.1	4.5
Sweet potatoes	12.4	10.8
	100.0	100.0

In an analysis of response of African consumers to price changes, William O. Jones describes these striking shifts as follows:

The market for foodstuffs in 1953 was marked by great increases in prices of bananas, sweet potatoes, and manioc, and by the stability of the price of corn. The general price rise was caused by poor crops in late 1952, resulting from inadequate rainfall; if government had not intervened, corn prices might have risen in the same way as did the prices of other staples even though corn stocks were fairly large. Through government control of distribution and supplies, however, the price of corn meal was kept fairly steady at between 27 and 30 cents per pound. In other years this would have been considered a high price for corn meal, but in 1953 it made it the cheapest of all the starchy staple foodstuffs in terms of calories (238, p. 117).

Prices of plantains per 100 calories were more than double what they had been in 1951 and were a similar margin over the price of maize in 1953 (Chart 8-1). By 1957 the relative cost of starchy-staples was again approximately what it had been in 1951, and expenditure on maize had fallen among two groups, the Batoro and Baganda, although not completely back to 1951 levels (Chart 8-1). Among the Banyankole it remained high.

A survey of six households on the island of Anjouan, Comoro Archipelago, for about a month just after harvest in 1961, shows maize to rank far behind rice, breadfruit, manioc, and banana-plantain, accounting for only about 2 percent of calories consumed (75, p. 75):

Foodstuff	% of total calories consumed
Rice	30.7
Breadfruit	23.9
Manioc	11.7
Banana-plantain	6.4
Maize	2.4

In western tropical Africa, consumption surveys show maize to be generally of much less importance than in the east and south. No maize was reported in a survey of 136 families in Dakar–Saint Louis–Thiès area of Senegal in 1957 (283, p. 73); and in nine villages in the Bongouanou area of Ivory Coast, surveyed for three periods of four months each in 1955 and 1956, yams and plantains accounted for the bulk of starchy foods consumed, and maize was insignificant, contributing less than 1 percent of the total (221, p. 84).

Surveys in four areas of Ghana conducted from 1952 to 1955 show the

CHART 8-1 — KAMPALA, UGANDA: EXPENDITURES ON STARCHY-
STAPLES BY AFRICAN LABORERS, BY ETHNIC GROUPS, AND
AVERAGE MARKET PRICES, 1949–57

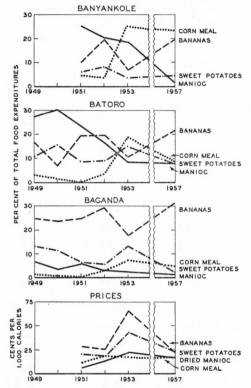

From W. O. Jones, "Economic Man in Africa," *Food Res. Inst. Stud.,* Food
Research Institute, Stanford, Calif. (May 1960), p. 118, based on Uganda [East
Africa High Commission], East African Statistical Department, *The Pattern of
Income, Expenditure and Consumption of African Labourers in Kampala, Septem-
ber 1950* (May 1951); idem., *The Pattern of Income and Expenditure and Con-
sumption of African Unskilled Labourers in Kampala, September 1951* (Jan. 1952);
ibid., *September 1952* (May 1953); ibid., *September 1953* (Jan. 1954); and ibid.,
February 1957 (June 1957).

contribution of maize to be slightly larger, but significant in only one
area, Sekondi-Takoradi, where maize ranked second (Table 8-2).

J. Périssé has provided, through his survey of Togo, a country which
roughly comprises a cross section of western tropical African climates, the
basis for analysis of the position of maize according to vegetation zone.
In each of five communities, well spaced from the coast to the northern

TABLE 8-2 — GHANA: RELATIVE CONTRIBUTIONS OF THE VARIOUS
STARCHY-STAPLES TO THE DIET IN KUMASI (1955), SEKONDI-TAKOR-
ADI (1955), SOUTHEAST AKIM ABUAKWA (1952/53), AND THE ODA-
SWERDU-ASAMANKERE REGION (1955)

	Urban		Rural	
Item	Kumasi	Takoradi	Southeast Akim Abuakwa	Oda-Swerdu-Asamankere
	% of total calories from starchy-staples			
Manioc and manioc products	37.5	46.3	50.4	41.5
Plantains and bananas	29.2	13.9	17.7	29.6
Yams	9.0	3.9	2.2	2.9
Maize and maize products	7.8	22.1	5.6	7.7
Rice	7.4	8.8	. . .	1.2
Taro	7.2	1.2	24.1	15.7
Bread	1.9	3.8	. . .	1.4
Total	100.0	100.0	100.0	100.0
	Total calories from starchy-staples			
Per person per day	1,364	1,260	1,435	1,312
	Sample characteristics			
Number of households	120	96	832	1,080
	30 days	30 days	12 months	3 months
	(Mar.– Apr.)	(Feb.– Mar.)	(June– May)	(Oct.– Dec.)

Data from T. T. Poleman, "The Food Economies of Urban Middle Africa: The
Case of Ghana," *Food Res. Inst. Stud.*, Stanford, Calif. (May 1961), p. 152.

extreme of the country (Map 8-2), Périssé selected 20 to 35 families
which seemed typical and measured their food consumption for five to six
days at three different times during the year.

His survey at Attitogon is the only consumption study in western Africa
in which maize was of outstanding importance. Maize and manioc together accounted for over 98.5 percent of total caloric intake (*349*, pp.
18 and 30, cited in *238*, p. 199). Maize supplied 41.0 percent and
manioc 58.5 percent of the calories coming from starchy-staples (Table
8-3).

TABLE 8-3 — TOGO: THE RELATIVE IMPORTANCE OF STARCHY-STAPLES IN DIETS ACCORDING TO FIVE CONSUMPTION SURVEYS, BY VILLAGE

		Village			
Foodstuff	Attitogon	Kouma Adamé	Akaba	Sahoude	Bombouka
		% of calories from starchy-staples			
Maize	41.0	20.2	9.4	3.5	0.8
Millets-sorghums	0.0	0.0	34.1	69.9	74.8
Rice	0.0	9.7	3.3	0.6	18.2
Yam	0.0	6.3	47.8	19.2	0.9
Taro	0.0	25.7	0.0	3.1	0.0
Manioc	58.5	33.3	5.4	1.6	2.2
Sweet potatoes	0.5	0.0	0.0	2.0	1.1
Other roots and tubers[a]	0.0	0.0	0.0	0.0	1.5
Banana-plantain	0.0	4.8	0.0	0.0	0.5
Total	100.0	100.0	100.0	99.9[b]	100.0
		Calories per person per day			
Calories from starchy-staples	1,703	1,715	1,650	1,309	1,000

Derived from J. Périssé, *L'Alimentation des populations rurales du Togo* (ORSTOM, Dec. 1959), Table 14. "Millets-sorghums" includes sorghum beer; "manioc" includes gari, a manioc product.

[a] *Coleus* potatoes.

[b] Percentages have been rounded.

Moving north from coastal savanna to short-grass savanna, maize became progressively less important, losing its place to manioc, taro, yams, and the millets-sorghums, in that order. In the northernmost village surveyed, Bombouka, on the drier edge of the short-grass savanna zone maize ranked sixth among the starchy-staples, supplying only 0.8 percent of starchy-staple calories in the diet.

These and other data from consumption studies support the hypothesis, suggested by per capita production estimates (Map 8-1), that maize is important in tropical African diets mainly in the savanna zones, and tends to become unimportant in both the short-grass savanna and the wet-forest zones. In addition to the Senegal studies already cited, a survey in the short-grass savanna of Cameroun in October 1954, January 1955, and June 1956 indicates that there maize accounts for less than 1 percent of starchy-staple calories (*279*, Table 4). Surveys in the short-grass savanna of Nigeria give similar results. The Ivory Coast survey already cited, and others in the wet-forest zone of Cameroun, Nigeria, Congo (Brazzaville), and the Congo (Leopoldville) discussed below, also indicate that maize is of only slight importance in the wet forest.

Surveys by B. M. Nicol provide data for 13 rural areas of Nigeria. The earliest of these surveys are three studies that were carried out in Niger Province: the food consumption of three families in each of three villages was measured over four periods of seven days each between March 1947 and March 1948, "the periods being distributed throughout the year in accordance with expected seasonal variations in availability of the staple foodstuff" (*315*, p. 27, cited in *231*, pp. 196 and 197). A survey of three villages in Warri Province in 1949 and 1950 and of seven other areas between 1954 and 1957 employed similar techniques. Maize was of only slight importance relative to other starchy-staples in all the drier savanna areas, representing less than 6 percent of total calories, except in Bunga, north of the Nigerian Plateau (Map 8-2), where maize accounted for 13 percent of total calories but was still insignificant compared with millets and sorghums. Nor was maize important in surveys in the forest zone (*316*, p. 297; *315*, pp. 25–43; and *317*, pp. 34–55, cited in *231*, pp. 194–95).

A study of cocoa farmers in southwestern Nigeria, conducted by Galletti, Baldwin, and Dina, reports food consumption by 187 cocoa farmers for the year 1951/52 and gives a more detailed account of the diets of 33 families each surveyed for two weeks in August and November 1951 and in February and June 1952. Galletti and his associates warn that the latter survey is likely to underestimate maize consumption because some of the periods were too early and others too late for the maize harvest. Hence it is of little help to us and we shall not review it.

In the larger survey, which covered the entire year, maize was of major importance only in Ibadan, where it supplied 24.6 percent of total calories (Table 8-4).

Bascoulergue and Bergot provide information on five rural areas and Brazzaville in Moyen-Congo, former French Equatorial Africa. In each village studied the sample of families surveyed was drawn equally from families with two to four, with five to eight, and with nine or more members. For each family observed, food consumption was measured for a week, except at Kibouendé, where the surveyors were in the village 15 months and every family was surveyed twice, for a week each time. Except to note that 258 families were studied in 35 villages, the authors do not give details as to the size of the samples drawn.

Maize was not recorded in two surveys, but these were each only a month or so in length and probably not in the season for maize. In the text of their report Bascoulergue and Bergot note that "Maize is cultivated everywhere but in small quantity. Most of it is consumed where it is harvested" (35, p. 33), probably meaning as roasting ears in the field. In none of the areas surveyed was maize important, being always an insignificant supplier of calories compared with either manioc and manioc products or banana-plantain (35, pp. 29, 31, 32, and 34):

Foodstuff	% of starchy-staple calories					
	Sou-anké	Min-douli	Kiboy-endé	Brazza-ville	Mas-sendjo	Madingo-Kayes
Maize	4.5	4.0	2.3	1.2	0.0	0.0
Manioc and manioc products	12.5	91.1	95.7	97.8	88.6	90.6
Banana-plantains	80.6	0.8	0.5	0.4	1.7	5.3
Yams	0.6	2.5	0.6	0.3	8.2	1.7
Sweet potatoes	0.6	1.1	0.9	0.3	0.6	0.6
Taro	1.1	0.5	0.0	0.0	0.8	1.7
Total	99.9[a]	100.0	100.0	100.0	99.9[a]	99.9[a]

[a] Percentages have been rounded.

A 1947 survey of three localities in Bas-Congo District of the Belgian Congo by V. Drachoussoff, based on interview rather than actual measurement, estimated manioc to account for from 47 to 73 percent of calories consumed; maize, rice, and banana-plantain were the next most important starchy-staples, accounting for from 1 to 3 percent each, according to locale (127, pp. 80–81, cited in 231, p. 202).

A survey near the mouth of the Congo River, in Vale de Loge (Cabinda District, Angola), reported on in 1956 at the Third Inter-African Nutrition Conference, Luanda (472), found maize not important enough to include among the starchy foodstuffs consumed; but probably some immature maize, at least, was part of the diet.

An exceptionally elaborate survey of diets carried out by G. M. Culwick found maize of only slight importance in Zande District of southwestern Sudan in 1947/48. The 37 to 47 Tabu households surveyed near

TABLE 8-4 — NIGERIAN COCOA FARMS: PERCENT OF TOTAL CAL-
ORIES SUPPLIED BY MAJOR FOODS, 1951/52, BY DISTRICTS AND TYPES
OF COMMUNITIES

Area	Maize %	Maize products %	Yams and yam products %	Manioc and manioc products %	Other roots %	Other cereals %
Ibadan	4.2	20.4	10.5	37.2	0.9	0.5
Ifé-Ilesha	2.0	7.9	25.6	24.6	0.2	5.6
Ondo	4.4	0.2	38.9	11.4	20.5	1.5
Abeokuta-Ijebu	1.0	2.9	3.1	51.3	3.9	9.1
All districts	3.0	9.5	19.9	30.4	4.4	3.8
Rural settlements	2.1	14.5	13.7	34.9	1.2	6.5
Market centers	6.5	3.3	29.0	18.7	7.3	1.2
Towns	2.1	5.4	24.6	30.4	8.2	1.3

Data from Galletti, Baldwin, and Dina, *Nigerian Cocoa Farmers* (London,
1956), pp. 491–92.

Yuba Station appeared to consume more maize than any other group,
but their maize consumption could not have been more than 13.2 percent
of starchy-staple calories consumed (Table 8-5).

Income Elasticity of Demand

Data from consumption surveys are not reliable enough to warrant calculation of the coefficient of income elasticity of demand for maize, but
they do suggest that the percentage of food outlays going for maize decreases as total expenditures increase (Chart 8-2).

Seasonality of Consumption

Maize consumption is highly seasonal where maize is of only slight importance in the diet. In such areas it is most often consumed immature
(as roasting ears); consequently the bulk of consumption is restricted
to a period of two to three weeks when the young grains are hard enough
to eat but not beyond stiff dough consistency. This is well illustrated in
Périssé's five surveys of Togo (see notes, Chart 8-3).

For the months when surveys were conducted, there was a good correlation between the variability of maize consumption and the impor-

tance of maize in the diet (Chart 8-3). From the coast northward, maize consumption progressively diminished from a daily average of 698 to 8 calories per person, and the range of consumption, relative to the mean, progressively increased:

Parameters	Attitogon	Kouma, Adamé	Akaba	Sahoude	Bombouka
(A) Range of maize consumption (highest month to lowest)	584	352	267	121	25
(B) Mean maize consumption	698.0	346.0	155.7	45.3	8.3
$\dfrac{A}{B}$	0.84	1.02	1.71	2.67	3.00

TABLE 8-5 — SUDAN: RELATIVE CALORIC CONTRIBUTION OF
STARCHY-STAPLES IN TABA DIETS, 1947/48
(Percent of calories from starchy-staples)

Foodstuff	Month			
	August (47 homes)	November (42 homes)	February (40 homes)	May (37 homes)
Maize (max.)[a]	13.2	4.2	3.7	2.8
Manioc and manioc products	72.3	68.7	59.6	81.4
Other starchy roots[b] and bananas	1.3	21.9	21.2	0.4
Eleusine (finger millet)	13.2	5.2	15.5	15.4
	100.0	100.0	100.0	100.0

Derived from G. M. Culwick, *A Dietary Survey among the Zande of the Southwestern Sudan* (Sudan, Ministry of Agriculture, 1950), p. 132, and W. O. Jones, *Manioc in Africa* (Food Res. Inst. Stud. in Trop. Devel., No. 2, Stanford, Calif., 1959), p. 145.

[a] Maize, sorghum, and rice are grouped together in Mrs. Culwick's tables, with a note that maize is the principal component of this category. The value shown here is the highest possible share that maize could represent; i.e. the percent obtained by assuming both sorghum and rice were zero.

[b] Mostly sweet potatoes.

CHART 8-2 — EXPENDITURES ON MAIZE AS PERCENTAGE OF
TOTAL FOOD OUTLAYS BY EXPENDITURE CLASS,
SELECTED BUDGET STUDIES

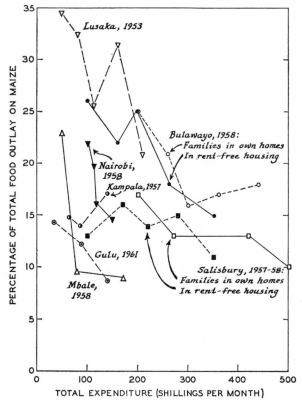

Data derived from H. Kaneda and B. F. Johnston, "Urban Food Expenditure
Patterns in Tropical Africa," *Food Res. Inst. Stud.*, 2, No. 3 (Nov. 1961): 232, 242,
244; from unpublished data calculated by Mr. Kaneda; from Southern Rhodesia,
Central African Statistical Office, *Preliminary Report on Urban African Budget
Surveys in Bulawayo, June 1958*, pp. 5–7; from Uganda, Ministry of Economic
Development, Statistics Branch, *The Patterns of Income, Expenditure and Con-
sumption of African Unskilled Workers in Gulu, February 1961* ([Entebbe], Aug.
1961), App. VI; and from files, Rhodes-Livingstone Institute, Lusaka, Zambia.
The number of months covered in the surveys was Nairobi, 4; Salisbury, 3; Lusaka,
2; Bulawayo, Mbale, Kampala, and Gulu, 1 each.

At Attitogon, maize consumption was lowest in May just before the
first harvest, while the high came in January, the month following the
second harvest. The highest value recorded at Kouma Adamé was in
June, the month of the main harvest, and was almost three times as large

CHART 8-3 — TOGO: SEASONAL VARIATION OF MAIZE
CONSUMPTION, SELECTED VILLAGES
(Calories per person per day)

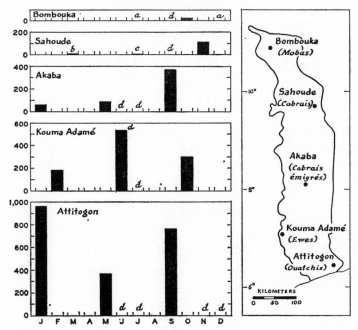

Derived from J. Périssé, *L'Alimentation des populations rurales du Togo*
(ORSTOM, Dec. 1959), Table 14. Surveys were conducted only in months for
which bars are shown here.

a Survey made but no maize found in diet.
b Seven calories per person per day.
c Four calories per person per day.
d Harvest month.

as the lowest (February). In the Akaba survey, maize consumption in
each of the two preharvest periods was only one-fourth to one-fifth as
much as in the survey two months after harvest. For Sahoude the largest
consumption in the preharvest period (March) was only one-eighth that
in the postharvest survey (November); and at Bombouka, the northernmost village, maize was found in the diet only in the postharvest survey.

In a 1954 survey at Evodoula, west-central Cameroun, much more
immature maize was purchased in the harvest months of June, July, and
December than in other months of the survey (*278*, Table 4, cited in
237, p. 143):

Period	*Grams purchased*		
	Immature ears of maize	*Maize grain*	*Total*
Feb.–Mar.	2.7	. . .	2.7
June–July	153.3	0.5	153.8
Sept.	. . .	1.2	1.2
Dec.	89.0	2.1	91.1

The survey of cocoa farmers in southwestern Nigeria in 1951/52 suggests a less marked seasonal pattern of total maize consumption. Yearly records of 187 families, reported by quarters, show the range of variation to be from 84 to 120 percent of the mean (*163*, pp. 489 and 891):

Period	*Calories per day*			*% of total food calories*
	Unprocessed maize	*Maize products*	*Total*	
June–Aug.	226	243	469	15.4
Sept.–Nov.	34	295	329	10.8
Dec.–Feb.	34	321	355	11.8
Mar.–May	86	321	407	13.0
Average	95	295	390	

The variation in unprocessed maize consumption, which reflects the seasonal availability of immature maize, was considerably greater, ranging from 36 percent of average in the dry season (September to February) to 238 percent of average during the main harvest of June to August. Consumption of maize products ranged narrowly, from 83 to 109 percent of average, and was greatest in the period when fresh maize was not available. The contribution maize made to the diet ranged from 10.8 to 15.4 percent of total food calories.

The most complete data on seasonal patterns of consumption come from a census of internal commerce in Ghana from October 1957 to September 1958.[5] Unless stocks or waste vary considerably monthly — and there is no reason to think that they do in Ghana [6] — these data should give a good notion of seasonal fluctuations in consumption.

There was considerable monthly variation in the amounts moving in commerce from one region to another; and for two sections for which data exist for earlier years, there was variation from year to year. In 1957/58

the coefficient of variation [7] in Sector I, the Keta area (Map 10-1, p. 180),
was 60, which was considerably larger than in the three preceding years:

	Coefficients of variation	
Year	*Sector I*	*Sector VI*
1957/58	60	40
1956/57	19	22
1955/56	42	38
1954/55	20	48

The profile of monthly movements in 1957/58 resembled that in 1955/
56 and 1956/57 fairly closely, but was inverse to that of 1954/55 for the
February to September period (Chart 8-4).

CHART 8-4 — GHANA: NET MONTHLY IMPORTS OF MAIZE,
SECTORS I AND VI, 1954/55–1957/58

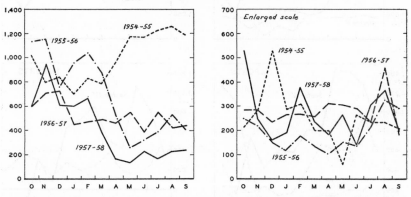

Data from files of the Ghana Government Statistician. See Map 10-1 for definition of sectors.

In Sector VI, the Sekondi-Takoradi area, the 1957/58 coefficient of
variation was considerably larger than the preceding year, but only slightly
larger than the 1955/56 figure and somewhat smaller than the 1954/55
coefficient. The pattern of movements of maize supplies resembles only
one of the preceding three years, 1955/56, in the October–June period,
although the profile fairly closely approximated each of the other years
in June, July, August, and September (Chart 8-4).

Only 1957/58 data are available for other areas; of these, the coefficient of variation ranged from 123 in Sector IX, comprising Northern

Ghana, roughly, where maize is consumed almost entirely as roasting ears, to 19 in Sector II (Map 10-1).

Exporting sectors generally had lower coefficients of variation; the average coefficient of variation was 36.7 for the three net exporting sectors and 65.5 for the six net importing sectors. In five of the nine sectors, maize shipments were largest in November, December, or January, and generally declined thereafter until May or June, rising to a secondary peak in July or August in most sectors (Chart 8-5).

CHART 8-5 — GHANA: NET MONTHLY EXPORTS AND IMPORTS
OF MAIZE, BY SECTOR, 1957/58 (metric tons)

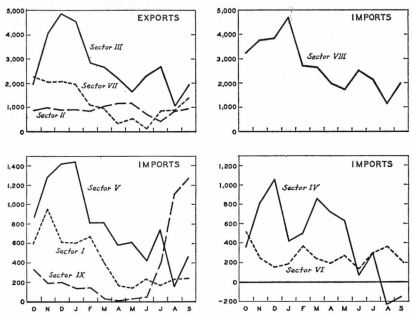

Data from files of the Ghana Government Statistician. See Map 10-1 for definition of sectors.

Sector IX, the area with the most atypical pattern, had poor harvests in 1957, and therefore imported unusually large supplies of maize. The rapid rise of imports from June to September probably reflects mainly shipments to relieve food shortage.

G. M. Culwick in her study of the Taba in southwestern Sudan recorded the percentage of house-days (defined as the number of houses times the number of days for which records were kept) maize was encountered between June 1947 and July 1948; the range was from zero in January and February to 48 percent in July, a harvest month (*111*, p. 145):

June	20	Dec.	2
July	48	Jan.	0
Aug.	44	Feb.	0
Sept.	18	Mar.	2
Oct.	5	Apr.	0.5
Nov.	7	May	0.7

Fluctuations of maize in the diet were roughly complementary to those of the millets and sorghums, sweet potatoes, yams, and bananas, but somewhat parallel to variations in the consumption of manioc, the major starchy-staple of the area.

9

MAIZE IN EASTERN AFRICA

MAIZE is the dominant staple in diets over relatively large areas of eastern Africa, but has become a major food only fairly recently. In much of the region it was developed as an export soon after colonization, and is still of considerable importance in trade.

RWANDA AND BURUNDI

One cannot establish with any certainty what the dominant staple crops of Rwanda-Burundi were before the advent of Belgian administration at the end of World War I, but it seems clear that manioc, maize, and sweet potatoes were grown very little, if at all, in most communities (*39*, p. 94, and *40*, p. 80, cited in *237*, p. 241). In fact, accounts of historical trade suggest that the inhabitants of Rwanda-Burundi may have obtained staple foods from the peoples of the valleys lying on either side of the high plateau containing the ancient kingdoms of Ruanda and Urundi, in exchange mainly for livestock and livestock products, beans, and peas (*260*, pp. 44 and 45). Such a pattern involves the type of specialization reported elsewhere in eastern and central Africa where differences in elevation have made the ecological zones occupied by neighboring peoples strikingly different (see *189* and *291*).

Beginning in 1922, the Belgian administration, alarmed by food shortages in one part or another of the country in nine of the previous twenty-five years, first encouraged, then ordered, Ruanda-Urundi farmers to grow sweet potatoes, Irish potatoes, and manioc because they were relatively resistant to drought and locusts. The campaign was intensified after a fairly severe famine was experienced in several regions in 1929 (*135*), and compulsory acreages continued to be an important part of policy for at least the next two decades.

There is some evidence that maize, although not encouraged by the government, became an important food crop in Ruanda-Urundi during

132

the same period (*136*, p. 585). In the parts of Urundi where it is a main staple, the elders are said to claim that it became a staple only in the past thirty or forty years (*71*).

UGANDA

Maize was apparently unknown in Uganda as late as the 1860's, and production was small as recently as forty-five years ago. In 1914 the Department of Agriculture reported that it was growing Hickory King and Yellow Hogan, imported varieties of maize, at Kadunguru Plantation "for introduction among the natives" (*435*, 1914, p. 13); and further details are given in its 1918 report (*435*, 1918, p. 13): "Maize production is being encouraged, and further supplies of seed have been distributed. It is mostly grown as a subsidiary food crop by the natives, although the grain-eating tribes are taking an increased interest in this important crop. Amongst the Buganda maize is chiefly grown for eating green, and as this tribe eats very little grain the extension of maize cultivation is slow in Buganda Province. The other provinces, however, are making fairly rapid strides in maize cultivation."

Thus in Uganda the government directly stimulated the production of maize in the second decade of this century. The government's role was also of notable importance in another way. Migrant labor, employed by the government and others (mostly as porters and workers for cotton gins or plantations), had, since the turn of the century, been mainly Baganda, who relied principally on plantains and sweet potatoes as staples. By 1918 the Baganda had turned from wage employment to the more remunerative production of cotton and coffee for sale; they were also hiring labor in order to increase their scale of production, and had become serious competitiors for available workers (*356*, p. 25). The government, forced to seek its labor elsewhere, seems to have obtained a predominance of "grain-eaters." Origin of laborers cannot be determined at all accurately, but the available evidence suggests that the Baganda were largely replaced by members of grain-eating peoples of the north and southwest: the Banyankole, Banyoro, Batoro, and Acholi (*356*, p. 36). Workers from these groups probably demanded grain for their ration, and may have been willing to accept maize.

There is also good economic reason to expect that it was maize they got. Where the government, mining companies, or plantations were employers, rations usually had to be imported; and only maize, among the starchy-staples, was both cheap — when account was taken of transport costs — and storable: roots, tubers, and banana-plantain could not be stored or transported cheaply without costly processing; rice and wheat were not cheap; and millets and sorghums, although competitive in price at the farm, were not so to the consumer, for their production was concentrated in a zone considerably farther from rail lines than the principal maize-producing areas.

Others besides laborers also received maize from the government on occasion: 1928 was a year of food shortage in some areas, and maize meal was distributed as relief, as it was in several later "famine" years.[1]

Here we have a hint of what was probably a major factor in the acceptance and spread of maize as a food crop: its preeminent importance following seasons of crop failure.

With harvests below normal, people anticipated short supplies and at the beginning of the next season frequently planted much more of their acreage than usual to an early-maturing variety of maize, having learned from experience that they could get an edible product from maize sooner than from any other starchy-staple. The result, when weather was favorable, was that considerably more maize was produced than could be consumed green, which provided scope and motivation for consuming a portion of the harvest not as roasting ears (a vegetable) but as a staple. This was possibly one of the principal situations in which dishes made from mature maize were tried. It may have been of key importance in the acceptance of maize as a staple rather than as a mere delicacy.

Reinforcing this development was the issuance of maize as a relief measure, for it was usually maize meal that was so distributed. At such times there was no choice but to devise ways of consuming it as a staple. In 1928 a further stimulus took the form of a reduction in the railway rates on maize flour. At the time, this was heralded by the Department of Agriculture as an event which extended the market of maize flour (imported) to all the protectorate (*435*, 1928, p. 12). A year later one finds reference to erection of several small maize mills in Buganda and Eastern provinces, the first mention of local production of products from mature maize among the plantain-eating peoples. The milling of maize was probably mostly for labor employed by plantations or the government,[2] but it certainly made maize more attractive as a staple, even if few consumed it that way at the time: neither plantain nor sweet potatoes lend themselves so well to mechanical processing, and in all likelihood an alternative product which could be mechanically processed was welcome.

In 1938 an agricultural officer of the northwestern corner of Uganda observed: "In Southern highlands portion of West Nile [District] also maize appears to be increasingly widely grown. There is at present no market for this maize and the fact that increased acreages of the same crop are being grown is presumably due to the fact that numbers of men have returned to the district with an acquired taste for maize as an article of diet" (*435*, 1938, p. 57). That there was no market for maize is questionable. The volume of interregional commerce in tropical Africa seems to be frequently underestimated; and since this area is adjacent to one of the mining areas of the Congo (Leopoldville), it is likely that maize surpluses were finding a market across the frontier. There may have been a trend toward increased per capita consumption, too, for there is a report that maize was introduced to the area only about 1925 (286), but thirty years later it seems to have been firmly established (392, pp. 242 and 243; and 391, p. 145). At present, qualitative evidence suggests maize to be of considerable importance as a staple in several of the northern and western areas. Perhaps migrant laborers generally, having received maize during a sojourn away from home, have attempted to continue their newly acquired dietary habits on their return.

During and immediately following World War II expansion of maize production was tremendous and deliberate. Uganda was called upon to produce as much maize as possible as part of her contribution to the war effort and to fill postwar deficits in Kenya and Tanganyika. Prices were guaranteed at a high level to encourage production, and in some years seed was issued. The African producer's response was immediate and in total impressive: acreage appears to have more than tripled before special incentives were removed in 1954 (435, various issues; and unpublished data provided by the Department of Agriculture):

Year	Acreage: all Uganda (acres of maize planted)	Price: Buganda Province (shillings per bag)
1939	93,183	a
1944	316,264	7
1945	157,721	8
1946	307,738	8
1947	258,233	10
1948	295,785	8
1949	314,643	10
1950	316,579	10
1951	267,965	14
1952	301,244	45
1953	661,902	30
1954	471,692	b
1955	379,564	b

a Price free; no data.

b Price free; estimated to have averaged 17 s. and 30 s. per bag in 1954 and 1955, respectively.

Increases in consumption of maize in rural areas must have been much less spectacular: exports were large; and the number of categories of labor given rations increased (*436*, 1946, p. 5), as did the labor force itself,[3] so that much of the additional production left after exports may have gone to laborers rather than to unrationed consumers. Even so, this was probably a period when consumption habits were changing, for when the maize campaign was relaxed in 1954 and Kenya prohibited further purchase of Uganda maize, in order to protect her own producers, acreages continued about the same. This may have been because of illegal exports to Kenya, where a high price was guaranteed. Kenya officials estimate illegal trade to have been on the order of 100,000 200-pound bags in 1955 (i.e. 48 percent of average gross exports to Kenya during the 1942/43–1952/53 period [*320; 420*, p. 1, col. 8]). However, unless illegal commerce was considerably larger — at least equal to that of the 1944–54 period — per capita consumption in Uganda must have increased, barring a drastic and sudden fall in yields. The labor force receiving maize as a ration appears to have declined slightly since 1953; and after 1954 there was a slight decline in the labor force itself from the level of the preceding five years (*436*, various issues).

An upward trend in maize consumption is suggested by surveys of expenditures by African laborers in Kampala, 1950–53 and in 1957. The increase was particularly striking among the Baganda, Batoro, and Banyankole (*423, 424, 428, 429*):

	Expenditure on maize as % of total food outlays			
Year	*Baganda*	*Banyankole*	*Batoro*	*Other Groups*[a]
1950	0.8	. . .	1.6	5.2
1951	0.7	4.4	0.1	9.4
1952	3.0	3.4	3.8	4.9
1953	7.7	24.9	18.4	28.2
1957	4.8	23.7	8.8	18.5

[a] Bakiya and Ruanda-Urundi, Congo, and Kenya groups.

The unusually high maize consumption in 1953 was largely because in that year maize was much cheaper per thousand calories, relative to plantains and manioc, than is normal.

KENYA

Prior to this century, maize appears to have been of little importance in diets in Kenya except along the coast and in the southeastern corner of the country. In the first decade of this century its use as a staple was beginning to spread. By 1907 the growing popularity of maize among African laborers of areas where heretofore it had been unimportant was striking enough to cause comment by at least two observers (*130*, p. 42; and *248*, 1907–8, p. 6). The Department of Agriculture, briefly analyzing this trend in its annual report, emphasized economic considerations: "An increasing desire on the part of the natives, in employment, for diet of mealie meal [maize meal] in place of matama flour [sorghum flour] has caused mealies to receive more attention lately and a larger area than usual was placed under this crop last season, while new and improved varieties have been introduced which is likely to have a marked effect on the yields as compared with those usually obtained from crops from the native seed" (*248*, 1907–8, p. 6). The following year it added: "Apart from its being a more palatable food than matama (Kaffir corn) [a variety of sorghum] so largely grown in the past, it is a more certain crop, requiring from four to five months to mature against seven months for matama. Two crops therefore can be grown within a year" (*248*, 1908–9, p. 13).

European production was expanding even more rapidly than that of Africans. In 1903 the production of the handful of settlers was of little significance. Quantities needed to feed railway gangs, African troops, porters, and the like were mainly imported from South Africa (*213*, p. 4). In 1904 came a large influx of immigrants, mostly from South Africa, and in 1908 and 1911 special parties were organized for "treks" from South Africa to Kenya (actually most of the journey was by boat; *213*, pp. 59 and 63). Maize was grown by most of these newcomers, but at first mainly for their own tables, as a ration for their African laborers, or as feed for their animals. Those near towns, forts, or labor camps probably sold sizable quantities, but high transport costs cut off markets more than a few miles away.[4] Most settlers were seeking their fortunes with other crops: ostrich farming, ranching, sisal growing were popular, and many crops were tried, usually to the farmers' regret. "This was the era of experiment. No one knew what to grow, when or where or how to grow it, or how to keep it alive. . . . Within the first decade of the century farmers tried almost everything" (*213*, p. 10).

An outbreak of east coast fever and other cattle diseases about this time, and disease difficulties with many of the crops introduced, together with a reduction in rail rates on maize and a favorable report on an experimental consignment of maize sent to London in 1909, encouraged those near the rail line to shift to maize. The value of maize exports increased from a little more than 1,000 to over 332,000 rupees between 1907–8 and 1911–12 (*245*, p. 8):

Year	Value of maize exported (rupees)
1907–8	1,154
1908–9	40
1909–10	46,740
1910–11	106,742
1911–12	332,541

During the First World War, because of a large demand by local military forces, exports of maize practically ceased, but production probably continued to increase. For 1916–17, the only war year for which data are available, sales to military forces alone were 143 percent of exports in the peak prewar year, according to the annual report of the Kenya Department of Agriculture (*248*, 1916–17, p. 6); and in all probability the emergency was accompanied by an increase in the civil labor force receiving rations. On the other hand, over 85 percent of the European men of the protectorate who were of military age are reported to have joined the armed forces (*213*, p. 32). With many farms unattended, an increase of production would have been difficult.

By 1923, a further stimulus to production came in the form of another reduction in the freight rate for maize, and it was changed to a flat rate to encourage production in the more remote regions, as the Economic and Finance Committee had recommended in 1923. Sir Charles Bowring, chairman of this committee, argued that specializing in maize production was in the economic interest both of the colony and of the railroad, which had considerable involuntary excess capacity owing to lack of freight. He noted that capital was scarce and that maize gave a quick return, providing funds with which the colonist could develop his holding. As for the African, "the cultivation of maize afforded an ideal occupation and one eminently suited to his method of life and social custom. Unlike the cultivation of other more valuable crops such as coffee, for instance, it presented neither the spread of disease by ignorant and negligent methods of cultivation nor the temptation of theft" (*247*, p. 1).

The government gave further aid to maize growers at the same time by an advance to the newly formed Plateau Maize Growers' Association "for the purchase of oxen and wagons to enable them to bring their crops to the railway" (*247*, p. 2). This group was composed primarily of Boers who had pushed far beyond the existing settlements on their arrival at the Uasin Gishu Plateau. They had been isolated and little affected by the initial development of an export market before the war of 1914–18, but in 1922 the railroad was being extended toward the plateau on its way to Uganda. A group of 113 farmers, foreseeing the possibility of furnishing maize for the construction gangs, formed an association in 1923 to negotiate for contracts with the railroad (*213*, p. 70).

Other developments had also been leading to a concentration on maize. Shortly before the First World War there had been a catastrophic slump in the market for ostrich feathers; and just after the war, in 1920, flax prices crashed (*213*, pp. 10 and 43).

In 1923 the first of five annual conferences on maize marketing was held, and arguments for grading the crop prior to export were made. The foundation had been laid for development of an export industry; with the number of settlers almost doubling in the 1920–30 decade (*204*, p. 3057), maize acreage increased almost every year until 1929–30 (*245*, p. 8):

Year	European maize (acres harvested)
1919–20	32,167
1920–21	30,846
1921–22	57,131
1922–23	74,747
1923–24	108,556
1924–25	129,647
1925–26	155,751
1926–27	177,987
1927–28	177,009
1928–29	204,945
1929–30	233,973

In the 1930's farmers responded to sagging world prices with smaller acreages. Production would have been cut back sooner had gold not been discovered in 1931 in western Kenya, which meant an expansion of domestic consumption to feed the mining labor (*248*, 1935, p. 98). By the end of the depression acreages had dropped considerably; in the 1939–40 crop year they were only 42 percent, and in 1941–42 a mere 29 percent, of the peak years of 1928/29–1930/31 (*245*, p. 8):

Year	European maize (acres harvested)
1930–31	200,926
1931–32	160,546
1932–33	164,018
1933–34	112,949
1934–35	a
1935–36	117,848
1936–37	a
1937–38	113,103
1938–39	a
1939–40	93,517
1940–41	a
1941–42	63,100

a No census.

While Europeans were discovering maize as a cash crop, so were Africans, and more important, discovering it to be a relatively productive and agreeable staple.[5]

Besides the great yields it offered, maize was popular because it gave a whiter flour than the traditonal millets and sorghums. This had not always been so. In 1903 when the Department of Agriculture began to concern itself with maize, colored varieties predominated. As in other parts of Africa, government policy in large measure precipitated a change in the pattern of starchy-staple foods grown, even if its influence was indirect: one of the first activities of the Department of Agriculture was to distribute the improved white varieties of maize from South Africa (213, p. 4). Where the export market developed, white varieties were found more suitable for sale overseas (245, p. 7); this provided further incentive for distributing seed. African areas near the railway got first priority, since they accounted for the bulk of the African crop marketed for export (248, 1925, p. 18); in these areas the Department of Agriculture attempted to eliminate existing colored varieties (204, p. 3067; and 248, 1930, p. 40). Around 1930 several district agricultural officers reported that colored seed had been almost entirely eliminated in their areas. For the same period there are a number of reports of increases in maize acreage at the expense of the millets and sorghums; but except around Nairobi and to the southeast of it maize was rarely of more than secondary importance as a staple (196, p. 2208; 312, p. 2262; 81, 2: 2362; 268, p. 1972; and 147, p. 977). Possibly these observers were merely noting the culmination of a gradual process that had begun two to three decades earlier; but it may also reflect a fairly close link between the availability of white maize seed and maize acreage. It is not unlikely that there was a fairly rapid shift in response to the seed issues of the Department of Agriculture, which not only were of the preferred color but also gave perceptibly higher yields than local maize or competing staples (335, p. 1047).[6]

Local administrative authorities at the time also cited the superiority of maize to sorghum in resisting attack by locusts, as an important factor in the trend toward maize for at least one ethnic group; this may have been important generally (57, p. 2379). Locusts invaded Kenya from 1929 to 1931, ruining crops in a number of areas. Where their destruction resulted in food shortage, it was usually maize that could be shipped to tide over a period of hunger. The result seems to have been that "many people tasted . . . [maize] flour who had never done so before" (57, p. 2379).

Thus, although the evidence is thin, the importance of occasional food shortages in initiating and stimulating consumption of maize in staple forms seems to have been much the same in Kenya and in Uganda.

In some African areas increases in the production of maize, not as a staple but as a cash crop, were even more striking. In the region around Lake Victoria and extending north to Mt. Elgon, many African farmers seem to have recognized the value of the plow and the significance of the railway extension as readily as the neighboring Europeans did. For instance, annual sales of plows in this zone are reported to have grown from 100 in 1928 to 200 in 1929, and then to 300 in 1930 (248, 1930, p. 39).[7]

Once the means for a much larger scale of production were available, a rapid expansion of acreage was possible, and in some areas phenomenal increases in maize marketed were achieved. In Kavirondo District the value of maize marketed in South Kitosh Division increased 29-fold between 1931 and 1936, and in North Kitosh Division it increased eight-fold between 1932 and 1935 (451, p. 36; and 248, 1935, p. 99):

	Long tons of maize marketed	
Year	South Kitosh	North Kitosh
1931	116	. . .
1932	. . .	410
1933	418	965
1934	982	2,100
1935	2,593	3,260
1936	3,325	. . .

In other areas of this region, the opening of gold mines greatly expanded the local market and thereby encouraged adoption of maize as a cash crop (*248*, 1935, p. 98).

During World War II Kenya, like Uganda, was called on to produce all the food it could. As soon as Kenya's role was clearly defined (in 1941), its government guaranteed maize prices to European producers of 6.34 shillings per bag, 134 percent of the level of the previous year (*213*, pp. 134 and 135). In 1942 and 1943 the support level was boosted another 23 and 38 percent, respectively. Farmers responded immediately, and by the end of the war acreage had about doubled (Table 9-1). After the emergency, guaranteed prices were steadily raised in order to subsidize European agriculture.

TABLE 9-1 — KENYA: EUROPEAN AND ASIAN PRODUCERS, MAIZE ACREAGE, MARKETINGS, AND PRICES RECEIVED, 1941–42 TO 1957–58

Year	Prices received by European and Asian producers[a] (shillings per bag, f.o.r.)	Acreage (acres planted)	Marketings (1,000 bags of 200 lbs.)
1941–42	6.34[b]	63,100	. . .
1942–43	7.80	81,561	. . .
1943–44	10.80	107,686	600
1944–45	11.40	119,934	528
1945–46	11.40	124,855	552
1946–47	15.90	110,211	508
1947–48	20.00	108,060	379
1948–49	20.00	120,925	616
1949–50	23.40	133,164	737
1950–51	28.80	144,777	763
1951–52	30.30	141,927	755
1952–53	42.25	140,510	638
1953–54	42.12	164,827	784
1954–55	40.35	173,998	1,202
1955–56	40.35	157,870	887
1956–57	42.48	166,285	867
1957–58	42.48	166,689	1,015

Data from Kenya, Department of Agriculture, *The Maize Industry*, Sessional Paper No. 6 of 1957/58 (Nairobi, 1958), Table A; and *idem., Food Shortage Commission of Inquiry Report, 1943* (Nairobi, 1943), p. 8.

[a] Includes the cost of the bag.

[b] Price paid by Kenya Farmers' Association, 1941–42.

African producers appear to have increased production during this period, but their response can be only roughly traced. Actual prices paid to African producers were fixed at a lower level through various deductions and taxes, some of which varied according to district; data on these are not available. Acreages planted by Africans are not known. Marketings increased on the whole, but varied considerably from year to year.

TANGANYIKA

At the beginning of the twentieth century maize was a staple in only small areas of Tanganyika and was probably unknown over much of the country. In the northeastern corner of the trusteeship, it was a staple crop of the Akamba, at least; in parts of the southwest and west it appears not to have been grown at all as late as 1880 (*415*, pp. 209 and 316). Throughout most of the rest of Tanganyika maize seems to have been known but unimportant (*415*, pp. 105, 268, and 317; and *396*, p. 651). No relevant data have been found for the first decade of this century; but by 1915 demand had been stimulated by the needs of the military forces, and production increases were strongly encouraged or possibly forced by the government.

During several years in the first decade after World War I the government distributed seed (*407*, various issues), and toward the end of the decade an agricultural officer noted that in the northeastern corner of the country "the maize crop is increasing in popularity with the planters [settlers] and native farmers" (*407*, 1929/30, p. 6). This was a period when not enough maize was marketed to meet the needs of sisal and other plantations; it had to be imported from Kenya to feed plantation labor, as it has frequently been since (*407*, 1928, p. 4, and 1931, p. 27). As the effects of the 1929 world depression were felt, the administration began to view imports as undesirable, and encouraged maize production as a move toward economic self-sufficiency (*407*, 1931, p. 27). By 1933 producers in northeastern Tanganyika were finding local needs much expanded because of the demands of the gold mines (*407*, 1933, p. 32, and 1935, pp. 26 and 39). African production increased, and European population in the Mt. Kilimanjaro area expanded (*407*, 1935, p. 39).

The next major influence on maize production was World War II; in 1942 prices were fixed to producers in an effort to meet wartime production goals, and bonus payments for acreage expansion soon followed (*407*, 1942, p. 1, and 1946, p. 37). Despite these incentives, demand for maize outran production; and during most of the war and early postwar years Tanganyika was a net importer, drawing on Uganda and Kenya. Fixed prices were continued and increased steadily for a decade following the war. When surpluses arose in the early 1950's, government responded by replacing fixed prices with support prices in 1955, and then in 1957 reducing them to 66 percent of the level of 1956.

In 1958 the Central Advisory Committee on Nutrition of the Ministry of Social Services requested district nutrition teams to evaluate the kinds of change in diet that had occurred with an increase in disposable income. Of 20 districts where trends were reported, maize was replacing millets, sorghum, or manioc in six. In another ten maize was already the staple; but in six of these ten, high income groups showed a tendency to consume wheat products or rice rather than maize (406). The overall impression conveyed by the reports of district nutrition teams is that maize is, or is becoming, the staple of the low and middle income groups, while those who can afford rice and wheat products have begun to substitute these commodities for maize.

MOZAMBIQUE

Maize was probably well established as a staple food in parts of Mozambique at the beginning of this century, but commercial production seems to have been of little importance. In a book on Mozambique's agricultural development published in 1913, Lyne states: "Maize is a staple crop with the natives, but no European has yet established maize-growing as his main business. The highlands of Quelimane may prove a good granary by and by. . . . The cultivation of maize has been carried to a high pitch of excellence in the Transvaal, under the guidance of Mr. Butt Davy. . . . The influence of the Transvaal is being already felt in Lourenço Marques, and maize-growing in the country will continue to develop under it" (264, pp. 133 and 134).

Exports increased from an average of 10,900 metric tons in 1911–15 to 30,900 tons in 1921–25 and reached 34,000 tons in 1926 (309, p. 146). Most of this trend is to be explained by development of production in the Chimoio Valley, then by far the most important area of European production (Map 9-1, Sec. A). A description of the Mozambique economy published in 1920 by the British Foreign Office underscores the rapid expansion of maize production in this area:

The cultivation of maize has made notable progress in recent years, especially in the territory of the Mozambique Chartered Company. A large tract of country between Massikessi and the coast plain has proved suitable for maize-growing, and settlers are readily taking up farms for this purpose. The advance in production is shown by the returns of maize exported from Beira; the figures were 2,325 tons in 1912, 6,673 in 1913, 9,745 in 1914, and 9,100 in 1916. Cultivation has been stimulated in the last few years by the action of the Portugese Government in commandeering the whole export for European consumption, and by the satisfactory system of grading and testing instituted

MAP 9-1 — MOZAMBIQUE: EUROPEAN MAIZE PRODUCTION AND TRENDS, AFRICAN MAIZE MARKETING TRENDS, AND PRINCIPAL AREAS PRODUCING EXPORT CROPS

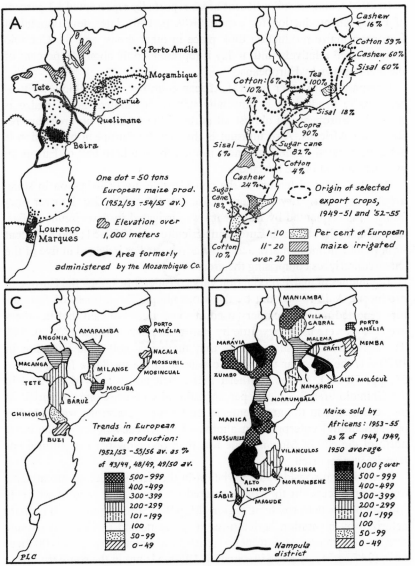

Data from, or derived from, Mozambique, Repartição Técnica de Estatística, *Estatística agrícola* (Lourenço Marques), various issues; and from Junta de Exportação do Algodão, *Esboço do reconhecimento ecológico-agrícola de Moçambique,* Vol. 1 (Lourenço Marques, 1955).

at Beira in 1914 by the maize expert of the Mozambique Company (*178*, p. 64).

In 1924 Chimoio and adjacent areas reportedly represented 83 percent of European production for export (*309*, p. 146); later development of European maize production took place in other areas, and the Chimoio area declined relatively until today it represents only about 48 percent of the maize grown by Europeans.

Compared with other tropical African countries, Mozambique's European maize production is unusually widely distributed. Some maize is grown by Europeans in almost all parts of the country; no areas are reserved for Africans. Also unusual is the fact the European production is not concentrated in the highlands; in fact, the southern belt of European production is all in the lowlands.

Another atypical feature is the considerable use of irrigation in some areas. In the fairly dry southern maize belt (Map 9-1, Sec. B) over one-faith of maize planted by Europeans was irrigated in two circunscrições, according to the census of European agriculture in 1950–51; and 8 percent or more of European maize acreage was reported as irrigated in five of the ten circunscrições comprising the area.

Techniques of maize production vary considerably among the European producers. A 1946 account by the Mozambique Department of Agriculture reported much machinery used in some areas but said that in others even plows were used very little by European maize farmers (*301*, p. 84). The agricultural census suggests that there was still wide variation in 1950–51, the last year for which census data are available (*300*, 1950–51, pp. 704–7). In the southern maize belt an average of 2.7 and in the Chimoio area 2.3 plows per agricultural enterprise were reported in the census; but in the area centered on Guruè the average was only 0.6 per agricultural enterprise. In almost all the circunscrições on the coast north of the city of Moçambique less than one plow per agricultural enterprise was reported.

There is also considerable variation in the size of holdings among European producers. In the zone centered on Guruè, the core of which is Mozambique's tea-producing region (Map 9-1, Sec. B) and which is characterized by plantation agriculture, 70 percent, and in Chimoio circunscrição 56 percent, of European agricultural enterprises were 100 hectares (247 acres) or more in extent in 1950–51; but in the southern maize belt and in the upper Zambezi Basin 70 percent or more — and in several circunscrições 100 percent — of European agricultural enterprises were less than 100 hectares (*300*, 1950–51, pp. 33–66).

Throughout Mozambique Europeans grow maize to feed their African laborers and to supply the needs of towns, cities, and other nonself-sufficient centers where numbers of Africans are employed (*301*, p. 83). In the southern maize belt, maize is grown to supply the requirements of cashew, cotton, and sugarcane growers (Map 9-1, Sec. B),[8] and to provision Lourenço Marques. Much of the European maize production in this region is in alluvial valleys where maize is grown with bananas (*301*, p. 84).

In central Mozambique, European maize production is mainly to meet the requirements of sugarcane and copra plantations, and the ports of Beira and Quelimane. The concentration of European production in the Chimoio area suggests that central Mozambique may be a surplus area supplying the cashew, sisal, and cotton plantations of areas where European maize production is relatively small. This was true a decade or so ago, but the surplus of central Mozambique has been falling, and records of coastal trade suggest the reverse in recent years. Central Mozambique appears to be a deficit area, for maize moves from the north to central and southern Mozambique (see Map 9-2). Since European maize production is small in the north, African producers must be responsible for most of the surplus of that area.

Although data from the agricultural census do not suffice to determine the scale of European agriculture, they support the impression of a mixture of small farms and plantations that one gets when traveling in northern and central Mozambique, and from observers who have visited the southern areas. Small holders probably account for a small part of total maize production. Only Mozambique, possibly other Portuguese possessions, and Malagasy in tropical Africa contain considerable numbers of small European farms which make little use of machinery. In economic terms Mozambique represents the opposite end of the spectrum from European maize production in adjacent areas — Tanganyika, Zambia, Rhodesia, and Malawi — and in Kenya.

In southern Mozambique, at least, techniques employed in African maize production are conspicuously more advanced than in most of tropical Africa. The Mozambique Department of Agriculture reported that several thousand plows were being used by Africans in the southern maize belt in 1944 (*301*, p. 86).

Trends in European Production in Mozambique

Quantitative data are not available on trends prior to 1929, and yearly data seem to begin only in 1939; but qualitative information suggests that European production increased steadily until 1929–30, when it stood at 41,000 metric tons (*301*, p. 83). Production declined sharply during the depression of the 1930's, when low maize prices caused farmers to turn to other export crops (*155*, p. 20; and *161*, p. 370). European production 1939–40 to 1943–44 and 1948-49 to 1955–56 was as follows (*301*, p. 83; *299*; and *300*, various issues):

Year	Metric tons	Year	Metric tons
1939–1940	28,993	1950–1951	23,871
1940–1941	30,327	1951–1952	28,323
1941–1942	32,884	1952–1953	25,740
1942–1943	30,477	1953–1954	28,516
1943–1944	27,812	1954–1955	27,180
1948–1949	25,568	1955–1956	31,278
1949–1950	34,976		

Mozambique's maize exports declined from an average of 28,000 tons in 1926–30 to 5,000 tons in 1934–38, all of which came from the area administered by the Mozambique Company, principally the Chimoio area, in 1932, 1933, and 1934 (*155*, pp. 61 and 82; *241*, p. 58; and *242*, pp. 16 and 78):

Year	Maize exported from area administered by Mozambique Company (metric tons)	Maize exported from other areas of Mozambique (metric tons)
1925	2,900	10,240
1927	20,796	8,693
1928	19,162	14,175
1930	6,641	25,015
1931	8,922	2,436
1932	4,616	0
1933	3,662	0
1934	4,590	0
1935–39	3,260	3,195
1940–44	1,957	827

Before the 1930's, maize marketing in Mozambique was unrestricted, except for local restrictions or incentives set occasionally by provincial governors to stimulate production of maize or to prevent it from being ex-

MAP 9-2 — MOZAMBIQUE: COASTAL MAIZE TRADE, 1953

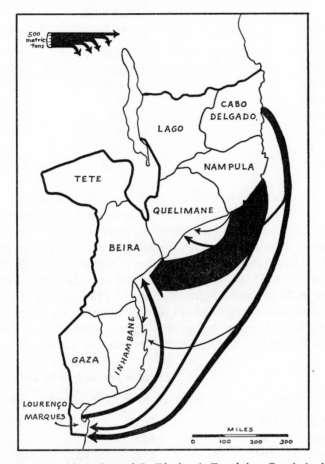

Data from Mozambique, Repartição Técnica de Estatística, *Comércio de cabota-gem* (Lourenço Marques, 1955), p. 11.

ported to other areas in times of shortages (*301*, p. 88). In 1936 the Mozambique Company created the Junta do Comércio do Milho e Sua Farinha to assist maize growers in the area it administered (*301*, p. 88). This body, and its successors — the Comissão Directora do Comércio do Milho and the Grémio dos Productores de Cereais do Distrito de Beira — set support prices and bought and sold maize. Prices paid by the Grémio and received by it from 1937 to 1944 were as follows (*301*, p. 90):

	Escudos per metric ton	
Year	Price paid to producers	Price paid by consumers
1937	630	727
1938	688	771
1939	688	771
1940	590	797
1941	701	797
1942	712	855
1943	750	891
1944	913	1,060

In 1938 the Junta de Exportação dos Cereais das Colónias was created by Decree No. 28,889 and given the authority to define grades; to control production, domestic commerce, and exports; to coordinate the activities of merchants in supplying the colonial and metropolitan markets; and to fix prices at farm and retail, subject to the approval of the Ministry of Agriculture (301, p. 88). This junta did not effectively exercise its authority in Mozambique before the end of 1944 (301, p. 88); in the meantime prices were regulated in Lourenço Marques, the most important urban market for maize, by another agency. Beginning in 1941, the Comissão Reguladora do Importação set prices as follows (301, p. 89):

	Escudos per sack of 90 kilograms		
Date	At farm	Wholesale	Retail
Feb. 12, 1941	70.0	. . .	85.5
Sept. 24, 1941	85.0	. . .	. . .
Aug. 22, 1942	85.0	93.0	105.0
July 19, 1944	125.0	. . .	140.0

By 1946–50 Mozambique was a net importer, and in the 1956–60 period her net imports averaged almost as much as net exports did in the peak years of the period before the depression of the 1930's (Table 9-2).

The change from a net exporter to a net importer of maize in the 1940's was probably the result of rapidly growing internal demand and unfavorable producer prices. Oliveira Boléo, in an analysis published in 1951, reported that commercial production had fallen off and was becoming irregular because of relatively low yields from maize and low, as well as irregular, prices for the crop (56, p. 443).

That internal demand has increased considerably in some recent years is

MAIZE IN EASTERN AFRICA 151

TABLE 9-2 — MOZAMBIQUE: NET EXTERNAL TRADE IN MAIZE,
SELECTED YEARS, 1911–60

Year	Net Exports (1,000 metric tons)
1911–15	10.9
1916–20	19.9
1921–25	30.9
1926–30	28.2
1934–38	5.0
1940–44	2.8
1946–50	− 1.6
1951–55	−12.0
1956	−28.7
1957	1.2
1958	−29.1
1959	−21.8
1960	−10.9

Data from C. de Melo Vieira, *L'Agriculture* [Mozambique], published for the Exposition Coloniale Internationale (Paris, 1931), p. 18; FAO, *Yearbook of Food and Agricultural Statistics*, Pt. 2: Commerce (Rome), various issues; and Mozambique, Direcção dos Serviços de Economia e Estatística, *Estatística agrícola* (Lourenço Marques), various issues. Negative amounts are net imports.

reflected in an increase in imports, and in amounts of maize marketed internally by Africans, while European production and consumption remained fairly steady (Tables 9-2 and 9-3).

Over the post-World War II period, for which data are available, the decline in total European production appears to have been arrested, but some areas have become less important while production expanded in others (Map 9-1, Sec. C). The areas with the sharpest increment of production all show large expansion of maize acreage, probably in response to greater demand by employers of African labor. The number of man-days worked by wage-earning Africans increased 11 percent from 1948 to 1954 (*299*, various issues):

Year	Thousand man-days worked by wage-earning Africans
1948	36,053
1949	36,446
1950	. . .
1951	37,920
1952	36,327
1953	39,848
1954	40,487

TABLE 9-3 — MOZAMBIQUE: TOTAL MAIZE AVAILABLE FOR CON-
SUMPTION, EXCLUDING CHANGES IN STOCKS, 1944 AND 1949–54
(1,000 metric tons)

Year	African marketings	European production less on-farm consumption	Net imports	Total maize available for consumption excluding changes in stocks
1944	27.9	18.2	−9.1	30.8
1949	35.0	22.9	3.7	53.1
1950	37.5	15.0	−6.1	46.4
1951	31.0	19.9	21.9	72.8
1952	29.9	17.8	30.4	78.1
1953	39.3	18.6	−1.5	56.4
1954	34.7	18.8	0.6	54.1

Data from, or derived from, Mozambique, Repartição Técnica de Estatística, *Estatística agrícola* (Lourenço Marques), various issues. Negative amounts are net exports.

The largest expansion of production was in areas supplying port cities. Most of the other areas that exhibit increasing production trends are isolated zones where maize was probably a much less attractive crop until its price increased or transportation costs were reduced, both phenomena that seem to be characteristic of the post-World War II period. The importance of transportation is suggested by the fact that even today European maize production is concentrated along the railroads (Map 9-1, Sec. A). Table 9-4 shows prices paid in 1944, 1949, 1950, and 1953–55 to African producers in areas of acreage expansion. European producers probably received price increases equal to or greater than those paid to Africans.

In two areas, Tete and Báruè, prices paid for maize were slightly lower in 1953–55 than in 1944, 1949, and 1950. In all of the other areas where acreage increased, prices were higher in the later period, and in the areas with the greatest growth of maize production — Porto Amélia, Mocuba, Amaramba, Angónia, and Macanga — they were considerably higher.

In Tete, Mossuril, and Milange circunscrições, improved yields help explain the expansion of production. Decline of yields is the primary cause of decline in production in Chimoio and Buzi circunscrições, the oldest zone of European maize production. Yields of Chimoio and Buzi circunscrições combined averaged only 0.71 metric tons per hectare in the 1948/49–54/55 period and were lower in the later part of the pe-

TABLE 9-4 — MOZAMBIQUE: AVERAGE MAIZE PRICES PAID
AFRICAN PRODUCERS IN SELECTED CIRCUNSCRIÇÕES,
1944, 1949–50, AND 1953–55
(Escudos per kg.)

Circunscrição	1944, 1949, 1950	1953, 1954, 1955
Milange	0.653	0.960
Tete	1.053	1.000
Angónia	0.700	0.875
Macanga	0.743	0.843
Mogincual	0.831	0.863
Báruè	0.937	0.920
Amaramba	0.656	0.807
Mocuba	1.000	1.063
Mossuril	0.913	0.950
Porto Amélia	0.726	1.010

Data from Mozambique, Repartição Técnica de Estatística, *Estatística agrícola* (Lourenço Marques), various issues.

riod than in the first years. The 1948/49–54/55 average was only 55 percent of the 1930 and 1931 yields for European maize in the area administered by the Mozambique Company, and at that time European maize of that area appears to have been grown chiefly in Chimoio and Buzi circunscrições. Yield declines may be largely a result of maize monoculture. Around 1930 there was already concern over yield reductions that had resulted from lack of rotations. J. Pyke, British consul for Mozambique, commented at the end of 1929 that yields were low because "Farming has been conducted without regard to the necessary rotation of crops, and a great deal of land is so thoroughly exhausted that it is unlikely to recover its former fertility . . ." (*359*, p. 26).

Acreage reductions explain most of the fall in production in Nacala circunscrição. Yields in areas with clear yield trends in the years 1944–45 to 1954–55 [9] were as follows (*299*, various issues):

Metric tons of maize per hectare

Circunscrição	1944-45	1948-49	1949-50	1950-51	1951-52	1952-53	1953-54	1954-55
Mossuril	0.91	0.58	0.79	1.45	1.15	1.06	1.03	0.98
Milange	. . .	0.81	1.00	0.72	0.98	1.06	1.05	1.08
Chimoio	0.98	0.77	1.10	0.58	0.82	0.58	0.66	0.62
Buzi	1.12	0.55	0.76	0.26	0.27	0.34	0.33	0.50
Nacala	0.59	0.78	0.63	0.92	0.69	0.58	0.63	0.69

Trends in African Marketings

Estimates of amounts of maize sold to stores by Africans suggest that African maize marketings in Mozambique have steadily increased in absolute terms as well as relative to European production (*299*, various issues):

Year	African marketings to stores (1,000 metric tons)	African marketings as % of European production
1939	17.1	59
1941–44	18.8	62
1949–52	31.2	110
1953–55	48.5	167
1956–58	33.7	. . .

Only in a section of the northern coastal region did marketings decline. In almost all areas on the western border they rose sharply (Map 5-1, Sec. D), which suggests that part of the increase may be explained by a differing movement of prices in the Federation of Rhodesia and Nyasaland and in Mozambique which would make it advantageous for Federation Africans near the border to smuggle their maize into Mozambique. The Mozambique Department of Agriculture has asserted that the increases in maize purchases in two of these circunscrições, Milange and Morrumbala, were sharply upward in the 1939–44 period — by 503 and 83 percents respectively — largely because of illegal shipments across the border from Nyasaland (*301*, p. 93). Price data available for Nyasaland suggest this has not been the case, however, for later years. Prices to African producers in Nyasaland were constant at 16s. 8d. per 200-lb. bag from 1949 to 1955, while in six of Mozambique's eight circunscrições on the Nyasaland border with strong increases in maize marketing in 1944, 1949, 1950 to 1953–55, maize prices fell during 1949–55 (*326*, p. 13; and *300*, various issues):

Circunscrição	Escudos per kilogram						
	1949	1950	1951	1952	1953	1954	1955
Maniamba	0.62	0.63	0.61	0.59	0.62	0.57	0.57
Vila Cabral	0.69	0.68	0.59	0.66	0.67	0.62	0.59
Morrumbala	1.04	1.25	1.00	0.82	0.89	1.01	1.00
Angónia	0.85	1.00	0.96	0.90	0.93	0.85	0.84

Macanga	0.81	1.02	0.99	0.94	0.90	0.85	0.78
Tete	1.22	1.25	1.00	1.01	0.94	0.92	1.02
Amaramba	0.75	0.75	0.79	0.86	0.84	0.80	0.78
Milange	0.64	0.79	1.10	1.01	0.94	0.92	1.02

The increased sales of African maize in Mozambique are probably to be explained by changes in the relative prices received for maize and other crops sold by Africans.

Decline in African maize marketings in Nampula District, the administrative division containing the circunscrições with downward trends, appears to reflect continuation of a trend that started in the 1930's. Pyke noted that in 1928 the maize surplus from Nampula District had increased "by more than 100 percent over the previous year, amounting to 18,200 tons" (359, p. 26). In 1944 Africans of this district sold 3,495, and Europeans produced 1,080, metric tons of maize, a total of only 4,575 metric tons, even assuming all European production was surplus, which is not likely. From 1949 to 1955 the maximum surplus possible was considerably lower yet (300, various issues):

Year	Purchases from Africans (metric tons)	European production (metric tons)
1944	3,495	1,080
1949	236	1,084
1950	502	1,528
1951	1,024	1,735
1952	1,201	1,616
1953	266	1,308
1954	412	1,649
1955	687	1,597

MALAWI

Maize probably gained its predominant position in Nyasaland diets after Livingstone's visits in the mid-1800's (467, p. 128; 359; and 330), and before 1910, the date of the first published report by British administrators which describes the protectorate's agriculture (328, 1910, p. 9). In that year the director of agriculture, commenting on export of maize for the first time, reported a steady rise in its price on markets in the British Isles during the preceding thirteen years, and said he thought that maize might become a major export when transportation costs were reduced by extension of the railway (*328*, 1910, p. 9). But after 2,000 long tons had been exported in both 1910 and 1911, drought struck areas near the rail line in 1912 and there was no surplus to export. Nor was any maize exported in the following years. Small exports, 90 and 523 tons, were shipped in 1915 and 1916 respectively.

In 1916 exceptional local demand created by troops stationed in Nyasaland reportedly caused the price to double in most areas (*328*, 1916, p. 8). In 1918 at least 6,000 long tons went for military rations, about half of which was obtained on contract with European farmers, and half from "arrangements . . . made with District Residents [administrators] to induce the natives to produce 56 lbs. of maize per hut" (*328*, 1918, p. 4). Similar techniques for stimulating maize production were employed the following year, but thereafter, with the end of the war and the end of larger than normal requirements, commercial production seems to have dropped sharply. No more maize was exported for nearly a decade, and very little after that (*328*, various issues). Requirements were confined to government employees plus plantation and other labor, and were largely met by produce from the fields of European farms and estates, the employers of most of the labor force.

The next sizable change in demand that can be traced was during World War II. To meet the needs of this emergency special marketing facilities were created; and later, price incentives were offered. The volume of maize marketed rose steadily from about 5,000 short tons in 1940 to some ten times that in 1952 and 1954 (*328*, various issues):

Year	Marketings (1,000 short tons)	Year	Marketings (1,000 short tons)
1940	5.0	1951	30.0
1941	4.9	1952	50.6
1942	12.0	1953	44.2
1943	9.0	1954	54.3
1944	9.8	1955	44.7
1945	8.5		
1946	14.0	1956	33.7
1947	7.5	1957	5.7
1948	7.0	1958	12.8
1949	5.0	1959	5.5
1950	10.0		

The sudden drop in marketings after 1954 was a result of government policy. Agriculture and conservation officials considered maize an undesirable crop; they refused to buy it in areas believed in danger of soil erosion, reduced the government-guaranteed price to all producers, and were thus able quickly to bring the maize surplus back to pre-1940 levels. The simultaneous slump in the world market meant that the relatively high guaranteed prices of the early 1950's could be continued only by a government subsidy, which was against official policy at that time.

ZAMBIA

Although one cannot determine when maize was introduced into Northern Rhodesia, it is fairly certain that there are no large areas where it was more than a minor food at the beginning of this century,[10] whereas today it is the major crop in most of the south-central and southeastern parts of the country. Over the same period the demand for maize by nonself-suppliers has increased strikingly (twenty-two-fold in 1921/25 to 1955: Chart 9-1); maize has become the main cash crop of African farmers, and a principal one of most European farmers.

Gains in the importance of maize in diets and commerce are related: nonagricultural industries which were initiated and developed in this period used workers who consumed large amounts of maize, and thereby created an increase in the quantity of maize demanded. Africans in favorable locations (i.e. those with relatively good soil and near the railway) were induced to grow maize as a cash crop, which in turn appears to have induced an increase in their own demand for maize.

Discovery of rich mineral deposits in the southern Belgian Congo during the first years of this century, and in adjacent areas of Northern Rhodesia somewhat later, led to investment of overseas capital in mining. Growth of this and related industries and facilities required large numbers of African laborers and food to feed them.

European farmers, who had begun to settle the area about the time of the birth of the mining industry, were occupied almost solely with supplying maize and meat to the mines, but their capacity to do so was exceeded considerably by the ever-growing food needs of the developing industries (351, p. 13). On the other hand, traditional African commerce was meeting strong competition from European traders, which made African traders all the more receptive to the idea of turning to a cash crop. Concomitantly, African capacity to supply maize was rapidly increasing because the geographical zone from which maize could be economically shipped to the mines was expanded by improvement of transportation,[11]

CHART 9-1 — NORTHERN RHODESIA: ESTIMATED MARKETED MAIZE
SUPPLIES REQUIRED, VARIOUS YEARS, 1921–55 (1,000 bags of 200 lbs.)

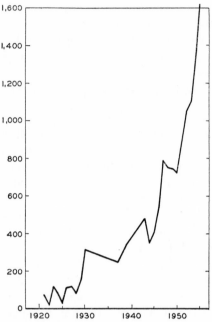

Data from S. Milligan, *Report on the Present Position of the Agricultural Industry* . . . (Livingstone, Northern Rhodesia, 1931), p. 6; Northern Rhodesia,
Department of Agriculture, *Annual Report* (Lusaka), various issues; and Federation of Rhodesia and Nyasaland, *Report of the Grain Marketing Board* . . . (Salisbury), various issues.

and because adoption of plows [12] and improved seed allowed an increase
in the acreage a farmer could plant, and resulted in larger yields per acre
as well.

African farmers who could profitably market maize switched from millets and sorghums as their staple to maize because, with an assured market
for the latter, there was a means of disposing of the surplus in years of
good weather, whereas the surplus from a bumper crop of millet or sorghum could not be exchanged so easily or so profitably for money. The
demand for money had increased about the same time because of taxes
imposed by the British administration and an increase in the range and
quality of imported goods available.

Prior to World War I, the principal market for maize was in the Katanga
mining areas of the southern Belgian Congo (*351*, p. 12). Supplementing
this demand were the needs of the laborers employed in building the

Northern Rhodesia railroad (*474*, p. 135). By 1914 the needs of the railway construction gangs had declined, but they were soon replaced, if not exceeded, by military demands: the forces stationed in Northern Rhodesia relied heavily on porters, and the ration given them was based on maize.[13]

After the war this demand of course ended, but it was partly replaced by growth of mining in Northern Rhodesia. During the boom of the late 1920's the demand for maize exceeded quantities marketed domestically. Consumption in 1929 appears to have been about 50 percent higher than the level of the previous three years, and over 100 percent higher than it had been in the three years before that. In 1930 it increased by roughly another 100 percent, and for the first time imports were larger than domestic production marketed by European farmers (Table 9-5).

With the depression of the early 1930's the Congo market for Rho-

TABLE 9-5 — NORTHERN RHODESIA: MAIZE IMPORTS AND EXPORTS TO THE BELGIAN CONGO AND SURPLUS MAIZE FROM EUROPEAN FARMERS, 1929–30
(1,000 bags of 200 lbs.)

Year	Estimated surplus maize for sale from European farmers	Imports	Exports to the Belgian Congo
1921	127	8	68
1922	81	7	75
1923	167	7	68
1924	101	16	45
1925	72	18	55
1926	140	24[a]	62
1927	214	6	104
1928	152	7	82
1929	168	43	61
1930	164	177	28

Data from S. Milligan, *Report on the Present Position of the Agricultural Industry* . . . (Livingstone, Northern Rhodesia, 1931), p. 6.

[a] The 1926 annual report of the Department of Agriculture contained the following comment on this relatively large quantity of imports: "The increase in the amount of maize imported from Southern Rhodesia, is explained by the fact that Biera and Moshonaland and Rhodesia Railways Companies are engaged in extensive work upon the line in Northern Rhodesia. A considerable amount of native labour is employed upon this work and meal for rations is purchased in Southern Rhodesia and imported" (*323*, 1926, p. 12). This may have also been true of other years.

desian maize disappeared, as a result of reduced mining activity, completion of a rail link between the Kasai maize area and Katanga, and adoption of a policy of self-sufficiency in the Congo (*323*, 1929, p. 6). Mining activity in Northern Rhodesia, although also reduced, remained large enough to absorb most of local production for two or three years. It was not until 1934 that production, relative to demand, was large enough to be considered a problem (*351*, p. 211). Production marketed was considerably greater than average in 1936 and reached a record high in 1937 (Table 9-6); but in the next seven years, because of "low prices, soil deterioration and poor seasons" (*229*, p. 3), it averaged only 68 percent of the 1936 and 1937 levels. By 1946 improvements in transportation and a good market were encouraging maize production in areas that previously had been unimportant, and from 1949 onward the distant Eastern Province contributed 10–15 percent of total marketings.

RHODESIA

How important maize was in 1892 when the first settlers arrived from Orange Free State cannot be determined, but the evidence available suggests that since that time it has become of considerably greater importance as an item of diet in many areas; the entire development of cash cropping based on maize appears to have taken place since the last decade of the nineteenth century.

Horne, in a book published in 1909, gives helpful information concerning the early development of European maize production:

The principal crop, which forms, and is likely to form the most important staple product in Rhodesian agriculture, is the mealie, or Indian corn.

The fact that farming is rapidly increasing and becoming more prosperous, and that many farmers are still confining their attention to mealie growing, is proof in itself that this industry is a profitable one and is likely to continue to be the backbone of Rhodesian agriculture . . . .

In 1901 a fearful cattle disease broke out on the eastern border of Southern Rhodesia . . . this latest disease, since known as African fever, spread worse havoc than rinderpest . . . . Strange though it may appear, the result of this fearful disease was to set in motion the first real stimulus towards progress in agriculture . . . old landowners . . . now collected together the remainder of their cattle, and as they were not allowed to let them stray on to other ground, set about to break up their land and put it under cultivation . . . .

It must also be mentioned that another stimulus to agriculture was given by the constant falling off of "trading with natives." In the earlier years traders made enormous profits by selling to the natives beads, salt, and Kaffir goods in exchange for grain and meal, but as the traders increased in the country and competition amongst them grew keener, they were unable to buy as much grain with the same amount of goods as formerly, and were further handicapped by the great drop in the selling price of grain and meal which oc-

TABLE 9-6 — NORTHERN RHODESIA: QUANTITIES OF MAIZE
MARKETED, 1933–57
(1,000 bags of 200 lbs.)

Year	Total	Areas served by rail		Eastern Province (race of producers not specified)
		European producers	African producers	
1933	128	91	37	. . .
1934	313	213	100	. . .
1935	169	132	37	. . .
1936	274	. . .	. . .	. . .
1937	440	240	200	. . .
1938	282	156	126	. . .
1939	217	153	64	. . .
1940	320	202	118	. . .
1941	158	120	38	. . .
1942	197	146	51	. . .
1943	204	144	60	. . .
1944	327	212	115	. . .
1945	475	273	202	. . .
1946	451	268	172	. . .
1947	264	190	54	. . .
1948	650	343	296	. . .
1949	397	283	61	53
1950	851	447	344	60
1951	761	391	290	80
1952	663	389	173	101
1953	1,166	602	435	129
1954	1,357	661	595	101
1955	1,069	615	320	134
1956	1,641	893	600	148
1957	2,082	1,176	823	83

Data from Northern Rhodesia, Department of Agriculture, *Annual Report* (Lusaka), various issues.

curred just at that period. Many of the traders, therefore, who had farms, found it more profitable to grow mealies themselves than to buy them from natives (*206*, pp. 198–201).

The annual report of the Department of Agriculture in 1910 suggests that maize and little else was being grown by Europeans because of "the simplicity of its cultivation, the sure demand and comparative certainty of a crop . . ." (*395*, 1910, p. 1506). Another authority claims that "until 1925 [maize] was the only important cash crop" (*464*, p. 83).

Certainly no other tropical African country has had so much of its agricultural production and development during this century centered on maize, with the possible exception of Kenya. The first acreage estimates for Southern Rhodesia (for 1913–14) place European maize at just above 161,000 acres. Over the next decade the trend was slightly upward, and reached a level of 220,000 to 230,000 acres by the 1922–23 and 1923–24 crop years. Over the same period, maize acreage represented on the average around 85 percent of the crop area planted by Europeans (*352*, 1925, p. 270):

Year	Grain (1,000 acres of maize)	Silage (1,000 acres of maize)	% of cropped area planted by Europeans to maize.
1914–15	167.0	2.9	91.5
1915–16	174.6[a]		88.0
1916–17	203.2	9.8	85.5
1917–18	192.2	6.2	86.2
1918–19	173.3	5.6	87.1
1919–20	173.5	4.9	84.5
1920–21	186.2	6.3	81.1
1921–22	181.7	12.4	85.1
1922–23	220.9	7.6	85.7
1923–24	231.6	11.3	84.6

[a] Combined figure for both grain and silage.

Southern Rhodesian farmers, like those in Northern Rhodesia, profited from the growth of mining activity in Katanga during this period (*69*, p. 4); in 1901 they began to export maize to Europe (*362*, 1909, p. 755); by 1914, 215,000 bags were exported (*393*, p. 29); and the figure rose to an average level of more than twice that in 1918, 1919, and 1920, presumably because of a war-induced increase in quantities demanded. Except in 1922, exports remained about or above the 1914 level in all of the next eight years following 1914 (*393*, p. 29):

Year	1,000 bags exported	Year	1,000 bags exported	Year	1,000 bags Exported
1914	215	1916	64	1918	237
1915	354	1917	256	1919	407

1920	617	1924	408	1928	647
1921	461	1925	416	1929	653
1922	84	1926	486	1930	485
1923	861	1927	568		

This appears to have been a reflection of prosperity abroad and in the Katanga mines.

A lowering of rail rates was interpreted by the Department of Agriculture in 1929 as making Southern Rhodesian maize much more competitive in the Katanga market (*323*, 1929, p. 7). Comments in 1929 by observers in Northern Rhodesia about the need to take measures to combat Southern Rhodesia's new policy of "dumping" maize in the Copperbelt suggest that indeed the lowering of rail rates had much the effect one might expect, considering that it was more to the advantage of Southern Rhodesian producers than of their Northern Rhodesian competitors (*323*, 1929, p. 7).

Between World War I and the depression of the 1930's there may also have been a general expansion in the consumption of maize by Africans. The report of the Maize Enquiry Committee of 1930, which was appointed to investigate ways of increasing the income of maize farmers, endorsed the view that "there has been a turn over to maize as a native food from other grains formerly preferred." This they explained as being "largely due to the facilities existing for the milling of maize, thus saving the drudgery of grinding it by primitive methods at the kraal. There is also the further evidence that mealie meal [maize meal] being the staple food of natives in employment, and the native having been educated to its consumption, he does not wholly revert to the other grains on his return to kraal life" (*393*, p. 10).

The committee considered another factor, adoption of plows, to be of little importance. "The increasing sale of ploughs was also commented on," they reported, "but it has not been proved to the satisfaction of your Committee that the more general use of the plough has led to increased production" (p. 11).

The committee's conclusion is perhaps questionable. The only real competitors of maize were the millets and sorghums, crops which do comparatively well during periods of drought. Under the rainfall conditions of much of Rhodesia, maize must be planted quickly at the beginning of the rains, or the rainy season will come to an end at a critical period for maize yields — the tasseling stage when the ear is forming. Use of the plow rather than the hoe permits a much larger acreage per household to be prepared and seeded during the optimum planting period. If the increase in the use of plows was large, one would certainly expect yield increases to have caused a shift from millets and sorghums to maize.

The Maize Enquiry Committee gave no statistics on the growth in number of plows used, but other sources report an increase from 3,402 in 1911 to 108,341 in 1941 (*230*, p. 175), with an increase of 246 percent (from 28,000 to 97,000) between 1926 and 1936 (*161*, p. 244 n.). It is highly doubtful that the rate of increase was any lower in the African sector than in the economy generally; and unless it was vastly lower, there is no convincing argument that plows were of little importance in increasing the productivity of African maize producers.

European marketings appear to have reached a plateau in the early 1920's and to have remained there through the Second World War, mainly because of a shift toward tobacco (*29*, pp. 126–31). African marketings, however, increased from about 200,000 bags in 1933–35 (Table 9-7) to over 400,000 bags in 1935/36, a level exceeded in the years of the Second World War for which data are available, suggesting a consider-

CHART 9-2 — SOUTHERN RHODESIA: ESTIMATED MAIZE MARKETINGS
REQUIRED FOR URBAN AREAS, VARIOUS YEARS, 1919–56
(1,000 bags of 200 lbs.)

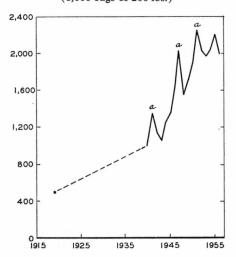

Data from E. A. Nobbs and F. Eyles, "Statistics for Crops Grown by European in Southern Rhodesia . . . ," *Rhodesian Agr. J.*, 15, No. 6 (Dec. 1918): 499; and Federation of Rhodesia and Nyasaland, *Report of the Grain Marketing Board . . .* (Salisbury), various issues.

[a] Years of poor harvest when relatively large quantities of maize were imported. The increase in amounts demanded in those years appears to reflect largely purchases by consumers who normally grow part or all of their own needs.

able shift from other crops to maize, or an increase in African productivity.[14]

The trend in aggregate consumption (European and African consumption are not distinguishable in the statistics) appears clearly upward since 1940 (Chart 9-2). Records of amounts bought by the government marketing monopoly from producers and sold by it to consumers indicate that the consumption has been sharply upward, reflecting mainly economic development since World War II, particularly the trend toward urbaniza· tion. The trend toward increased maize consumption may now be revers-

TABLE 9-7 — SOUTHERN RHODESIA: QUANTITIES OF
MAIZE MARKETED, 1930/31–1956/57
(1,000 bags of 200 lbs.)

Crop year	Total	European	African
1930/31	1,076	1,076	. . .
1931/32	1,418	1,418	. . .
1932/33	826	826	. . .
1933/34	1,419	1,202	217
1934/35	1,009	805	204
1935/36	1,848	1,406	442
1936/37	2,055	1,463	592
1937/38	1,249	941	308
1938/39	1,051	727	324
1939/40	1,441	1,047	394
1940/41	687	687	. . .
1941/42	700	700	. . .
1942/43	894	894	. . .
1943/44	1,421	964	457
1944/45	1,334	859	475
1945/46	1,111	804	307
1946/47	603	397	206
1947/48	1,768	1,089	679
1948/49	1,072	681	391
1949/50	1,826	978	848
1950/51	666	463	203
1951/52	2,094	1,402	692
1952/53	2,263	1,354	909
1953/54	2,625	1,735	890
1954/55	2,487	1,780	707
1955/56	3,791	2,419	1,372
1956/57	3,399	2,568	831

Data from Federation of Rhodesia and Nyasaland, *Report of the Grain Marketing Board* . . . (Salisbury), various issues.

ing, however, if the opinion of some local authorities is correct. Wadsworth, commenting in 1956, notes that "there are distinct signs that the African, as a bulk consumer, is turning over increasingly to consumption of wheat in the form of bread and is cutting down his maize requirements" (450, p. 56). Some support is provided for this view in estimates of wheat consumption in the Federation of Nyasaland and Rhodesia, which increased from 7.2 kilograms per capita per year in 1951/54 to 9.3 in 1957 (232, p. 2).

BECHUANALAND

Only the southeastern fourth of Bechuanaland has enough rainfall for maize, and even there fairly frequently the crop is very poor (185, p. 180, and fig. 32, p. 181). Maize needs usually exceed production considerably. Maize is the principal foodstuff supplied to African laborers, and maize imports averaged over twice estimated production from 1946 to 1958 (see Chapter 6), while in years of low rainfall they were much larger (182, pp. 176–77):

Year	Imports of maize and maize meal (1,000 bags of 200 lbs.)	Year	Imports of maize and maize meal (1,000 bags of 200 lbs.)
1947	132.3	1953	36.0
1948	35.8	1954	12.1
1949	37.9	1955	13.9
1950	55.4	1956	25.0
1951	52.7	1957	47.9
1952	122.1	1958	49.7

THE MALAGASY REPUBLIC

The Malagasy Republic is unusual compared to the rest of tropical Africa in that it is one of the principal maize exporters, and the commodity is a relatively old export; but maize is of major importance in the diet only in a few small, scattered areas.

The island of Madagascar was exporting maize to other islands of the Indian Ocean, particularly Réunion and Mauritius, certainly as early as 1841 (121, pp. 177–78), but possibly earlier.[15] Maize was apparently one of the foodstuffs given to slaves on sugar plantations from the beginning of sugar exports; and with the rapid expansion of sugar exports from 25 metric tons in 1815 to 30,610 metric tons in 1841 and 68,469 metric tons in 1860 (215, p. 608), a foodstuff deficit developed which has remained until the present.

Little effort seems to have been made to develop maize exports in the first few years after 1896, when Madagascar was made a French colony. From 1896 to 1899 the colonial administration was occupied with wars of pacification, and since maize was not a ration for either the Algerian, Senegalese, Somali, or Malgache troops or porters involved in the campaign (*199*, pp. 47–48), there is no reason to suppose its production was stimulated through administrative policy during the wars against the Malgache rebels.

By the end of the wars of pacification, agricultural production had been severely curtailed. Before these wars Madagascar was an exporter of "several thousand metric tons" of rice, which was fairly widely the island's staple food; but in the first three years of peace it had sizable imports and was not a net exporter again until 1907 (*13*, p. 86; and *145*, p. 89):

Year	Net exports (metric tons)	Year	Net exports (metric tons)
1900	− 7,566	1907	2,129
1901	−26,030	1908	4,560
1902	−15,440	1909	3,891
1903	− 2,689	1910	8,198
1904	− 5,570	1911	6,176
1905	− 2,833	1912	7,420
1906	− 553	1913	10,664

The high cost of transportation to the coast [16] was cited in 1909 as the major obstacle to further development of rice as an export (*13*, p. 73), and the same was probably true for maize. In 1909 the railway from the coast reached Tananarive, the capital, located on the central plateau (*102*, p. 110); this, together with extensions in the next few years, provided a considerable stimulus to maize production. Exports, however, for some time remained oriented toward nearby markets. The long ocean voyage to Europe limited maize exports to what could be absorbed in Mauritius and Réunion, which was, in the main, a quantity that varied inversely with the world price of sugar (*367*, p. 9):

Year	Maize exported (metric tons)	Year	Maize exported (metric tons)
1911	279	1916	1,491
1912	350	1917	531
1913	581	1918	1,665
1914	281	1919	1,536
1915	1,149	1920	2,815

France's needs grew rapidly in the 1920's, and so did Madagascar's maize exports (*159*, p. 57; and *367*, p. 9):

Year	Maize exported (metric tons)
1921	2,806
1922	3,786
1923	11,120
1924	16,467
1925	15,889
1926	10,048
1927	4,105
1928	8,644

Government efforts to encourage plowing may have contributed considerably to the expansion of maize acreage during this period. That some African farmers were early eager to adopt plowing is suggested by a report by A. Fauchèrie in 1914 that the Sakalaves of the Sambriano Valley near the island of Nosy Bé were asking European settlers to plow their fields for them (*145*, p. 77). Beginning in 1920, plows were first given to Africans by the government, then later sold to them at half price. Between 1920 and 1924 the number of plows issued by the government increased from 34 to 1,547 per year (*267*, Jan., 1926, p. 74):

Year	Plows distributed
1920	34
1921	42
1922	726
1923	700
1924	1,547

(According to estimates published in 1926, about 30 man-days are required to prepare a hectare using the traditional spadelike implement of the Malgache, whereas a plow can do the same task in four hours [*267*, Jan. 1926, p. 73].)

Also probably of importance was expansion of irrigation. August Chevalier describes the 1905–22 period as one of rapid expansion of irrigation facilities in the arid southwest, allowing expansion of "sugar cane, maize, sisal, manioc, and coconuts" (*101*, p. 3). This is the area that contributed over 75 percent of maize exports at the peak of their expansion in the late 1930's (*413*, p. 444; *160*, p. 346; and *102*, p. 206).

The onset of the depression of the 1930's brought a sharp setback in export-oriented maize production. In 1931 maize prices had fallen to 44 percent of their 1929 level (*255*, p. 120); maize exports declined from 12,100 to 4,800 metric tons over the same period. Production incentives were restored with a preferential tariff imposed by France in 1932 to stimulate colonial production (*417*, p. 421; see also discussion of French West Africa, Chapter 10 below). Response was slow at first, but in the course of six years exports grew about thirteen-fold (*102*, pp. 206–7):

Year	Maize exported (metric tons)
1928	8,644
1929	12,100
1930	6,100
1931	4,800
1932	4,100
1933	5,500
1934	9,800
1935	9,900
1936	15,900
1937	34,000
1938	53,800
1939	45,600

During World War II maize exports dropped to an average of 2,200 metric tons per year,[17] then increased somewhat in the early postwar period to a peak of 9,500 metric tons in the 1951–55 quinquennium, only to decline once more (*102*, pp. 206–7; and *144*, various issues):

Year	Maize exports (metric tons)	Year	Maize exports (metric tons)
1940	5,800	1947	3,500
1941	6,100	1948	6,900
1942	1,200	1949	2,100
1943	100	1950	1,400
1944	1,500	1951	5,900
1945	2,100	1952	9,500
1946	6,800	1953	9,400

1954	5,400	1958	6,500
1955	7,700	1959	1,300
1956	2,700	1960	5,200
1957	2,100		

Characteristics of Maize Production in the Malagasy Republic

It is not clear that maize is the major starchy-staple anywhere in Malagasy; and it is reported as a principal starchy food only in two fairly small areas, one comprising the high altitude zones on the central plateau around Tananarive and Betafo, and the other in the extreme south (*119*, pp. 170–71; *216*, p. 203; and *367*, p. 9).

Maize is grown as a cash crop throughout the island, by small and large farmers alike. About 1953, settlers accounted for an estimated 2.4 percent of maize acreage but undoubtedly a much larger proportion of production (*216*, p. 203).

Along the eastern and northern coast many of the settlers are Creoles from Réunion and Mauritius who, like many of the Portuguese farmers in Mozambique, practice small-scale peasant agriculture. Most of the Creoles are sharecroppers (*214*, pp. 102–3 and 116).[18] Elsewhere non-Malgache agriculture ranges in organization from small estates to large plantations operated by giant corporations.

The organization of agriculture among Malgache farmers has no parallel in the rest of tropical Africa because (1) land can be bought and sold in most areas; (2) in parts, if not most, of the densely populated central plateau, irrigation and other agricultural matters are regulated by complex communal organizations; (3) some Malgache farmers, like the Creoles, operate as sharecroppers; and (4) there is no tsetse problem, and cattle are kept throughout the country (*106*, pp. 20–24 and 156–89; and *336*, pp. 22–23).

Preparation of maize fields varies greatly, and in distinction to the rest of tropical Africa, the hoe is not used anywhere. Along the eastern coast most vegetation is cut and burned, a hole is made in the ash with a pointed stick, maize seed are dropped in and covered (*367*, p. 8). On the central plateau fields are plowed in many communities or, alternatively, are worked with an *angady*, a spadelike tool with a long handle that was traditionally the implement used to till the land. In the southwest, the most important maize region of the island, plowing has spread slowly; a tool much like the angady is still widely used (*119*, p. 169); and the slash-and-burn method is found in some areas (*413*, p. 443). In this region maize is often irrigated in valleys and grown throughout the year (*413*, p.

444; and *353*, p. 283). In the extreme southwestern tip of the island, the entire surplus for export reportedly comes from irrigated fields (*413*, p. 444), and this may be true for other areas of the south and west.

Throughout the island red and yellow varieties of maize are frequently grown, another striking contrast with the rest of tropical Africa. Part of the dislike for white maize may stem from the vulnerability of some white varieties to weevils (*353*, p. 283), but preference of Réunion and Mauritius consumers for yellow maize is apparently the major reason (*367*, p. 9).

In most regions of the island some of the cattle kept are fed and their manure is used for fertilizer, even if they are not used for draft purposes (*310*, p. 218; and *388*, p. 30). Whether maize is a crop that is usually fertilized is not clear; [19] but maize stalks, if not the grain, are of some importance as cattle feed not only among the Malgache, who often keep their cattle in a pit while fattening them (*388*, p. 30), but, on the central plateau and in the south and southwest, by nonindigenous farmers or estates that fatten cattle purchased from the Malgache (*214*, p. 111). In parts of the central plateau, and probably more generally, maize is also fed to hogs (*164*, p. 92).

Marketing

In the extreme south the coastal people carry on an active trade with those on the plateau, exchanging livestock for maize, and to a lesser extent for rice, manioc, and sweet potatoes. No estimate is available of amounts of maize sold in this interregional trade, but from 1939 to 1941 the number of cattle involved annually reportedly ranged from 5,000 to 8,774 head (*413*, p. 439).

In other areas maize is generally bought up by landowners who have sharecroppers or by village storekeepers: in the east predominantly Chinese; in the west Chinese and Indian; and in the south Merina (Malgache from the central plateau), Chinese, and whites of various nationalities (*102*, pp. 101–3). These merchants have manufactured goods for sale and buy agricultural products from small farmers. Commodities purchased move on to larger merchants who provision the urban areas and channel the surplus overseas.

Trends in Maize Production

Estimates made of staple crop acreages in 1905, five years after the colonial administration finally brought the entire island under its control, suggest that maize was then less important than either rice or manioc, or

TABLE 9-8 — MALAGASY REPUBLIC: ESTIMATED CHANGES IN
ACREAGE OF THE MAJOR STARCHY-STAPLES, EXCLUDING
MILLETS AND SORGHUMS

Crop	1905	1934–38	1948–52	1959–60
	(% of area in starchy-staple crops listed)			
Maize	8.1	10.1	8.2	7.5
Manioc	21.5	26.5	19.4	16.5
Rice	56.5	50.0	61.5	69.7
Sweet potatoes				
and yams	12.5	12.3	8.9	4.3
Irish potatoes	1.4	1.1	2.0	2.0
Total	100.0	100.0	100.0	100.0
	(1,000 hectares)			
Aggregate area in				
crops listed	655	1,006	1,005	1,130
Area in maize	53	102	83	85

Data from A. Chevalier, "Cinquante années d'efforts scientifiques et sociaux pour
le développement de l'agriculture Malgache," *Rev. Bot. App. et Agr. Trop.,* Supplement, Sept. 1946, p. 343; and FAO, *Yearbook of Food and Agricultural Statistics,*
Pt. 1: Production, various years. Millets and sorghum areas were together reported
as 60,000 hectares in 1948–50 and 84,000 hectares in 1959–60 by the FAO, but
data are not given for other periods.

sweet potatoes and yams taken together (Table 9-8). Production estimates are not available, but all these crops frequently give larger yields per
acre than maize where they are relatively important (see Chapter 11 below); hence it is almost certain that the position of maize was no better —
and probably not as good — as the acreage data indicate.

Qualitative data also suggest that maize was generally less important
than most of the other starchy-staples. The first annual report of the colonial administration, a document which describes the agriculture and economic activities of each province, military territory, and cercle, reports
maize among the food crops in all parts of the country, but mentions it as
the staple only among part of the Sakalaves of the west (*157*, pp. 205–
374). It was described as a major commodity in local commerce only for
the Morondava area on the west coast (*157*, p. 308).

Data available do not suffice to indicate clearly changes in the position
of maize in the diet, but throughout much if not all of the island rice is reportedly preferred to maize or manioc (*160*, pp. 125, 271, and 345).
There is some evidence that rice is gaining at the expense of maize.

After the end of World War II, and following a striking expansion of irrigation,[20] rice acreage increased steadily — and over part of the period rice exports were declining — suggesting a considerable increase in domestic rice consumption (*143* and *144*, various issues):

Year	Acreage (1,000 hectares)		Net exports (1,000 metric tons)	
	Maize	Rice	Maize	Rice
1934–38	102	500	24.7	4.2
1941–45	68	530	2.2	9.8
1946–50	81	563	4.1	2.1
1951–55	81	693	7.6	24.6
1956	. . .	730	2.7	30.2
1957	90	830	2.1	16.9
1958	93	800	6.5	58.2
1959	75	792	1.3	17.3
1960	96	762	5.2	0.4

The same conclusion is suggested by the decline in the acreage planted to roots and tubers since 1934–38 (Table 9-8).[21]

Estimates of maize acreage indicate that considerably less land is given to this crop than before World War II, but on the other hand maize exports are much less; thus it is not certain that domestic utilization is declining, although this seems probable considering that in much of the period since World War II either maize rust (*Puccina polysora*) or locusts have lowered yields (*160*, pp. 43 and 126).

THE SMALL ISLAND ECONOMIES
OF EASTERN TROPICAL AFRICA

Maize appears not to be of major importance in the diet in any of the small island economies of eastern tropical Africa, and varies from a minor foodstuff in Zanzibar, Pemba, the Seychelles, and the Comores to a foodstuff of primary importance in parts of Réunion. All of these small island economies specialize in export crops and import some of the starchy-staples they require. Réunion and Mauritius produce sugar and little else; Zanzibar and Pemba are highly specialized clove producers; the Comores produce mainly vanilla and copra; and the Seychelles export principally copra, cinnamon, and cinnamon products. Only Réunion includes significant amounts of maize in its foodstuff imports (*144*, various issues):

Area	Net maize imports 1957–60 (1,000 metric tons)	Net maize imports 1957–60 (Kgs. per capita per year)
Réunion	14.3	44.5
Mauritius	3.8	6.2
Seychelles	0.2	5.3
Zanzibar and Pemba	0.1	0.4

Except for Réunion, all these islands appear to produce less maize than they import; hence consumption must be relatively small — probably less than 50 calories per person daily, at the maximum. If Réunion's maize production of 14,700 metric tons per year for 1957–60 is added to net imports, average maize consumption for the whole island is probably on the order of 300 calories per capita daily (*143*, various issues); and the figure is considerably higher for the interior hills and mountains where maize is the dominant starchy-staple (*215*, p. 621). Throughout the islands of eastern tropical Africa, maize assumes greater importance when rice is dear (*384*, 1949, p. 7; and *276*, 1943, p. 2).

Trends

During World War II an order was issued in Mauritius requiring all plantations to grow foodstuffs, and maize was encouraged at the expense of sweet potatoes (*276*, 1943, pp. 2 and 3). In 1945 compulsory acreage allotments were lifted, and from 1947 to 1949 a bonus payments scheme was implemented to encourage production of maize and other food crops (*276*, 1945, p. 4; 1948, p. 4; 1950, p. 12). Maize acreage in Mauritius has fallen steadily since subsidies were stopped in 1949, and maize imports have increased sharply to help make up the foodstuff deficit (*281*, p. 91; *276* and *144*, various issues):

Year	Maize acreage (arpents)[a]	Maize imports (1,000 metric tons)
1945	. . .	11.8
1946	2,973	8.5
1947	10,000	1.7
1948	9,682	. . .
1949	8,078	. . .
1950	4,874	. . .
1951	4,429	. . .
1952	4,244	. . .

1953	. . .	. . .
1954	. . .	. . .
1955	3,345	2.8
1956	2,405	1.7
1957	1,597	2.8
1958	883	3.5
1959	908	5.2

ª 8.5 acres.

Réunion, like Mauritius, has tended to increase its maize imports in the post-World War II period, but among the small importers the trend is downward (*144*, various issues):

Net maize imports (1,000 metric tons)

Year	Réunion	Mauritius	Seychelles	Zanzibar and Pemba	Total
1945	2.1	11.8	. . .	. . .	. . .
1946	. . .	8.5	1.1	0.5	. . .
1947	7.6	1.7	1.7	0.4	11.4
1948	5.9	. . .	1.3	0.3	7.5
1949	3.8	. . .	1.3	0.9	6.0
1950	12.6	. . .	0.9	1.1	14.6
1951	9.3	. . .	1.6	0.7	. . .
1952	13.6	. . .	1.9	0.5	. . .
1953	11.3	. . .	1.6	0.7	. . .
1954	10.6	. . .	0.5	0.2	. . .
1955	15.0	2.8	0.4	0.5	18.7
1956	9.8	1.7	0.3	0.5	12.3
1957	8.1	2.8	0.1	0.2	11.2
1958	17.0	3.5	0.2	0.1	20.8
1959	14.2	5.2	0.3	0.2	19.9
1960	18.0	3.8	0.3	. . .	22.1

10

MAIZE IN WESTERN
AND CENTRAL AFRICA

I N much of Angola and in a fairly large portion of Congo (Leopoldville), maize is as important in diets and commerce as it is in most of
eastern Africa; but for the rest of central Africa and almost all of western
tropical Africa — with the exception of the Cape Verde Islands and a
zone extending from southwestern Nigeria to south-central Ghana — it
appears to be of slight importance in either diets or commerce.

In most areas of western and central Africa, however, maize seems to
have clearly become more prominent in diets in the past hundred years; in
a number of areas the amount of maize marketed is increasing; in some
areas trade in maize seems to have fluctuated. Following suppression of
the slave trade in the latter part of the nineteenth century, trade in maize
declined, but development of maize exports brought a revival for a short
time around the turn of the century in coastal regions of western Africa
and a later, but lasting, revival in the Belgian Congo and Angola.

WESTERN AFRICA

In a commentary on the prospects for maize along the Guinea Coast
in 1910, August Chevalier noted that maize from western tropical Africa
was not known to Europe before 1903 (*98*, p. 225). Until then neither
the colonial administrations, nor the traders along the coast, had dreamed
that African farmers had surplus maize to sell; in Togo, Dahomey, and
western Nigeria cotton was the primary concern of the governments and
the railroads (*28*, p. 49). However, despite considerable capital expenditure on transportation facilities and cotton gins, and experimenting with
plantation production, returns on investment were mediocre. In 1904
M. H. B. Russell asked the Nigerian administration to divert part of its

effort in the cotton campaign to maize (28, p. 50); and about the same time the John Holt Company, long a buyer of African produce, advertised in African villages that it would buy maize. The purchases in the first fortnight were promising enough for the Holt Company to order shelling machines to be distributed (some as gifts) among the Africans (28, p. 52).

Exports of maize grew rapidly after 1903. Lagos exported 2,484 metric tons in 1903/04 and 4,688 metric tons the next year. Shipments from Togo were almost twice as much as from Nigeria in 1904/05 (8,707 metric tons). The exports of both countries included sizable purchases from Dahomeans who did not sell at home because relatively high freight charges by the railroad and wharf companies made the price there considerably less (28, p. 50).

A great drive was made to increase production in Nigeria from 1904 to 1908 (318). In Togo development of the railroad from Lomé to Palime in 1906 was given credit for an almost threefold increase in maize exports (285, p. 234); by 1907 maize led in earning foreign exchange (73, cited in 14, p. 119):

Commodity	% of total exports, by value
Maize	28.5
Rubber	26.1
Palm nuts	23.1
Palm oil	10.0
Cotton	5.5
Ivory	3.1
Cocoa	1.2
Peanuts	0.9
Manioc	0.8
Shea butter	0.3
Copra	0.3
	99.8[a]

[a] Percentages have been rounded.

In the Ivory Coast, free maize seed was distributed about the same time to stimulate production there (53, p. 24). By 1910, however, maize supplies on the world market had increased to such an extent that prices fell to a level which discouraged exports (318; and 285, p. 233). Despite a growth in western African maize exports from near zero in 1903 to 65,000 metric tons in 1910 (roughly 5 percent of present production and at least seven times the peak of exports during the slave trade), export shipments dwindled in the next few years, and had become insignificant by the end of the First World War (*128*, p. 114; *28*, p. 50; and *98*, p. 225).

During the 1930's France made an effort to increase exports from her colonies because of an increasing deficit at home, and adopted a preferential tariff in 1932. Imports by the *metropole* from colonies increased from 8.5 percent of the total in 1932 to 82 percent in 1937 (*417*, p. 421). Maize exports from Dahomey increased from 1,600 metric tons in 1935 to 45,000 metric tons in 1939; and in Togo the increase was from 8 to 25,000 metric tons between 1936 and 1939 (*158*, pp. 113 and 213; *114*; and *417*, p. 424):

Maize exports (1,000 metric tons)

Year	Dahomey	Togo	Ivory Coast
1934	. . .	. . .	0.1
1935	1.6	. . .	. . .
1936	2.6	8.0	. . .
1937	18.3	16.0	1.5
1938	35.4	21.0	. . .
1939	45.0	25.0	. . .
1940	0.0	11.0	. . .
1941	13.9	6.0	. . .

Maize acreage reportedly expanded considerably throughout French areas of western Africa over the same period. P. Tissot, in an article published in 1939 analyzing progress made in meeting France's domestic maize deficit, gives official estimates showing from 30 to 700 percent increases in maize acreage between 1926–30 and 1937 in French colonies of western Africa (*417*, pp. 423–34):

Acreage increase per 1,000 hectares

Year	Niger	French Sudan	Dahomey	Senegal
1926–30	5.0	35.0	150.0	14.0
1937	35.0	135.0	225.0	18.5

In the Ivory Coast the increase was from 195,000 hectares in 1934 to 250,000 in 1937; in French Guinea it was from 50,000 hectares in 1925–34 to 65,000 in 1937 (*417*, p. 423).

There was no revival of exports in British areas of western Africa. Maize exports from Nigeria, the only British colony that was a significant exporter in 1903–10, were trivial during the 1930's (*318*):

Period	Maize exports (metric tons)
1903–04	2,484
1905–09	11,794
1910–14	5,636
1915–19	520
1920–24	208
1925–29	47
1930–34	97
1935–39	48

Since 1940 maize exports from western Africa have steadily declined, and since 1950 the region has been a net importer, with Ghana and Senegal being the major deficit areas (*144*, various issues):

1,000 metric tons net maize exports

Year	French West Africa	Togo-land	French Cam-eroons	Ghana	Nigeria	Total
1934–38	14.6	11.6	3.5	...	0.1	29.8
1947–48	0.6	0.3	...	...	...	0.9
1948–52	− 2.8	...	...	−2.4	...	− 5.2
1953	...	1.3	...	−1.3	0.2	0.2
1954	− 4.4	0.9	...	−0.6	0.1	− 4.0
1955	− 3.2	0.4	...	−0.2	...	− 3.0
1956	− 5.2	0.1	...	−1.1	...	− 6.2
1957	− 8.0	0.8	...	−1.2	...	− 8.4
1958	− 8.3	0.5	...	−0.4	...	− 8.2
1959	−14.4	0.4	...	−0.2	...	−14.2

Net maize imports into Senegal from 1956 to 1959 were (in metric tons): 1956, 4,000; 1957, 8,000; 1958, 8,300; and 1959, 14,400.

It is difficult to estimate with any accuracy the quantities of maize moving in internal trade; but for Ghana, almost one-third of the crop appears to have moved into commercial channels in 1957–58 (Map 10-1), according to data derived from a census of commerce described earlier (p. 62).[1]

Deficit areas were five of the coastal zones (sectors I, IV, V, VI, and VIII), one of which is the city of Accra and another contains Sekondi and

MAP 10-1 — GHANA: MAIZE SURPLUS AND DEFICIT AREAS, NET
IMPORTS AND EXPORTS SHOWN IN METRIC TONS, 1957–58

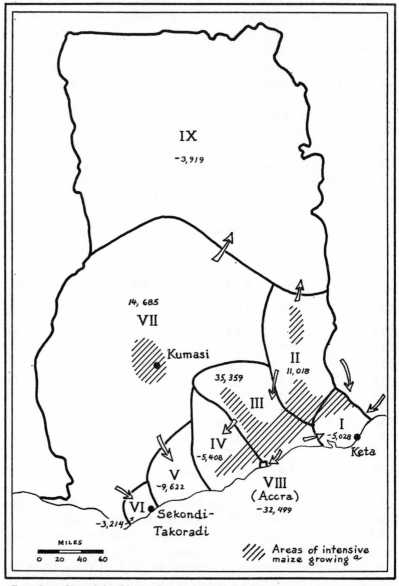

Data from files of the Ghana Government Statistician.
ª Intensive maize-growing areas according to W. R. Stanton, "Progress Report
on a Maize Survey of West Africa," West African Maize Rust Research Unit,
Second Annual Report, 1954 (London, 1955), App. map.

180

Takoradi; and northern Ghana (sector IX). Accra was by far the largest of the net importers, accounting for 32,499 metric tons, or just over half of the total commerce in maize. Of the three surplus sectors, number III, a sector with a relatively large area of intensive maize production, accounted for 35,359 metric tons of net exports, which was more than twice as much as either of the other sectors. The Trans-Volta sector (II) had net exports of 11,018 metric tons, and the Kumasi sector (VII) had 14,685 metric tons.

One-third of maize production in Dahomey is estimated to be commercialized (115, p. 44); and in Western Nigeria maize marketings appear to be certainly not less than one-third of production and are very likely more.[2] In a survey of the Nigerian cocoa belt, the major maize-producing region, 187 families sampled during four different months in 1951–52, each in a different season, purchased an average of 20 pounds of maize per family during the four periods (equivalent to 28 percent of their maize production) and 582 pounds of maize products — 580 percent of their production of these items (163, p. 717).

The principal deficit areas, about 1950 (May 10-2), appear to be the cities of Western Nigeria between the coast and Oyo — especially Ibadan, a city of half a million, Lagos, and Abeokuta — Kano, the Jos Plateau, and Enugu. The major surplus areas are a zone extending about a hundred miles northeast and the same distance south of Ilorin; and area in the extreme southeast adjacent to Dahomey, which helps supply that country, Togo, and Ghana, as well as Lagos and Ibadan; an area around Benin City; a zone immediately southwest of the Jos Plateau; and the Bamenda Highlands.

Information is not available on trade within other western African countries; but whatever the proportion of the crop marketed, it probably is considerably greater than at the turn of the century when transportation costs were much higher; internal trade has possibly become a good deal larger, relative to production, than exports ever were. One can only speculate on noncommercial trends, but a divergence is evident between the coastal areas and the interior. There is reason to think maize has become less important in the past century or century and a half along the Gold and Slave coasts because of gains made by manioc (236, p. 110; 116, p. iii; and 78, p. 321).

An economic report on Senegal published in 1920 notes: "Maize is increasingly cultivated, especially in upper Gambia and Futa. . . ." (177, p. 27), one of the few areas in the western African interior where maize is now even of secondary importance in the diet (Map 8-1; and 363, p. 193). As was noted earlier, in northern Ivory Coast and French Sudan

MAP 10-2 — NIGERIA: MAIZE SURPLUS AND DEFICIT AREAS,
ABOUT 1950

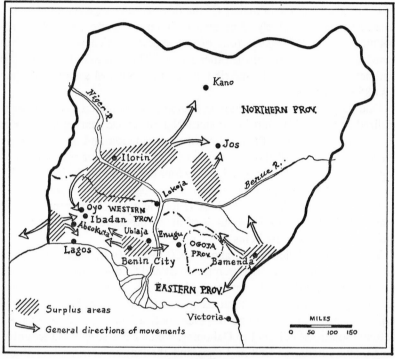

For regions south and west of the Niger River and for the Bamenda Highlands,
data are from a market survey by the author, described in Chapter 5 above; for
other areas data are from A. R. Prest and I. G. Stewart, *The National Income of
Nigeria, 1950–51,* Col. Res. Stud. No. 11 (London, 1953), App. A, Map No. 3.

maize acreage was estimated to have quadrupled in the 1926–37 period
(*417,* pp. 423 and 424). For French Niger, a sevenfold gain was noted
for the same period. In Bamenda Province, West Cameroons, maize
seems to have been of very slight importance in the diet until the present
century; within the memory of living men it has become a major staple
throughout, and in several areas the main one, at the expense of the
millets and sorghums (*27* and *21*). The same is probably true of neighboring peoples to the east. The Mum, now maize eaters, say they once
depended on millets as their starchy-staple, but they do not indicate when
millets were replaced by maize (*123,* p. 628). Observers report maize
consumption seems to have increased considerably in the French Cameroons since World War II (*278,* p. 11). Mr. La Anyane of the Economics Section of the Ghana Department of Agriculture argues that in eastern

Ghana, an area in which he has done considerable field work, maize has become increasingly important since World War II because of the need for a cash crop to compensate for loss of income resulting from damage to cocoa plantations by swollen shoot disease (*19*).

THE ISLAND ECONOMIES OF WESTERN AFRICA

The Cape Verde Islands, São Tomé, and Príncipe, like the small islands off the eastern coast of continental Africa, specialize in export crops and import much of their starchy-staple foodstuffs. The main exports of the Cape Verde Archipelago are coffee and fish; cocoa and copra are the principal products of São Tomé and Príncipe. Both groups of islands import enough maize for it to be at least a secondary foodstuff. Maize imports in São Tomé and Principe were sufficient to provide over 300, and in the Cape Verde Islands over 200, calories per person daily from 1957 to 1960 (*144*, various issues). In the Cape Verde Islands maize is described as the dominant starchy-staple by a large margin (*100*, p. 843; and *176*, p. 23). Estimates of crop acreages in these islands in 1934 give maize 62 percent of land cultivated and sweet potatoes and manioc, the only other significant starchy-staples, only 14 and 6 percent respectively (*375* cited in *100*, p. 839):

Crop	Acreage (% of culti-vated land)
Maize	62
Sweet potatoes	14
Purgueira (an oilseed related to castor bean)	14
Manioc	6
Sugarcane	2
Coffee	1
Other	1
	100

Characteristics of Maize Production (Cape Verde Islands)

Several systems of agriculture are found, ranging from small independent farmers to sharecroppers and large plantations (*176*, pp. 25–26; and *100*, pp. 838, 841). Generally some sort of irrigation is followed, but in some areas rainfall suffices for early-maturing maize varieties, a popular one of which matures in seven weeks (*100*, p. 844).

Hoe culture prevails. Plows were introduced as early as 1878 (*176*, p. 25), but were used very little as late as 1935 (*100*, p. 837). Debris left on fields from previous crops is burned to get ash for fertilizing fields, but often by the time fields must be prepared all the maize stalks from the previous crop have already been used for fuel and little debris is left. Goat manure is applied to fields near the homestead, but typically is not carried to distant fields or to those on slopes above the homestead, because beasts of burden are not available (*100*, p. 838). Beans are often grown with maize, the seed being placed in the same hole with maize kernels.

Trends

Maize production in the Cape Verde Islands appears to have declined fairly sharply relative to needs over the last half century or so. J. Bacellar Bebiano, in an analysis of the economic problems of the archipelago published in 1959, says that "during the nineteenth century much maize was exported to the *metropole*" (*38*, p. 149); and about 1920 the colony was still typically a net exporter of maize, although in bad years — such as 1913 and 1914 — maize had to be imported (*176*, pp. 23 and 33). Compared with the late 1930's, maize imports are larger in both the Cape Verde Islands and São Tomé and Principe; but since 1945 there has been no obvious trend in net imports in either group of islands (*87*; and *144*, various issues):

Year	Cape Verde Islands (1,000 metric tons)	São Tomé and Príncipe (1,000 metric tons)
1934–38	0.1	1.5
1945–47	8.1	1.9[a]
1948–52	9.8	3.5
1953	1.2	3.4
1954	0.2	3.2
1955	1.5	3.4
1956	2.5	3.4
1957	2.5	3.0
1958	1.9	2.6
1959	4.9	3.3
1960	18.5	3.2

[a] Average of two years, 1945 and 1947.

CENTRAL AFRICA

There is no evidence that commercial maize production has ever been important in former French Equatorial Africa or the Sudan; maize either has lost its place in preference hierarchies in most of this area or was never firmly established as a staple. Most of the Sudan is too dry for it, but it is not clear why maize is of such minor importance in former French Equatorial Africa.

Former French Equatorial Africa is a very small maize importer in some years; maize imports averaged 100 metric tons in 1934–38 and 200 in 1956; in other post-World War II years there was apparently no external trade in maize (*144*, various issues). The Sudan exported small amounts of maize immediately before the war, averaging 3,500 metric tons in 1934–38. Maize exports increased to 22,300 and 20,900 metric tons in 1947 and 1948 respectively, but registered a fairly consistent decline from 1951 to 1960 (*144*, various issues):

Year	Maize exports (1,000 metric tons)	Year	Maize exports (1,000 metric tons)
1934–38	3.5	1951	11.8
		1952	9.9
1945	0.1	1953	5.3
1946	0.0	1954	5.6
1947	22.3	1955	5.4
1948	20.9		
1949	1.3	1956	6.2
1950	0.0	1957	5.5
		1958	1.6
		1959	1.4
		1960	3.0

Angola

Maize seems to have been well established in the diet of much of Angola by the beginning of the present century. As has already been noted, accounts of food consumption along the northern Angolan coast suggest that it was a major food as early as the sixteenth century. V. L. Cameron noted the importance of maize from the central Angolan plateau for provisioning coastal settlements when he crossed Angola from east to west in 1875 (*84*, p. 424). H. Capello and R. Ivens found maize to be a major crop in much of the interior during their exploration of Angola in 1877 which disproved the existence of the legendary Lake Aquilunda (*88*, 2:248), and in their trip across Africa from Angola to Mozambique in 1884–85 they noted that maize was especially important to the south of the central Angolan plateau in the Cubango River Valley (*89*, 1:267).

The early development of European production is obscure, but Europeans in Angola apparently were growing maize in quantity long before development of European maize production elsewhere in tropical Africa. There was notable European agriculture as early as 1850, when Angola's governors sought to find a profitable alternative to the newly prohibited slave trade by attempting to colonize the hinterland of Luanda on an agrarian basis (125, p. 11). Whether these colonists grew significant amounts of maize is not known, but the British consul at Luanda in 1874 lists maize as a main crop of the area, and in 1875 noted that 525 bags (27 metric tons) of maize and 86 bags of maize flour came down the Cuanza River in launches between May and December of that year (175, p. 1542). These were probably shipments to provision the city of Luanda, which had a population of about 6,000 as early as 1836 (125, p. 11).

The position of maize in the southern part of the country is better known; colonists there definitely grew maize as one of their main crops in the latter part of the nineteenth century. The Boers who reached Angola in 1879, after a five-year trek in which they lost about half their number in the Kalahari Desert (220, p. 259), may — like their counterparts in Kenya and Southern Rhodesia — have played a leading role in initiating large-scale maize production. An article written in 1898 by Charles Ivens, for a while Belgian vice-consul at Mossâmedes, attributed to the Boers the introduction of many new agricultural techniques in southern Angola (220, pp. 262–63), although he does not specifically mention maize, other than to note that maize and sorghum were then the two principal crops in the southwestern corner of Angola.

The first colonists in southwestern Angola arrived in 1840, after fleeing Brazil for political reasons (366, p. 38). In 1885 the total number of settlers stood at 30 Portuguese and 40 Boer families (366, p. 38). Additional immigrants, mostly Portuguese, who arrived in 1886–89 brought the total number of colonists to over four thousand by 1889. Their maize production was reported at 5,875 tons in 1891 and 17,620 tons in 1908–10, but the statistics may be grossly in error since the same figure is given for 1891 and 1908–10 for two of the colonies (366, p. 40; and 5, p. 559):

	Maize production (metric tons)	
Colony	1891	1908–10
Chibia	55	9,700
Huila	. . .	2,100
Humpata	3,320	3,320
Lubango	2,500	2,500
	5,875	17,620

João de Almeida estimates that, counting African maize, total maize production was considerably larger yet and that southwestern Angola could have easily exported 8,000 to 10,000 metric tons of maize in 1908–10 (5, p. 559). There is, however, no record of exports from this region [3] or other parts of Angola until 1910–14, and maize exports averaged only 1,400 metric tons in that quinquennium (409, p. 3).

It was west-central Angola — the Bié and Benguela plateaus — that first developed a sizable maize surplus, and this region still accounts for 85 to 95 percent of maize exports [4] (Map 10-3). Cameron's description of the economic activity on the western approach of the central plateau in 1875 suggests that at that time the central Angolan plateau already produced a considerable maize surplus: "Caravans continued to pass us, bound up country; and nearly the whole number seen by us during the day traded only between Bailunda [on the western edge of the Benguela plateau] and the coast. They carry thither the flour of Indian corn and cassava, on which slaves at Benguela [a settlement on the coast] are fed, and receive in exchange salt, aguardiente, and sometimes cloth" (84, p. 424).

In 1903 initiation of construction of the Benguela Railway, which runs from Lobito on the coast to the Katanga Copperbelt, promised greatly to reduce the transport costs between the central plateau and the coast. However, owing to financial difficulties and difficult terrain, it was not until 1914 that the rail line reached the heart of the central plateau. This date roughly marks the beginning of Angola's maize exports (211, p. 17):

Year	Maize exports (metric tons)
1912	460
1913	2,118
1914	4,052
1919	15,968
1920	17,925
1921	27,274

As the railway continued to advance across the central plateau, after nine years of delay at Chinguar, local observers became enthusiastic about the role of maize in developing the plateau region. A. B. Hutcheon, British consul in Angola in 1923, said in a report on the economic conditions of the country:

MAP 10-3 — ANGOLA: ZONES OF SURPLUS MAIZE PRODUCTION,
1949 and 1950

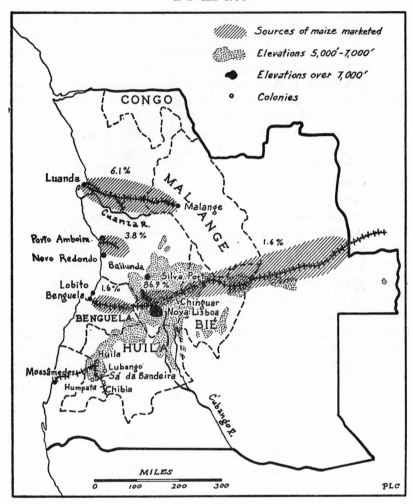

Data from files of Grémio do Milho do Ultramar, Lisbon.

Maize is cultivated extensively, particularly on the Benguella plateau,
where, owing to the advent of the railway, production has increased greatly
in recent years. Although classed among the low value products (*géneros po-
bres*) of the colony, it is now one of the most valuable of exports, while in
regard to bulk, it is by far the most important. The greater part of the crop
is grown by natives . . . . Apart from connecting the Katanga and the Atlantic, it [the Benguela Railway] will open up a large territory in Angola
which is eminently suited to European settlement. The country through which
it passes has already increased greatly in prosperity, and large areas have been

brought under cultivation which were formerly undeveloped (*211*, pp. 7 and 17).

Hutcheon's prophecy appears to have been close to the mark. A description of Angola by the Angola Institute in 1953 says maize "was the product which has mostly contributed to the settlement of European people in the plateaus of Benguella and Bié" (*10*, p. 89).

Hutcheon's report of exports by value showed maize to be the leading agricultural export in 1921 and second only to coffee in 1922 and 1923 (*212*, p. 31):

Commodity	% of value of total exports		
	1921	1922	1923
Maize	16.5	10.9	13.3
Coffee	14.6	30.5	17.8
Palm kernels	12.6	7.5	5.3
Palm oil	8.3	4.6	3.2
Wax	5.5	5.5	4.1
Sugar	3.9	1.8	5.5
Diamonds	24.6	28.5	37.5
Others	14.0	10.7	13.3
	100.0	100.0	100.0

Other reports suggest that in later years maize has consistently been second to coffee among agricultural exports, in terms of value (*74*; and *144*, various issues).

Maize exports increased steadily from an average of 1,400 metric tons in 1910–14 to 106,000 metric tons in 1940–44 (*55*, p. 176; and *144*, various issues):

Year	1,000 metric tons exported	Year	1,000 metric tons exported
1910–14	1.4	1935–39	103.1
1915–19	8.7	1940–44	106.0
1920–24	31.8	1945–49	80.0
1925–29	49.5	1950–54	117.8
1930–34	71.6	1955–59	106.2

Unlike most tropical African maize-exporting countries, Angola continued to expand its maize exports during the depression of the 1930's, and the government conducted a campaign to increase production (*465*, p. 248).

Imports of maize were expanding in Portugal, the principal market for Angolan exports, from 1931 to 1934, but fell in the next three years (*409*, p. 5):

	Maize imported by Portugal (1,000 metric tons)		
Year	*For bread*	*For feed*	*Total*
1931	56.9	0.0	56.9
1932	65.6	0.3	65.9
1933	64.3	4.7	69.0
1934	75.1	18.0	93.1
1935	19.6	19.8	39.4
1936	14.7	21.6	46.3
1937	26.4	2.9	29.3
1938	60.6	21.0	81.6
1939	28.5	18.3	46.8
1940	23.9	23.0	46.9
1941	79.9	30.2	110.1
1942	62.6	17.4	80.0
1943	43.0	7.5	50.5
1944	63.0	3.3	66.6
1945	55.4	27.1	82.5

Since Angola is considerably nearer to Portugal than is Mozambique, the only other Portuguese colony with a comparable maize surplus at the time, Angola was in a better position to compete for the Portuguese market. The reason for the continued expansion of Angolan maize exports from 1935 to 1940 in face of reduced maize imports by Portugal is not clear.[5]

During the 1951–57 period Portugal considerably reduced its imports of Angolan maize because of larger production at home and possibly because of a consumer shift from maize to wheat (*180*, p. 37), or a reduction in maize production in Angola resulting from a shift to other crops (see Chapter 13 below). Madeira has taken slightly larger amounts, on the average, in recent years; and Mozambique took a sizable portion of the exportable surplus in 1951 and 1952 (*11*, various issues):

	Angolan maize exports (1,000 metric tons)								
Destination	*1949*	*1950*	*1951*	*1952*	*1953*	*1954*	*1955*	*1956*	*1957*
Portugal	60.3	135.5	35.7	41.3	40.8	47.2	6.4	10.8	2.2
Madeira	9.1	14.4	11.5	14.6	15.8	15.3	12.8	16.7	16.7

Cape								
Verde 13.8	1.9	1.2	3.6	1.2	0.6	1.2	2.8	3.0
São Tomé								
and								
Príncipe 3.1	3.7	3.8	3.4	3.2	3.5	3.4	3.5	3.2
Mozambique 5.5	1.8	31.4	28.4	4.2	3.6	0.4	0.0	0.9
Non-Portu-								
guese								
countries 0.0	34.1	50.0	0.0	11.8	28.0	27.6	98.6	3.0
Total 91.8	191.4	133.6	91.3	77.0	98.2	51.8	132.4	29.0

Angolan maize exports recovered to 117.8, 149.2, and 117.1 thousand metric tons in 1958, 1959, and 1960, respectively, for reasons not evident in data available (*144*, 1961, p. 92).

Characteristics of Angolan maize production. In Angola, maize is a basic ration for laborers (*341*, p. 4). Antero Jacques Pena, in an attempt to construct a food balance sheet for Angola in 1952, estimated that some 300,000 laborers received maize as part of their ration at that time (*348*, p. 4). If these laborers received 800 grams of maize per day from their employers, the amount reported for the coffee plantations of the Uigé Plateau in northern Angola in 1950 (*341*) and a figure in line with rations given elsewhere in tropical Africa, 87,600 metric tons of maize per year — almost as much as average exports in the 1950–55 period — are required to feed the Angolan labor force.

In 1949 and 1950, 86.9 percent of maize sold to the Marketing Board came from a small zone extending about eighty miles each way along the railroad from Nova Lisboa (Map 10-3). The area around Luanda accounted for 6.1 percent, the Porto Amboim–Novo Redondo area was third with 3.8 percent, and other portions of the Benguela Railway zone contributed 1.6 percent each.

The Angola Institute distinguishes four categories of agriculturalists in Angola: small African tillers, African farmers, European farmers, and European plantations. Small African tillers practice exclusively unirrigated hoe culture. However, the other category of African agriculturalists, African farmers, often use plows and in many instances irrigate their crops. "The areas cultivated by each family are, in this case, a little larger. . . . Particularly during the harvest season, they often try to obtain the cooperation of other natives, whom they pay . . ." (*10*, p. 74), European farmers are "the great mass of settlers, living in the plateau zone, devoted to the tillage of the so called 'poor products,' such as: cere-

als, beans, potatoes, fruit-growing, and, sometimes, tobacco" (*10*, p. 76).
They raise cattle and employ irrigation and organic fertilizers. Hoe culture
is completely replaced by the plow among the European farmers, but
oxen remain the principal draft power. Tractors are used only to a limited
extent (*10*, p. 76). In 1953 the Angola Institute reported that in Angola
"according to a recent calculation, there are 2,746 European farmers . . ."
(*10*, p. 76), and that they are distributed by province as follows:

Congo	415
Malange	110
Bié	270
Benguela	1,146
Huila	805

Plantations generally belong to societies and companies and are located
on the coast and in the subplateau regions; they grow mainly sugarcane,
sisal, and coffee.

Most of the export surplus, certainly, and probably much of total maize
production come from what the Angola Institute calls African and European farmers. African farmers are probably found principally south of
the Benguela Railroad, for it is estimated that only about 10 percent of
Angola's cattle population is found north of the Benguela Railway Zone,
and farmers using plows must have cattle (*374*, p. 45).

On the central plateau Africans typically grow maize with beans and
sell or barter both to local stores, which sell them to consumers or to the
Grémio do Milho do Ultramar, the Marketing Board, for export, at prices
fixed each season by the Grémio.

In the 1920's there were complaints about the poor quality of Angolan
maize because of its mixed color and high moisture content. The value of
grading and drying machinery was clearly recognized at the time, but —
as with the Benguela Railway — capital was difficult to obtain and progress was delayed. In 1924 a large drying and grading plant, capable of
handling considerably more annually than was then being exported, was
started at Lobito by a Portuguese firm; because of legal difficulties with
the Angolan government and Banco Nacional Ultramarino, the plant was
still unfinished a decade later (*74*, pp. 20–21). In 1933 rules limiting the
purchasing date on maize for export, and thereby ensuring that it was
fairly dry before being sold, were imposed as a substitute measure. It is
not known when the Lobito plant finally went into operation, but there

was still comment in 1937 that maize-cleaning machinery was badly needed (*337*, p. 23).

In 1934 the government drew up a plan for expanding and improving maize production (*465*, p. 248), and in 1937 it provided 30,000 contos (£270,000) to assist African agriculture (*337*, p. 33).

Beginning in 1945, the Estação de Melhoramento das Plantas of the Cereals Marketing Board (Junta de Exportação de Cereais) began a breeding program to improve maize and attempted to replace colored varieties with white ones. In seven years it was able practically to replace unimproved maize with selected varieties in the zones producing maize for export (*188*, 1956, p. 9):

	% of total maize exports	
Year	Selected varieties	Unselected varieties
1949	8.7	91.3
1950	20.6	79.4
1951	38.6	61.4
1952	67.3	32.7
1953	86.7	13.3
1954	89.7	10.3
1955	94.2	5.8
1956	96.2	3.8

Recent trends in consumption. Consumption trends in Angola cannot be estimated quantitatively, but there is evidence that maize consumption may be increasing with rapid growth of urban population (Table 10-1). Irene S. Van Dongen, in a detailed study of recent trends in the economic activity of Luanda, the largest city in Angola, reports that population growth had by 1957 greatly reduced both the maize and manioc surplus of Luanda's hinterland and had prompted the local administrative authorities to stimulate maize production (*125*, p. 20).

The Congo (Leopoldville)

Maize appears to have been well established throughout the Congo Basin by the time the first explorers came, as was noted in Chapter 7. It was probably a major provision for trading caravans long before colonization, but the earliest documentation that I have found of its use as a ration is in the mining industry. Because of its economic characteristics maize was

TABLE 10-1 — ANGOLA: TRENDS IN URBAN POPULATION, 1930–50

	(1,000 inhabitants)		
City	1930	1940	1950
Luanda	50.6	61.0	141.6
Nova Lisboa	14.1	16.3	28.3
Lobito	12.0	13.6	23.9
Benguela	12.7	14.2	14.7
Sá da Bandeira	7.7	8.5	11.7
Malange	4.3	5.3	9.5
Silva Porto	4.2	4.7	8.8
Mossâmedes	4.6	4.9	8.6

Data from *Zaire* (Mar. 1954), p. 308.

ideal for laborers' rations, and it was so used in southern Katanga, the principal mining region of the Congo (Leopoldville) [Map 10-4].

From the beginning of mining activity around the turn of the century, southern Katanga appears to have been a food deficit area. In the years before the First World War, the only food surplus areas Katanga had access to by rail were the Rhodesias, which shipped in some 10,000 metric tons of maize in 1927 (*190*, p. 893). Maize shipments to Katanga from Northern Rhodesia alone ranged from 4,050 to 9,360 metric tons between 1921 and 1928, the year when the rail link between Katanga and Kasai — the principal maize-producing area of the Congo Basin — was completed (*287*, p. 6):

Year	Maize imports from Northern Rhodesia (metric tons)	Year	Maize imports from Northern Rhodesia (metric tons)
1921	6,120	1926	5,580
1922	6,750	1927	9,360
1923	6,120	1928	7,380
1924	4,050	1929	5,490
1925	4,950	1930	2,520

Belgian authorities had been encouraging maize production in Katanga for several years. In northern Katanga improved maize seed was distributed in the late 1920's because a blight had sharply reduced manioc yields (*80*, p. 327).

Completion of the railway connecting Kasai and Katanga in 1928 (*369*,

MAP 10-4 — THE BELGIAN CONGO: PERCENTAGE OF MAIZE PRODUC-
TION MOVING IN COMMERCIAL CHANNELS, 1956 and 1957

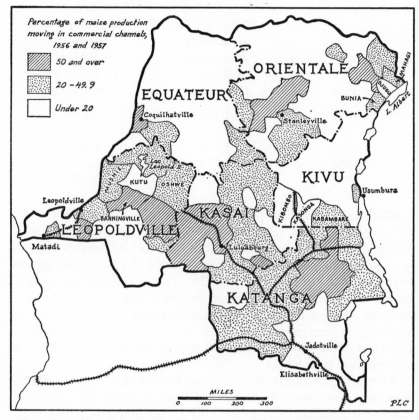

Data from files of the Institut National pour l'Étude Agronomique du Congo Belge.

p. 8) opened a market for Kasai maize which, with efforts by the railway company (and possibly also the government), in following years (*401*, p. 223) greatly stimulated maize production along the railway, and brought about a rapid expansion of Kasai's maize surplus. By 1934 Kasai was producing over 4,000 metric tons more maize than it needed, and Katanga was able to stop imports from the Rhodesias (*190*, p. 893). Growth of the surplus would have been even greater except that Kasai's own mines — principally the diamond mines south of Luluabourg — were apparently taking considerably larger amounts, too. The difference between maize entering commercial channels in Kasai and amounts shipped to other provinces grew from zero to almost 5,000 metric tons between 1933 and 1937 (*17*, p. 459; and *47*, p. 175):

Year	Maize entering commercial channels in Kasai (metric tons)	Maize shipped to other provinces or exported (metric tons)
1933	1,175	1,175
1934	6,227	4,262
1935	5,538	4,784
1936	8,319	6,478
1937	17,575	12,705

Mines in Kivu Province purchased 507 metric tons of maize in 1935, 520 tons in 1936, and 1,205 tons in 1937 (*47*, p. 175; and *16*, p. 267). In Leopoldville Province maize moving in commercial channels — mainly to provision the city of Leopoldville — stood at 1,772 metric tons in 1936 and 1,618 tons in 1937 (*17*, p. 426). Thus in 1937 total maize moving into commercial channels in the Belgian Congo was 21,500 metric tons, not counting Equateur and Orientale provinces. (Information on marketings in these two provinces is not available for 1937; they marketed 1,400 and 2,500 metric tons of maize respectively in 1949, the first year for which data are at hand.)

A temporary decline in domestic needs because of a decline in the African labor force probably contributed to development of a surplus of maize over domestic needs in the early 1930's. Exports to Europe increased from 73 metric tons in 1933 — when, because of the depression, the African labor force had declined to 80 percent of the 1926–33 average — to 1,810 metric tons in 1935, and 23,773 metric tons in 1938 (*42*, various issues):

Year	Metric tons of maize exported	African labor force
1917–20	0	81,700
1921–25	0	216,600
1926	0	417,000
1927	0	427,000

1928	0	415,000
1929	0	420,000
1930	0	399,000
1931	0	327,000
1932	0	392,000
1933	73	318,000
1934	450	339,000
1935	1,810	377,000
1936	4,245	410,000
1937	11,353	492,000
1938	23,773	528,000
1939	19,693	. . .

Nearly all of the increased marketing of maize came from African production. In the early 1950's European farms and plantations produced 3,100 to 3,400 metric tons of maize, which was only about 1 percent of estimated African production for the same years (42, various issues). There is nothing to suggest that European production was ever a larger proportion of the total.

Little information is available on noncommercial maize production in the Belgian Congo before 1917; and for 1917–30 analysis of crop competition in the Belgian Congo is made difficult by governmental policy. Beginning with 1917, compulsory acreages were imposed for certain crops (principally rice and cotton, but others were included). Rice growing was encouraged in the northern and eastern forest areas of the Congo Basin and in the savanna belts which stretch across the north and south of the Belgian Congo (257). What one can infer about the effect of this on maize (a crop which seems not to have been strongly encouraged in many area until later) depends on assumptions about the behavior of Congolese farmers: if one is inclined to believe that they were cultivating about as much acreage as they could, forced planting of new crops would have necessitated reduction of the acreage of some or all of the old crops — perhaps of maize. But if one sides with the pessimistic official opinion of the time which held that the African was lazy and had considerable excess capacity, greater production of both rice or cotton and traditional crops — perhaps maize — as well would have been possible.

Another possibility is that the African's productivity increased considerably at about the same time, not because he was forced to change his allocation of time between work and leisure, but because he came into contact with superior techniques or organization of production. The government and private concerns as well distributed a good number of hoes, axes, and machetes between 1925 and 1928 (257, p. 648); and undoubtedly considerable increases in productivity came with introduction and dissemination of superior crop varieties. With increased productivity, it may have been possible to grow the crops dictated by the government while changing maize production little, if any, or even increasing it. (The timing of labor demands for rice or cotton and maize is largely complementary.)

The effect of the imposition of obligatory acreages, per se, is, then, indeterminate. However, other aspects of the campaign clearly favored substitution of rice for maize. The price of rice was guaranteed; and transportation and processing were provided. Stable, and probably relatively high, prices coupled with reduced processing costs would certainly have favored increased production or consumption of rice at the expense of maize.

Reasons of price and marketing seem to have encouraged cotton at the expense of maize, at least in the southern savannas. Two factors suggest that cotton was more remunerative about 1930: its price per pound was double that of maize; and buying stations were better dispersed so that cultivators typically had to carry loads less than a day's walk, whereas a three- or four-day journey was often required with maize (257, p. 659). However, the value of maize as a crop in the new crop rotation introduced with cotton somewhat offset factors that were working to diminish its importance. Maize was found to be a good crop to grow immediately before cotton; hence in areas where maize was not already well established expansion of cotton acreage also meant expansion of maize acreage.

Another factor was competition from manioc, which was continuing to spread. In the early part of this century manioc was not yet important in several regions (for example, 126, p. 2); but the government placed emphasis on this crop in some areas in order to establish a famine reserve. On the other hand, in most of the region south and east of a line extending through Luluabourg and Lake Albert, maize is reported to be becoming ever more important in diets (357; 408; and 444, p. 19), partly because the introduction of mechanical milling has greatly reduced the costs of processing maize but has not had much effect on manioc-processing costs.

An increase of 118 percent in the number of African laborers employed in the Belgian Congo between the early 1930's and late 1940's suggests that demand for maize by employers may have risen considerably over this period (46, p. 162; and 42, various issues):

Year	Number of Africans in the labor force
1930	399,000
1931	327,000
1932	392,000
1933	318,000
1934	339,000
1947	775,000
1948	775,200

Maize exports fell fairly sharply during and immediately after World War II, but by 1947 exceeded the previous peak, then declined in the 1950's as growing internal demand took an increasing share of domestic supplies (*42*, various issues; and *218*):

1,000 metric tons of maize

Year	Total maize production	Maize production moving in commercial channels	Maize exports
1939	. . .	. . .	19.7
1940–44	. . .	. . .	12.1
1945	. . .	. . .	3.8
1946	. . .	. . .	4.6
1947	307.0[a]	. . .	31.5
1948	. . .	. . .	27.5
1949	304.2	61.1	17.2
1950	336.6	67.9	17.7
1951	313.3	69.2	23.9
1952	305.7	56.3	0.2
1953	324.1	. . .	4.6
1954	321.6	. . .	20.4
1955	325.4	81.8	8.8
1956	315.2	99.9	− 4.4
1957	330.0	111.7	11.9

[a] African production only.

The fall in production in 1951 and 1952 is attributed mainly to an epidemic of *Sclerospora maydis* in Kasai Province, and a rust, *Puccinia polysora*, in Equateur Province (*42*, 1951, p. 25; and *42*, 1953, p. 44). By 1954 these diseases were under control, but production recovered weakly partly as a result of cessation of official efforts to expand maize acreage in Leopoldville Province and parts of Kasai Province because it was feared that Africans were developing a monoculture of maize. The amount of maize that the administration required Africans to plant was reduced in Leopoldville Province from 45,900 hectares in 1953 to 5,600 hectares in 1957 (*42*, 1954, p. 51; *17*, p. 425; and *218*):

Year	Total maize area planted (hectares)	Maize hectarage imposed by Belgian authorities (hectares)
1936	. . .	10,610
1937	. . .	9,950
1952	47,100	36,400
1953	51,000	45,900
1954	50,300	19,700
1955	44,345	. . .
1956	48,277	20,560
1957	51,595	5,600

In Katanga Province a steady expansion of the African labor force from 125,000 in 1948 to 189,800 in 1956 required either an expansion of local maize production or increased imports from neighboring provinces. Maize consumption in the Jadotville-Elisabethville mining zone increased 17 percent between 1954 and 1958 (*444*, p. 18; *44*, 1957, p. 180; and *44*, 1958, p. 166):

	Metric tons of maize consumed in Jadotville-Elisabethville mining zone		
Year	Total	Elisabethville	Jadotville	Mukula–Kula Kamina
1954	31,603	. . .	. . .	. . .
1957	34,935	15,174	16,362	3,435
1958	36,924	18,623	15,727	2,504

To keep pace, compulsory acreages of maize imposed by local authorities in Katanga were increased from 2,800 hectares in 1952 to 4,800 hectares in 1957 (*218*; and *444*, p. 19):

Year	Hectares of maize imposed	Maize marketed within Katanga (metric tons)
1949	. . .	8,200
1950	. . .	8,714
1951	. . .	11,360
1952	2,800	10,351
1953	3,400	11,812
1954	4,400	14,700
1955	4,200	. . .
1956	4,500	13,900
1957	4,800	13,500
1958	. . .	22,300
1959	. . .	23,400

Although amounts of maize marketed within the province increased from 8,200 metric tons in 1949 to 23,400 metric tons in 1959, the Jadotville-Elisabethville mining complex still relied mainly on Kasai for its maize supply in 1958 (44, various issues):

	1,000 metric tons supplied by			
Year	Kasai	Kivu–Upper Katanga	Southwestern Katanga	Total
1952	25.8	4.4	0.5	30.7
1953	31.8	6.8	1.3	39.9
1954	20.0	6.3	1.2	27.5
1955	18.6	6.3	1.1	26.0
1956	33.3	4.2	0.8	38.3
1957	36.7	7.1	1.3	45.1
1958	21.2	10.1	1.8	33.1

In Kasai Province maize consumption by mines, towns, and cities appears to have increased sharply in recent years. Between 1949 and 1957 the amount of maize marketed but not exported to other provinces or abroad increased from 4,521 metric tons to 32,376 metric tons. Over roughly the same period the African labor force grew from 8,600 to 109,000 (42, various issues; 43, 1957, p. 54; and 218):

Metric tons of maize

Year	Maize moving in commercial channels	Maize exported to other provinces or abroad	Maize available for local mines, towns, and cities	African labor force
1948	. . .	. . .	. . .	86,800
1949	31,471	26,950	4,521	. . .
1950	44,809	37,178	7,631	92,200
1951	42,929	36,373	6,556	98,000
1952	. . .	. . .	. . .	98,600
1953	. . .	. . .	. . .	104,400
1954	. . .	. . .	. . .	105,600
1955	. . .	. . .	. . .	114,200
1956	48,774	27,320	21,454	109,900
1957	66,423	34,047	32,376	. . .

It is not possible to derive estimates of the proportion of marketings retained for local use elsewhere, but Map 10-4 shows that in 1956 and 1957, except in the Kasai and upper Katanga areas, maize marketings are large relative to estimated production principally around towns, cities, and mines; Matadi, Leopoldville, Coquilhatville, Stanleyville, and Usumbura (which draws on Congo areas for provisions) all are in or near areas where 20 percent or more of maize production is estimated to move in commercial channels. The zone of commercialized production in the northeastern corner of the Congo (Leopoldville) supplies the Kilo-Moto gold mines.

In Djugu, Bunia, and Mahagi *territoires,* three of the administrative divisions producing provisions for the Kilo-Moto mines, maize marketings were sharply up between 1949 and 1955–57 (*284,* p. 229; and *218*):

Metric tons of maize marketed

Year	Djugu	Bunia	Mahagi
1949	250	300	50
1955	1,629	400	2,400
1956	1,234	751	2,500
1957	5,410	471	1,500

Maize may have increased greatly in importance around Lake Leopold II in recent decades, even though production and marketings from this area are still a small part of the total for the Congo Basin. An extract from the 1924 annual report of the agricultural officer of the area, published in the *Bulletin Agricole du Congo Belge*, states that maize had only recently been introduced and that maize commerce was "rather important" then (*15*, p. 401). No quantitative data are given; but a little over a decade later, in 1937, maize marketings were estimated at 138 metric tons, and over twice that amount in 1939. Since 1949 two of the four territories around Lake Leopold II — Banningville and Mushie — show an upward trend in maize marketings, probably in response to the growing needs of Leopoldville for provisions; Oshwe territoire shows no clear trend, and in Kutu territoire maize marketings have been declining (*365*, p. 676; *17*; and *218*):

Metric tons of maize marketed

Year	Banning-ville	Mushie	Oshwe	Kutu	Total
1937	...	...	...	...	138
1939	250	40	14	6	309
1948	115	30	46	108	299
1949	120	27	39	31	216
1950	81	22	48	56	208
1951	73	15	36	26	150
1956	247	57	7	14	325
1957	334	65	47	15	461

A similar diversity of recent trends in maize marketings appears to be characteristic of western Kivu Province. The trend seems to be upward in the southwestern corner of the area — Kasongo and Kibombo territoires — between 1951 and 1957, but to have been horizontal or downward elsewhere (*195*, p. 25; and *218*):

Metric tons of maize marketed

Year	Kasongo	Kibombo	Kindu	Kabambare	Pangi
1951	35	11	13	...	83
1952	101	14	15	600	58
1953	118	13	11	580	...

1955	127	20	15	200	...
1956	103	20	15	200	...
1957	...	20	13	200	...

For other regions, provincial aggregates suggest that maize moving in commercial channels increased a little over fivefold in Orientale Province between 1949 and 1957 but considerably less in Equateur and Kivu provinces, while declining slightly in Leopoldville Province over the same period (*42*, various issues; and *218*):

<table>
<tr><td colspan="5" align="center">*Metric tons of maize marketed*</td></tr>
<tr><td>*Year*</td><td>*Oriental*</td><td>*Equator*</td><td>*Kivu*</td><td>*Leopoldville*</td></tr>
<tr><td>1949</td><td>2,500</td><td>1,400</td><td>500</td><td>16,700</td></tr>
<tr><td>1950</td><td>3,100</td><td>1,600</td><td>700</td><td>9,000</td></tr>
<tr><td>1951</td><td>3,200</td><td>600</td><td>200</td><td>10,900</td></tr>
<tr><td>1955</td><td>9,300</td><td>1,600</td><td>1,300</td><td>...</td></tr>
<tr><td>1956</td><td>10,000</td><td>2,400</td><td>1,300</td><td>15,400</td></tr>
<tr><td>1957</td><td>13,200</td><td>2,300</td><td>1,400</td><td>14,900</td></tr>
</table>

11

ECONOMIC DETERMINANTS OF PRODUCTION

WHY maize is important in tropical Africa and why there are considerable differences geographically in its importance are difficult questions to answer simply. One helpful device is to think of crops as competitors, with different environmental and physical requirements and with different capabilities.

If consumers act more or less rationally, we would expect the dominant staple food to be one which provides the greatest utility for a given cost, or, stated another way, a given amount of utility for lowest price. Whether Africans act fairly rationally — whether, as a rule, they attempt to maximize the value or utility of a resource, or of a whole complex of resources, at their disposal — has been questioned. Many casual observers have thought to detect a marked difference between the economic behavior of tropical African peoples and that of Western Europeans and North Americans; and in some quarters the idea has become widespread that in tropical African societies the most basic of economic axioms — the maximization principle — lacks validity. This is not the assumption made here. Indeed, there is no substantial evidence that African peoples fail to maximize economic welfare any more than do individuals in Western societies. It is not held, of course, that either is completely rational.[1]

One might assume à priori that costs dominate in starchy-staple competition in tropical Africa, for if the level of living is thought to be extremely low, the elasticity of substitution between starchy-staple commodities would be extremely high: under such conditions, consumers cannot afford the luxury of a relatively expensive staple food.

The level of income in tropical Africa cannot be estimated with any confidence, published estimates of national income notwithstanding, and there are undoubtedly great geographical variations. Although there

205

may be sizable areas where levels of living are so low that preference is given little expression, there are clearly large areas where earnings from export crops alone have made it possible for Africans to indulge their preference for relatively expensive foods.

If one assumes that levels of living are high enough for considerable expression of preferences, the elasticity of substitution between starchy-staple commodities might still be high enough for costs to dominate, if starchy-staple commodities are sufficiently close substitutes. Again, there are measurement difficulties; at present we cannot estimate the substitutability of these commodities with enough accuracy to answer this question, although we do know that they are not perfect substitutes and that African consumers distinguish them in terms of such characteristics as color, texture, digestibility, and flavor.

Many African peoples say they prefer a staple with a relatively high fiber content, other things being equal, because it takes longer to digest, and therefore "stays in the stomach longer," the merits of which can be seen when one considers that reliance on such a commodity reduces the number of daily meals required. This has obvious attraction for people who must frequently work long hours in a field located quite a distance from their hearth. A number of ethnic groups say they prefer maize to manioc or plantain for this reason. However, the digestibility of starchy-staples varies considerably not only with the variety of the crop but with processing techniques, in which there are often great differences among ethnic groups. As to color, there is strong evidence that African consumers prefer a foodstuff which will yield a dish light in color. A prejudice against yellow varieties of maize exists practically everywhere in tropical Africa, and there is opinion to the effect that in Uganda, Kenya, and Zambia, at least, white varieties of maize are preferred to the millets and sorghums for the same reason.[2]

The focus will be on costs in this chapter, then, not because preferences are thought unimportant but because relatively little is known, or knowable at present, about them, about the degree to which they can be expressed, and about differences in preferences among the several hundred ethnic groups of tropical Africa. Most of what can be said about preferences comes from budget surveys and information on color and texture preferences; these are taken up in more detail later.

PRODUCTION FACTORS

Physical Yields

Table 11-1 summarizes three sets of information about the yields of major starchy-staples in western tropical Africa. It shows the relatively

TABLE 11-1 — APPROXIMATION OF STAPLE FOOD CROP YIELDS,
CALORIE VALUES, AND INDEX OF CALORIE YIELD PER HECTARE,
WEST AFRICA, ABOUT 1950

Crop	(a) Approximate yield[a] (metric tons per ha.)	(b) Growth period (months)	(c) Calories[b] per 100 grams	(d) Index of calorie yield per ha.
Millet-sorghum	0.6	2–6	345	100
Maize	0.7	2–5[c]	360	122
Rice	0.7	2–6[c]	359	121
Manioc	8.0	7–24	109	421
Yams	6.0	7–12	90	261
Taro (cocoyam)	3.0	6–18	86	125
Sweet potatoes	4.0	3–6	97	187
Plantains	8.0	8–18	75	290

Based on B. F. Johnston, *The Staple Food Economies of Western Tropical Africa,*
Food Res. Inst. Stud. in Trop. Devel., No. 1 (Stanford, Calif., 1958), p. 126.

[a] "Crude" approximations by B. F. Johnston "based on available statistics of
production and area for West African territories as of about 1950. The yam and
cocoyam yield figures have been adjusted to a 'net' basis by a deduction for seed
requirements. No attempt has been made to adjust any of the yield figures for milling loss or a waste factor."

[b] Data from FAO, *Food Composition Tables — Minerals and Vitamins — for
International Use,* Nutr. Stud. No. 11 (Rome, 1954), pp. 10–12 and 18.

[c] "Under comparable conditions, the growth period for maize would be shorter
than for rice. For the Itimbiri region of the Belgian Congo, Edgar Pauquet indicates
a growing period of 3½–4 months for maize and 4½–5 months for rice" ('La
Culture du riz en région Itimbiri,' *Bull. Agr. du Congo Belge,* Oct. 1955, p. 993).
The growing period for floating rice may be in excess of six months (*231*, p. 126).

short growth period for maize, the high caloric content of its grain, and its
relatively low yield per hectare. These yield data are rough estimates for
West Africa, a large heterogeneous area; but the yield relationships por-
trayed — although not the absolute level of yield — appear to hold generally. (See, for example, Charts 11-1 and 11-2.)

In terms of calories per hectare — a relevant criterion in a number of
areas where population pressure on land appears high for current techniques of production, and a criterion which is likely to be widely relevant
in the near future — maize is rarely the most productive starchy-staple.
In nearly all areas where manioc can be grown, it surpasses maize considerably in physical yield; and in the more humid areas plantain, rice, sweet
potatoes, taro, or yams generally give more calories per hectare; while in

CHART 11-1 — NIGERIA: YIELDS OF MAIZE, MANIOC, AND YAMS BY
VEGETATION ZONE, 1950–51 (million calories per hectare)

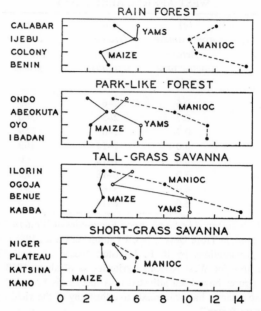

Data from W. O. Jones, *Manioc in Africa*, Food Res. Inst. Stud. in Trop. Devel.,
No. 2 (Stanford, Calif., Stanford Univ. Press, 1959), p. 261; and Nigeria, Department of Statistics, *Report on the Sample Census of Agriculture, 1950–51* (Lagos,
1952).

the parklike forest belts yams, millets, or sorghums usually give superior
yields. In the short-grass savanna millets and sorghums dominate because
of their relatively low moisture requirements; their ability to withstand
drought, which gives them an advantage if rainfall is unreliable, whether
or not it is scanty; their ability to thrive on relatively poor soils; and their
wide range of temperature tolerance — only maize, of the major tropical
African starchy-staples, will grow at higher elevations (*347*, p. 111; *104*,
pp. 3–8; *146*, pp. 136–43 and 150).

Charts 11-1 and 11-2 illustrate the considerable margin between maize
yields and those of other starchy-staples in Nigeria and the Belgian Congo, two countries where yield data appear to be relatively good.

For most of tropical Africa, yields per hectare are less important than
yields per unit of labor, for labor appears often to be the limiting input of
production. Therefore one would expect farmers to attempt to maximize
returns per unit of labor rather than per unit of land.

CHART 11-2 — BELGIAN CONGO: YIELDS OF STARCHY-STAPLES
BY DISTRICTS, 1952–54

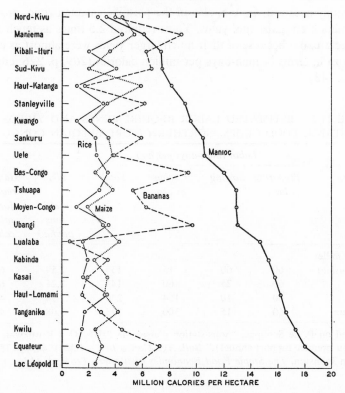

After Jones, *Manioc in Africa* (Stanford Univ. Press, 1959), Chart 10-1, p. 259.

Only a few attempts have been made to measure the labor costs of producing crops in tropical Africa, and techniques and organization of production may vary enough to make the estimates we have characteristic of
only a small part of tropical African agriculture. Nevertheless, the studies
that have been made suggest that the farm cost of producing maize is much
nearer that of other starchy-staples than yield data indicate, and that
when processing, storage, and transportation are taken into account,
maize may be nearly as cheap to produce as manioc, if not cheaper.

Labor Expenditures in the Field

A study by Pierre de Schlippé of the Logo people who live in the parklike savanna of the northeastern Congo Basin shows the labor cost of
producing maize to be slightly less per million calories than for sorghum,

considerably lower than for millet, and less than a fifth of the cost of rice (Table 11-2).

A study at Ejuru, Ghana, also in the parklike savanna zone, provides information on maize and yams. Yams required 2.5 times as much labor per hectare, but because of their much larger yields were almost as cheap as maize in terms of man-days per million calories (*209*, p. 226, cited in *231*, p. 143).

TABLE 11-2 — ESTIMATED LABOR REQUIREMENTS AND YIELDS FOR STAPLE FOOD CROPS, NORTHERN ITURI, BELGIAN CONGO

Crop	Labor (man-days per ha.)				Yield (metric tons per ha.)	Man-days required for one million calories
	Preparing land	Sowing	Caring for crop	Total		
Finger millet (*Eleusine*)	60	60	15	135	2.59	63.9
Rice	60	25	60	145	2.21	60.2
Maize	60	10	154	224	1.94	40.1
Sorghum	60	15	300	375	3.08	42.0

Based on P. de Schlippé, "Sous-station d'essais de l'INÉAC à Kurukwata (Extraits du premier rapport annuel)," *Bull. Agr. Congo Belge,* June 1948, pp. 388–93, cited in Johnston, *The Staple Food Economies of Western Tropical Africa,* p. 138.

J. Noyen reports on the relative returns of maize and manioc at Gandajika in the Kasai area of the Congo (Leopoldville). Manioc required 43 percent more labor per hectare, but cost much less than maize (roughly one-third as much) in terms of man-days per million calories (*324*, cited in *237*, p. 264):

Labor required
(man-days of 5 hours per hectare)

Crop	Clearing	Preparation seedbed	Preparation of cuttings	Planting	Hoeing	Harvest	Total	Yield (metric tons per ha.)	Man-days required to produce one million calories
Maize	6	11	...	3	30	7	57	1.5	10.67
Manioc	6	...	12	12	12	40	82	22.0	3.42

E. S. Clayton's estimates for millet, sorghum, maize, and rice in Kenya show the first two to be cheaper than maize in man-days per hectare and in man-days per million calories, but rice was more expensive than maize according to both criteria (*104*, p. 29, cited in *231*, p. 141):

Crop	Total labor required (man-days per ha.)	Yield (metric tons per ha.)	Man-days required to produce one million calories
Sorghum	17.3	1.2	4.5
Millet (on ridges)	37.0	1.4	8.2
Maize (on ridges)	44.5	1.4	9.3
Rice	156.0	2.8	15.3

A similar relationship between maize and sorghum is reported by N. R. Fuggles-Couchman for Kingolwira in eastern Tanganyika. This study gives data on maize and manioc grown together for one year, on manioc for one year, and on sorghum for three years during which "the only improvements made in local native practice were line planting of the grain crops, groundnuts and cassava" (*162*, p. 293). With the exception of 1936, maize required about the same or a little less labor per hectare than sorghum; but it required six or more times as many man-days to produce one million calories (*162*, p. 394):

Crop	Labor required (man-days per hectare)					Yield (metric tons per ha.)	Man-days required to produce one million calories
	Clearing grass	Planting	Hoeing and thinning	Harvesting	Total		
Maize and Manioc 1936	21.6	19.7	16.0	4.9	62.3	0.2	121.9
				37.0	94.5	2.2	40.7
Manioc 1937/38	37.0	37.0	28.4	58.0	160.4	4.1[a]	35.9[a]
Sorghum 1936	23.5	5.6	16.0	12.3	57.4	0.8	20.7

Sorghum							
1937	12.3	22.3	12.3	16.0	62.9	1.5	12.3
Sorghum							
1938	14.2	6.2	22.3	23.5	66.2	1.2	16.3

[a] Yields for manioc in 1937/38 not given; yield here was derived by assuming manioc yields in 1937/38 increased as much over 1936 as sorghum yields did.

The relationship between maize and manioc was roughly similar to that between maize and sorghum, although the difference in cost per million calories was not as striking. The exceptionally high cost of maize was possibly because of poor rainfall in 1936, when it yielded only a fifth of a metric ton per hectare. If data were available for maize in other years, its costs in terms of man-days per million calories would probably be considerably less, although it is not likely that they would be lower than the cost of manioc or sorghum.

A study in Genieri, Gambia, in 1949 by Miss Haswell also shows maize to be more expensive than sorghum to produce in the short-grass savanna zone; but it was cheaper than millet or rice (*197*, p. 57, cited in *231*, p. 139):

Crop	Man-days of 5 hours required to produce one million calories
Sorghum	54.5
Maize	61.9
Late millet	126.0
Early millet	122.3
Swamp rice	87.0
Upland rice	333.5

Jean Minelle reports the following estimates of labor requirements to be typical of the Malagasy Republic (*288*, p. 321):

Crop	Man-days per hectare
Banana-plantain	25–30
Maize	115
Manioc	170
Irish potatoes	215
Irrigated rice	350

Minelle reports such wide range of yields that meaningful estimates of labor costs per million calories cannot be made. In terms of labor outlay alone, however, banana-plantain required only about one-fourth as much effort as maize, while manioc required almost 50 percent more; Irish potatoes nearly twice as much; and irrigated rice — which is transplanted in the Malagasy Republic — over three times more labor than was needed for maize.

Postharvest labor costs

Only three of the studies on labor requirements of starchy-staples give information on postharvest cost; these provided data on maize, millets, sorghum, rice and manioc.

Pierre de Schlippé found that among the Logo the cost of processing maize was a little above the cost of processing rice, and about the same as processing millets or sorghums (*377*, pp. 388–93, cited in *231*, p. 138):

	Man-days per metric ton of processed product — ready to be cooked			*Man-days required to produce one million calories*		
Crop	*Processing immediately after harvest*	*Additional processing prior to cooking*	*Total postharvest*	*Field operations*	*Postharvest operations*	*Total*
Rice	42	136	178	60.2	49.8	110.0
Sorghum	47	143	190	42.0	55.4	97.4
Finger millet *(Eleusine)*	77	120	197	53.9	58.6	112.5
Maize	43	166	209	40.1	58.7	98.8

J. Noyen's estimates give information on maize and manioc for the southern Congo Basin: the difference between the cost of these two crops in terms of labor cost per million calories was considerably reduced by inclusion of processing costs: manioc increased from 32 to 59 percent of the cost of maize (*324*, cited in *237*, p. 264):

	Man-days of 5 hours per million calories				
Crop	*Shelling or peeling*	*Grinding*	*Total post-harvest*	*Field opera-tions*	*Total all opera-tions*
Maize	4.68	54.32	59.00	10.67	69.67
Manioc	6.67	30.03	36.70	3.42	40.12

R. Chambon and M. Alofs report maize to be almost twice as expensive as manioc in labor costs per million calories for field operations in Tanganyika District of Katanga Province (*95*, pp. 116 and 124):

	Man-days per million calories		
	Manioc		
Operation	*Light soil*	*Heavy soil*	*Maize*
Preparation of land	3.7	4.8	30.9
Preparation of cuttings	2.6	2.6	. . .
Planting	2.9	2.9	7.5
Cultivation	1.5	1.5	9.4
Harvest	19.4	22.8	10.3
Total field operations	30.1	34.6	58.1
Peeling or husking and shelling	41.1	52.1	41.2
Transportation to processing plant	9.5	26.8	. . .
Drying	1.5	1.5	0.6
Removing fiber	13.2	15.4	. . .
Transport to commercial center	12.8	9.2	13.4[a]
Total postharvest operations	78.1	105.0	55.2
Total all operations	108.2	139.6	113.3

[a] Derived by assuming that it costs the same to transport maize from field to commercial center as manioc from field to processing plant and thence to commercial center; hence this figure probably overestimates the cost of maize by at least the expense of the extra loading and unloading involved in processing manioc.

Maize, on the other hand, appears considerably less expensive for post-harvest operations, but exactly how much less cannot be precisely estimated from the experiments in Tanganyika District because of lack of detail in data on transportation. However, even assuming it costs the same to transport maize from field to commercial center as to transport manioc to the processing plant, unload it, load it again after processing, and transport it to commercial centers, the lower cost of maize in post-harvest operations is sufficient to make the total cost of maize only 5 per-cent greater than that of manioc grown on light soils. And on heavy soils maize was the cheaper crop by some 20 percent when account was taken of all operations.

How processing costs can be important in determining the position of maize vis à vis plantains and sweet potatoes is well illustrated in Uganda and Rwanda-Burundi, countries where these last two are of considerable importance, and where maize appears to have a markedly different posi-tion owing mainly to postharvest costs.

Compared with plantains and sweet potatoes, maize has the advantage of being less bulky relative to value, and therefore easier to transport and store, if central storage is necessary. Compared to the dried products of these starchy-staples, maize does not have a cost advantage in trans-portation and storage, but it is probably more easily processed; it can be machine-ground with little preparation (only husking, shelling, and a brief drying in cases where the moisture is too high), whereas the starchy fruits and roots, which contain roughly four to five times as much moisture at harvest, not only must be peeled but require much more drying.

In Rwanda-Burundi these postproduction costs are of relatively slight significance because of the structure of the economy. There is no large off-farm population or labor force to feed, and transportation and proc-essing costs are of slight importance: the first because there is little central marshaling of supplies requiring haulage over several miles; and the latter because the locus of production and processing is a household where the processor is the housewife. Such processors are in a position to consume much of their production directly from the field, thus avoiding the necessity of drying it for storage; and with the techniques used they can process (pound) a fresh fruit, root, or tuber as easily as a dry one. Therefore in Rwanda-Burundi harvest and preharvest costs and demand predominate; each starchy-staple competes successfully only in a fairly well-defined ecological zone.

By contrast, in the economy of Uganda the basic producing unit in some industries is relatively large (besides sugar plantations, mining, manufacturing, and processing industries, a number of large African coffee and cotton producers are found), and there is a sizable nonself-sufficient group of urban dwellers and laborers.[3] Feeding this population requires transport from farm to centralized locations, processing and storage there, and further transportation in distribution.

Maize thrives in the well-watered, fertile area of Uganda bordering Lake Victoria on the north and west, but so do plantains and manioc; hence maize is not competitive in calories per acre or per unit of labor. Nevertheless, it competes exceedingly well. Roots, tubers, and banana-plantain cannot be stored or transported so cheaply, and advantages they have in costs of production seem not to be offsetting.

Price Data

Market prices in areas where prices are uncontrolled may give an indication of the relative cost of producing maize. If markets are perfect, prices in them should equal marginal cost at farm plus transportation, handling, and returns to middlemen. Many food markets in tropical Africa seem to be characterized by a number of sellers and considerable competition, but how perfect market information is cannot be determined. However, unless market imperfections have widely caused the price of maize to be lower or the price of other staples higher than they would otherwise be, or unless inaccuracies in the basic data consistently distort price relationships, data available tend to support the hypothesis that because of its relatively low postharvest costs maize is of considerable importance in a sizable portion of tropical Africa, particularly in urban communities. Thus although both yield data and estimates of labor costs in field operations suggest that maize should not be a major competitor, its cost to the final consumer appears to be generally less per 1,000 calories than for other starchy-staples — with the exception of manioc products in some areas and millets or sorghums in the extremely dry zones (Table 11-3).

Table 11-4 compares prices of maize meal with various starchy-staple foodstuffs. These data yield less information than one would like because meaningful inferences can be drawn only when maize meal is the cheaper (since maize meal is a processed product, it should be more expensive, other things being equal, than an unprocessed foodstuff). However, plantain in Uganda (except for Jinja in 1952); fresh manioc in Dakar, Saint-Louis, and Dar es Salaam; and rice in Dakar, Saint-Louis, Luanda, and Cotonou were all more expensive than maize meal (Tables 11-3 and 11-4).

CATEGORIES OF MAIZE COMPETITION

There appear to be five principal categories of economic and ecological conditions under which maize is grown. Four divisions are made in its role as a food crop; these are called here "use as a delicacy," "insurance against famine," "secondary staple," and "primary staple." The fifth category is production of maize as a cash crop. Categories I and II, use as a

MAP 11-1 — CATEGORIES OF MAIZE COMPETITION
IN TROPICAL AFRICA

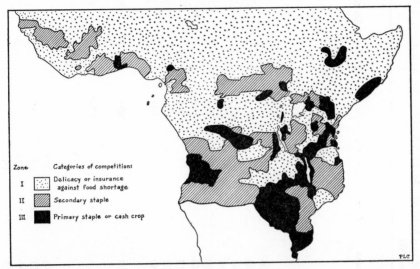

Zone	Categories of competition:
I	Delicacy or insurance against food shortage
II	Secondary staple
III	Primary staple or cash crop

Categories were derived from per capita production data and information on the
magnitude of amounts marketed relative to production.

delicacy and as insurance against famine, overlap, and together take up by
far the largest area (Map 11-1).

Use as a Delicacy

Throughout tropical Africa, as noted earlier, maize in the form of
roasting ears is a prized food and even a delicacy. When maize consumption does not exceed 25 kilograms per capita per year (see Map 8-1), this
is probably the primary form in which it is consumed; maize beer is the
only other notable food use of maize in these areas.

So consumed, maize is indeed a luxury, for neither beer nor roasting
ears are efficient modes of utilizing this crop. If left until maturity, roasting
ears would provide roughly 360 calories per 100 grams instead of 80 or
so; thus they are approximately four times as expensive in terms of energy
provided. With beer the difference is of similar magnitude. However, although use as a luxury is probably the predominant use in Zone I (Map
11-1), in some areas maize is for a brief season an important staple, and
sometimes a hunger breaker.

Insurance Against Famine

Over much of the savanna country, particularly the short-grass savanna,
maize makes a small contribution to total yearly food supplies (probably

TABLE 11-3 — INDICES ON STAPLE FOOD PRICES PER 1,000 CALORIES FOR SELECTED TROPICAL AFRICAN TOWNS AND CITIES (Maize=100)

Area	Maize	Sweet potatoes	Gari	Manioc	Yams	Taro	Plantain	Rice	Millet	Sorghum
RAIN FOREST										
Ivory Coast, Abidjan										
1957/58	100	227	...	171	...	...	263	228	144	...
Guinea, Conakry, 1957	100	...	...	140	...	...	...	150	157	...
Nigeria, 1952–55										
Delta[a]	100	...	64	...	205	...	...	...	...	...
Ijebu-Ode	100	...	63	...	243	...	...	...	...	...
Benin[b]	100	...	57	...	143	...	...	...	...	...
Colony-Agege	100	...	68	...	331	...	...	...	...	...
Onitsha	100	...	56	...	300	...	...	186	...	...
Calabar	100	...	56	...	183	...	...	161	...	...
Port Harcourt	100	...	75	...	314	...	...	211	...	...
Ahoada	100	...	51	...	222	...	...	199	...	...
Orlu	100	...	68	...	249	...	...	207	...	...
Ghana, 1953–55										
Kumasi	100	...	120	...	295	228	...	306	...	130
Ghana, 1956										
Kumasi	100	...	133[c]	...	...	220[c]	...	257[c]	...	88[c]
PARKLIKE SAVANNA										
Nigeria, 1951–52										
Ibadan	100	...	120	140	236	144	275	...	...	...
Abeokuta	100	...	86	42	133	124	112	85	...	...
Ifé-Ilesha	100	...	102	118	199	137	120	...	...	...
Ondo	100	...	115	78	224	159	101	...	...	...

TABLE 11-3, *continued*

Area	Maize	Sweet potatoes	Gari	Manioc	Yams	Taro	Plantain	Rice	Millet	Sorghum
Nigeria, 1952–55										
Ibadan	100	…	112	…	219	…	…	…	…	…
Abeokuta	100	…	59	…	219	…	…	…	…	…
Ondo-Akure	100	…	54	…	196	…	…	…	…	…
Ogoja	100	…	82	…	262	…	…	232	…	…
TALL-GRASS SAVANNA										
Ghana, 1953–55										
Tamale	100	…	136	136	383	337	…	261	…	136
Ghana, 1956										
Tamale	100	…	200c	131c	…	248c	…	191c	…	99c
Nigeria, 1952–55										
Oyo	100	…	58	…	179	…	…	…	…	…
Kabba-Okene	100	…	…	114	254	…	…	351	…	102
SHORT-GRASS SAVANNA										
Ghana, 1953–55										
Accra	100	…	143	217	547	476	…	290	…	149
Sekondi	100	…	103	67	349	271	…	236	…	144

Data from, or derived from, Johnston, *The Staple Food Economies of Western Tropical Africa*, pp. 146 and 292–93; and Jones, *Manioc in Africa*, pp. 267–68.

a Sapele, 1952 and 1953; Effurun, 1954 and 1955.
b Benin, 1952 and 1953; Irrua, 1954 and 1955.
c 10 months' average.

TABLE 11-4 — COMPARISON OF MAIZE MEAL PRICES WITH THE PRICES OF OTHER STARCHY-STAPLE FOODSTUFFS FOR SELECTED TROPICAL AFRICAN CITIES
(Maize meal=100)

Area	Maize meal	Manioc flour	Fresh manioc	Yams	Plantain	Rice	Millet
Uganda, 1951							
Kampala							
Nakawa	100	183	100	. . .	233	. . .	. . .
Kampala	100	116	92	. . .	215	. . .	. . .
Wandegeya	100	154	77	. . .	192	. . .	. . .
Katwe	100	175	83	. . .	283	. . .	. . .
Nakulabye	100	133	66	. . .	258	. . .	. . .
Jinja	100	200	116	. . .	133	. . .	. . .
Uganda, 1952							
Kampala							
Nakawa	100	100	77	. . .	122	. . .	. . .
Kampala	100	111	77	. . .	155	. . .	. . .
Wandegeya	100	122	89	. . .	139	. . .	. . .
Katwe	100	. . .	50	. . .	110	. . .	. . .
Nakulabye	100	94	77	. . .	172	. . .	. . .
Jinja	100	. . .	77	. . .	89	. . .	. . .
Tanganyika, 1955							
Dar es Salaam	100	125	200	. . .	. . .	. . .	. . .
Senegal, 1956							
Dakar	100	. . .	196	. . .	. . .	174[a]	84
Saint-Louis	100	. . .	194	. . .	. . .	108[a]	57
Dahomey, 1956							
Cotonou	100	67	. . .	. . .	. . .	124[a]	. . .
Angola, 1956							
Luanda	100	162	. . .	. . .	. . .	180	. . .

Derived from Johnston, *The Staple Food Economies of Western Tropical Africa*, p. 293, and Jones, *Manioc in Africa*, p. 270.

[a] Local rice.

less than 25 kilograms of grain per capita per year); but it is the dominant staple for a short season prior to harvest of the staple crop, and at such times is usually consumed immature. In these areas, even though maize is more costly than any of the other starchy-staples, it has the advantage of a shorter growing period, and is grown mainly to provide for a period when the dominant staple is in short supply. In years when supplies of the basic staple are ample, maize is still welcome.

Secondary Staple

The area where maize is a secondary staple (i.e. where production amounts to roughly 25 to 100 kilograms per capita per year) is predominantly open forest with some tall-grass savanna; maize is apparently more costly to produce here than yams and manioc but cheaper than taro, millet-sorghum, and banana-plantain (hatched areas in Map 11-1). An exception is Uganda and parts of the Congo (Leopoldville) and Rwanda-Burundi, where soils particularly favor the banana-plantain.

Primary Staple or Cash Crop

It is in the parklike and tall-grass savanna, and at high altitudes too cold for the other major tropical African starchy-staples, that ecological conditions give maize its greatest competitive cost advantages. Over most of this zone millets-sorghums, manioc, and sweet potatoes are the only starchy-staples that offer serious competition, except for limited areas on the more humid side which have relatively fertile soils, where banana-plantains can successfully dominate. In Rwanda-Burundi not starchy-staples but beans and peas offer the most competition at high altitudes. Even though manioc and sweet potatoes do fairly well, this is not their optimum environment; hence differences in their yields and those of maize are narrowed, to the advantage of maize.

Maize is a major cash crop almost anywhere there is need to transport food over considerable distances. This is much of Africa south and east of the Congo Basin, especially parts of Kenya, Tanganyika, Zambia, Rhodesia, and Malawi. Roots, tubers, and plantains cost too much to transport, even if production costs are competitive; for the millets and sorghums, if costs are competitive, demand is too weak. Only dried manioc and manioc flour appear to be major competitors.

Taking the proportion of the maize crop marketed as the criterion, Angola, Zambia, Rhodesia, Kenya, Uganda, and Congo (Leopoldville) are the principal geographical areas of the cash crop category (Map 11-2). But these data are rough and incomplete. Possibly maize is important in internal commerce over a considerably larger area. Also needed is information on internal trade in other starchy-staple commodities, but such data are available for only a few areas.[4]

A large share of maize marketed is grown by European farmers, but of areas with sizable European production, European and African marketings are clearly distinguishable in the official statistics only for Mozambique, Rhodesia, and Kenya. In Kenya and Mozambique Africans account for 60 to 65 percent of maize sold, but in Rhodesia for only 33 to 38

MAP 11-2 — AREAS OF TROPICAL AFRICA WHERE MAIZE
IS IMPORTANT AS A CASH CROP

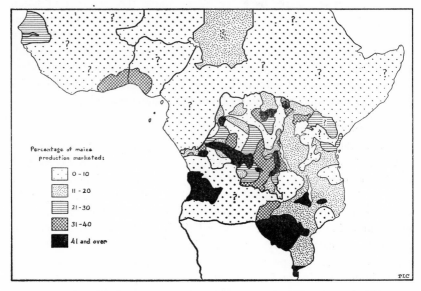

Data principally from sources cited in Table 11-5, but also from République du
Sénégal, *Comptes économiques, 1956*, p. 15; République du Tchad, *Comptes économiques, 1958*, p. 76; and République du Niger, *Comptes économiques, 1959*, p. 10.

percent (Table 11-5). For Zambia and Tanganyika, one can get only a
rough idea of maize sales by Africans.

Because marketings from Eastern Province, Zambia, are not identified
by source in the statistics, one can only establish an upper and lower limit
for the share of marketings contributed by Africans. If all maize sold in
Eastern Province came from African farmers, their total share would be
about 40 percent for 1946–50; if only European farmers marketed maize
in Eastern Province, the total share for Africans in Zambia would be
only 36 percent. The proportions are similar for the following quinquennium for the lower limit, but the upper limit is 47 percent (Table 11-5).

In Tanganyika, quantitative estimates are not available for sales of
maize to plantations for labor rations, but the African share of known
marketings averaged 53.5 percent in the period 1952–54. In the Congo
(Leopoldville) not less than 96 percent of maize sold is marketed by
Africans.

Of the remaining areas where maize is known to be of some significance
as a cash crop, Uganda, Ghana, Togo, Dahomey, Nigeria, and Cameroun
have virtually no European farmers; hence all maize marketed can be

TABLE 11-5 — SHARES OF MAIZE MARKETINGS CONTRIBUTED BY AFRICAN AND EUROPEAN FARMERS IN SELECTED COUNTRIES

Country	Period	% of total marketings		1,000 bags of 200 lbs.	
		African	European	African	European
Kenya	1945/46–1949/50	64.7	35.3	987.9	538.7
	1950/51–1953/54	59.1	40.9	1,074.3	744.6
Southern Rhodesia	1945/46–1949/50	38.1	61.9	486.4	489.9
	1950/51–1954/55	33.7	66.3	685.6	1,346.8
Northern Rhodesia	1946–50 max.[a]	40.5	59.5	208.0	306.0
	min.[a]	36.0	64.0	185.0	329.0
	1951–55 max.[a]	47.0	53.0	472.0	532.0
	min.[a]	36.0	64.0	363.0	641.0
Mozambique	1949–54	65.1	34.9	380.2	203.8
Tanganyika	1952–54	53.5	46.5	20.2[b]	17.5[b]
Nyasaland	1945	78.0	12.0[c]	13.0	85.0
	1946–50	72.0	18.0	19.0	87.0
	1951	92.3	7.7[c]	25.0	300.0
Belgian Congo	1956–57	96.1	3.9[c]	1,163.8	45.4

Data from Kenya, Department of Agriculture, *Annual Report*, various issues; Federation of Rhodesia and Nyasaland, *Report of the Maize Marketing Board*, various issues; Northern Rhodesia, Department of Agriculture, *Annual Report*, various issues; files of the Tanganyika Department of Agriculture; Nyasaland, Department of Agriculture, *Annual Report*, various issues; files of the Institut National pour l'Étude Agronomique du Congo Belge; and Mozambique, Repartição Técnica de Estatística, *Estatística agrícola*, various issues.

[a] Sales from Eastern Province are not distinguished by race of producer; if all Eastern Province marketings came from Africans, the maximum figures would apply; if all of it was from Europeans, the minimum figures would apply.

[b] Does not include sales to plantations for feeding African laborers.

[c] Production; no marketing estimates available.

safely assumed to be African. For Angola there is no basis for making a reasonably reliable estimate of maize marketed by Africans, because although sales by Europeans are known, they often represent amounts bought by merchants or farmers from Africans.

In several portions of the cash crop zone, maize quickly found its place as a cash crop because ecological conditions were unfavorable for other crops which had a market and because such areas were near the coast, providing easy and comparatively cheap access to international markets. The coastal areas of Ghana, Togo, Dahomey, and Nigeria were producing maize as a cash crop, a commodity sold to slave ships, as early as the seventeenth century. Dahomey and Togo maize continued to be an important export crop in recent decades mainly because the areas served by rail or near the coast grew little which was of value to the mother country except products of the oil palm and maize.

In all the major African maize-exporting countries, the geographical distribution of commercial production is determined as much by the location of railroads, cities, mines, and plantations employing large numbers of African laborers as by ecological conditions. Since maize will grow almost everywhere, although yields are low if the environment is far from optimum, it has not infrequently been encouraged by governments, through coercion or price incentive, in areas near railroads, roads, and rivers that had no other cash crop; low yields have been offset by proximity to cheap transport.

PROSPECTS FOR MAIZE

In earlier chapters we have seen that increased per capita maize production has come about both from greater maize acreage and from the better yields obtained. Gains in productivity per acre have been attained mainly through adoption of superior cultural techniques and organization of agriculture and better inputs, e.g. improved seed.

The demand for maize can be estimated only roughly, but budget surveys provide some data on what consumers' attitudes toward maize will be when levels of living are raised.

Most existing budget surveys cover groups of different income levels, and where they reveal consistent differences in diet with increased income, there is evidence of the kinds of dietary change that can be expected with economic progress. However, it must be born in mind that use of such data as a guide assumes that low income groups will exhibit the same habits of expenditure that upper income groups now have when their purchasing power increases. A better guide, if we had it, would be evidence of the changes in diet historically with changes in per capita disposable real income.

Available budget data suggest that meat and alcoholic beverages are clearly preferred to starchy-staples when incomes allow. Of the starchy-staple products, wheat and rice universally seem to edge out maize preparations (Chapter 8). Qualitative data suggest that maize dishes often rank higher than manioc, millet, sorghum, and taro dishes. The position of yams, sweet potatoes, bananas and plantains in relation to maize is obscure, and undoubtedly varies considerably by area, but it seems clear that they rank below rice or bread.

Roasting ears and maize beer unquestionably command a much higher place than maize porridge and other staple maize dishes; and beer, and perhaps other of the nonstarchy preparations made, or obtainable, from competing starchy-staples, probably rank above dishes made from maize. However too few surveys have been sufficiently detailed to tell us much about the magnitude of such differences. To get an accurate estimate not only should each maize category be subdivided and each major use weighed by the volume of maize production it accounts for — another unknown — but this would have to be done for each of the other starchy-staples.

If increased productivity means costs of production are lowered in tropical Africa, relative to other maize- and feed grains-exporting countries, it is of course conceivable that there might be a large increment in exports. No meaningful forecast can be made for more than the very short run, however; and even for that period the prospects vary so much among tropical African countries according to location, domestic and foreign governmental policies, and costs of production that no general appraisal can be made.

Key variables in determining the extent to which tropical African countries can be competitive in export markets are changes in their costs of production relative to competitors, the sort of trade restrictions adopted by importing countries, and the nature of the supply functions of African producers.

Estimates by the Foreign Agricultural Service of the United States Department of Agriculture indicate that world trade in feed grains (of which maize is the most important) has increased fairly steadily over the 1950–58 period from an average of 13.5 million metric tons in 1950–54 to 21.2 million metric tons in 1958 (*442*, p. 16). This was attributed mainly to "upward trends in consumer purchasing power and consumption of livestock and meat products in many countries" (*442*, p. 13); but the analysis suggests that recent rates of expansion are not likely to continue:

Feed grain production has increased in all major deficit countries in recent years but not fast enough to satisfy rapidly increasing demand. While prospects for the immediate future indicate continued expansion in world import requirements because of increasing livestock numbers, the expansion cannot be expected to continue indefinitely at the rate of recent years. Several European importing countries have already indicated intentions to shift from continued encouragement of a high level of domestic wheat production by means of price supports and other incentives to a higher level of feed grain production by the same methods. This would result in checking the upward trend in demand for imported feed grains (*442*, p. 19).

Moreover, even if there were a substantial increase in quantities demanded by importing countries, it is unlikely that costs of production in tropical African countries can be lowered as much in the short run as by their competitors in temperate zones, where, unlike tropical Africa, widespread adoption of hybrid maize varieties is a short-run possibility and, in fact, is being widely achieved.[5]

Costs of production would probably be considerably lowered for the more important of current tropical African maize exporters — Kenya, Zambia, and Rhodesia, for example — if competition were reintroduced into domestic marketing by abolishing the existing statutory marketing monopolies, and inefficient producers were thereby eliminated. However, it is not possible to establish what quantities a free-market price would call forth, because the supply schedule of producers cannot be established. It is possible that while costs of production would be lower free-market prices might be too low, or too variable, to induce production of a surplus over domestic needs.

If we ignore the possibility of expanding exports, the prospects for maize within tropical Africa seem the following: Per capita maize consumption will increase in the short run and the intermediate period of the next decade or two, depending on the rapidity of economic development. Maize will continue to gain at the expense of millets, sorghums, and manioc more than it loses to wheat, rice, meat, sugar, fats, and nonmaize alcoholic beverages. In the long run it will have taken as much ground as possible from the less preferred staples and can only lose by the substitution of wheat and rice for maize, and by a trend toward a more varied diet and a less starchy one.

This is as direct human consumption. Increased use of maize in other ways may be partially — even completely — offsetting. One would expect a wider use of maize in production of European-type beer as a substitute for the relatively dearer rice and barley. Creation of a distilling industry could account for considerable increases in maize consumption; production of some or all of the many industrial products which use, or can use, maize as a raw material is probable, and could mean considerable expansion of the demand for maize.

Because maize is the best of livestock-fattening feeds, as is well demonstrated in the Corn Belt of the United States, spread of the livestock-feeding industry, based on an increased productivity of maize growers, seems an obvious direction for economic development of tropical Africa to take. At present, however, cattle are not kept in many areas because of the tsetse fly; and where cattle are found, they usually are not deliberately fattened. Nor are swine or sheep common in many areas, although goats are found almost everywhere. Development of a livestock-feeding industry might, under these circumstances, seem to involve such fundamental changes in the existing rural economies as to be strictly a long-run possibility, not likely to be realized in the next two or three decades.

A fairly good argument can be made, however, that this is not the case. In most of tropical Africa game, historically the major source of meat for most ethnic groups, was fairly abundant as little as two or three decades ago. It has become scarce in recent decades because of the growing population, increased availability of guns among Africans, and the incursion of non-African hunters. Many of the latter have shot merely for sport, but significant numbers of them, in areas such as Kenya, Tanganyika, parts of the Congo Basin, Zambia, and Rhodesia, killed game to supply European enterprises — e.g. farming and mining — which relied on Africa's wild life for much of their food so long as game was easily obtainable.

Disappearance of game, the traditional source of meat in the diet of Africans, has brought about a very rapid expansion in fishing and fish trading in Katanga, Zambia, Rhodesia, and Malawi, and possibly in Uganda, over the past decade; this development appears also to have been characteristic of the Ivory Coast, Upper Volta, Ghana, Nigeria, and elsewhere (295; and 110, p. 7).

But substitution of fish for meat is not likely to be the ultimate solution. Even if the supply of fish can be expanded enough to replace the loss of game, it is likely that the income elasticity of demand for fish is low compared to meat. Therefore, as incomes rise, consumers can be expected to turn increasingly to meat, and, unless tropical African countries can spare a considerable portion of their foreign exchange earnings needed for the purchase of resources required in economic development which must be imported and have high opportunity costs, importing meat is not an efficient solution, and development of local livestock- and poultry-feeding industries will in all probability be the answer.

The question of the efficiency of maize as the base for the livestock-feeding industry remains, however, for in tropical Africa maize is not, as in the American Corn Belt, widely the cheapest source of carbohydrates. In much of the area manioc is probably a cheaper feed, provided the distance between the feed-producing and feed-consuming industries is not more than a few miles. In the drier areas millets and sorghums are frequently cost-competitive, and in the more humid zones manioc usually is. Although manioc is of somewhat lower quality as a feed, its yields are generally enough greater to be offsetting (237, p. 274).

But these are present cost relationships. There is reason to think that in the course of the next few years the costs of producing maize are likely to fall more than those of competing feeds.

This is a somewhat different conclusion than that of William O. Jones, who, in the concluding chapter of his *Manioc in Africa*, argues that "As population and income of the African economies grow, it can be anticipated that manioc's cost advantage over other local starchy staples will increase. Machinery can effect the same economies in labor needed to produce manioc as it can for other roots and cereals. Economies in processing may even be greater for manioc. And as land costs become an increasing part of production costs, manioc's superior yields will continue to give it an advantage" (*237*, pp. 269–71). Although maize has strikingly lower physical yields per acre than manioc, its economic yields are possibly not lower, and maize has special characteristics which may cause even its physical yields per acre to be higher relative to manioc in the future.

The present physical yield disadvantage of maize relative to manioc appears to be in preharvest costs. Manioc is much more expensive to harvest and prepare for storage. The data are rough, but as shown earlier they suggest that lower harvest and postharvest costs for maize largely offset its higher preharvest costs.

Maize yields currently realized in tropical Africa are rarely more than half of what is possible, and frequently only a third or a fourth. Furthermore the maize breeder can be expected continually to extend the capability of the maize plant. No other starchy-staple seems to reward breeding efforts so liberally; but even if some offer unrecognized latitude for yield improvement, the publicity maize has received through the spectacular gains from hybrid seed, and the greater number of men and larger research funds devoted to maize — not only in the tropics but in other parts of the world — favor a continued gain for maize.

In addition, where mechanization of production becomes the rule, maize is likely to achieve a further cost advantage relative to competitors (except, perhaps, the millets and sorghums). Maize production has already been almost completely mechanized in the world's principal producing regions. If production of other starchy-staples can be so cheaply mechanized, it will, in all probability, be only in the distant future, whereas mechanization of maize involves mainly borrowing. Mechanization applied to production, then, will probably favor maize relatively more than its competitors, just as it has where it has been applied to processing.

Of considerable import, too, will be government policy. Maize will probably continue to receive harsh words from those preoccupied with soil conservation, but there will undoubtedly be some of the opposite opinion. Prominent among these are likely to be officials who find mounting imports of wheat, barley, and rice adding to their balance-of-payments problems. The nutritionist who is concerned that maize is sure to bring pellagra conceivably could be influential in formulation of government policy in the next few years, although in the long run maize is not likely to be important enough in the diet as a staple to cause comment from even the alarmist. Also, nutritionists who believe maize necessarily brings pellagra when it becomes the principal staple are growing rare, and even those who fail to keep pace with nutritional developments seem to realize that the incidence of this nutritional disease is low among the populations in tropical Africa who rely heavily on maize.

The encouragement of competing crops as "famine" reserves appears on the wane; and with increases in per capita productivity, with the extension and improvement of transportation systems that accompanies economic growth, the compulsory manioc and sweet potato acreages, and the less forceful campaigns to extend these crops, will remain more a feature of the past than of the future. In the drier areas millets and sorghums will probably continue to have official favor, but development of early-maturing maizes may do much to win support for maize.

In summary, maize is likely to increase in importance as a food in tropical Africa in the short run but will almost certainly lose ground to wheat, rice, meat, fruits, and vegetables in the long run. There is little prospect for increased exports in the short run and no meaningful long-run forecast can be made. Use of maize as a feed is not likely to increase in the short run, but with development of a livestock-feeding industry it could increase greatly in the long run.

12

INCREASING EFFICIENCY
OF PRODUCTION

TECHNIQUES of maize production employed at agricultural experiment stations in tropical Africa often yield two or three times as much maize per acre as African farmers get, but the farmers have rarely adopted any of these cultural techniques. Some of the superior techniques are too costly at present; some require skills and knowledge not yet widely available among African peasants; and others have not been properly introduced.

IMPROVEMENT OF SEED

The spectacular increases in yield that followed adoption of hybrid varieties of maize in the United States Corn Belt have made a deep impression on many who concern themselves with problems of increasing productivity of agriculture; and it is often assumed that productivity of African agriculture can also be doubled or tripled in a single stroke by simply substituting improved seed for that farmers now plant. Probably no agricultural experiment station of any note in tropical Africa lacks a program for developing improved varieties of maize, and nearly all of these research bodies have demonstrated with their creations at least a 100 percent yield increment over that achieved by local peasant farmers (*71, 85, 329,* and *394,* p. 5):

Country or area	Yield increase of improved over unimproved seed (percent)	Level of yield with improved seed (kgs. per ha.)
Nigeria	100	. . .
Dahomey	50–82	354–382

230

Congo Basin
Ruzizi Valley	300	. . .
Gandajika	34	2,000
Yangambi	28	2,300
Rwanda-Burundi	100	2,300
Rhodesia	72[a]	1,560[a]
Malawi		
Central Region	52	900
Southern Region	36	685

[a] Four-year average, 1949/50–1952/53.

The primary problem at this juncture is not to develop superior seed but rather to distribute the improved seed now available. In explaining why there is such a great divergence between potential and actual maize yields obtained, nearly all the major problems of increasing the productivity of African peasants are underscored, including unfamiliarity of research workers with African diets and systems of farming, lack of education among Africans or of adequate extension services, and shortage of capital and low interest credit.

Although hybrid maize usually gives strikingly better yields than openpollinated varieties, it cannot at present be widely disseminated among African farmers because of the cost and the requirement that seeds harvested from hybrid plants not be planted.

With other types of improved maize it is not necessary to buy seed each year, but many other difficulties arise. In most areas these have so far proved to be insurmountable. Improved seeds invariably do well only in a fairly restricted area; they are bred for specific climatic and edaphic conditions, and when taken from these often do less well than the unimproved varieties Africans now employ. African farmers not infrequently give some of the improved seed they have been issued to a friend or relative who lives in an area for which it was not bred.

Another problem is keeping seed pure. Because of the ease with which maize varieties cross, it is almost futile to introduce improved varieties of maize piecemeal. Unless nearly all the farmers in an area adopt improved seed and there is strict care not to plant other varieties, the old and new types cross and in most instances quickly degenerate to a level of yield nearer that of the old than the new, if not below that of the old type.

The only instance known in which improved seed has been reasonably successfully introduced and established for an area circumscribing several hundred African farms is an area in Rwanda-Burundi, and there this achievement was possible only with strict control and compulsory replacement of old seed with improved varieties (71).

Probably the chief reason Africans have been reluctant to adopt improved varieties is the failure of plant breeders to create higher-yielding varieties with the characteristics African consumers want. Exactly what the desired characteristics of maize are varies from ethnic group to ethnic group, but generally an acceptable maize kernel must be of a light hue and have a starch neither too hard nor too soft. And in most areas the plant which produces it must do so in a certain number of days to fit into the farmer's agricultural calendar; otherwise he will not have the requisite labor to tend it.

Explanations of the Dahomey Department of Agriculture in 1957 for their failure to get wide adoption of improved maize are illustrative: "The principal causes seem to be criticism by producers . . . a longer vegetative period for the improved variety than for the local maize (4 months in place of 3 to 3½ months); greater attack by weevils on the improved than on local maize; total absence of rust at present, hence the rust resisting ability of improved maize could not be demonstrated. The season when improved seeds were issued corresponded to a season when maize was in short supply and much of the issued seed was consumed . . ." (115, pp. 48–49).

Failure of plant breeders to take cognizance of the preferences of African consumers almost certainly has its roots in the same failure to consult the African which I think caused European agricultural officers largely to waste their efforts and tropical African resources trying to remake African agriculture in the European image.[1] Because Africans generally have little formal education and a crude technology, it is frequently assumed that nothing can be learned from them.

Nor is this a problem which is confined to Africa. A similar failure of research and extension officers has been recorded among the Spanish-American farmers of the Rio Grande Valley where, like African peasants, farmers were reluctant to adopt maize varieties which gave much better yields but were of vastly inferior quality (20, pp. 42–43).

A prerequisite of any successful program for developing or introducing maize varieties with superior yields, then, must be study of how the recipients use maize and what characteristics of grain they require. In addition, in most areas, as much attention must be given to distributing superior seed as to developing it.

Probably the cheapest way of establishing a demonstrably higher-yielding, acceptable variety is one tried at Kizozi experiment station in Rwanda-Burundi. In the first season, the experiment station exchanged its superior seed for the existing planting stock in a given area. Peasants in that area were simply given a quantity of improved seed equal to that which they brought from their own granaries. They were instructed to plant none of their old seed, should they still have some. Inspectors toured to make certain farmers were following instructions. The inferior seed received in exchange was ground into meal and stored. At harvest time farmers in the area which had received improved seed, with the exception of those on the extreme fringe of the zone, were required to return an amount of seed from their harvest equal to what they were issued. For this they were given an equal amount of meal.

As the next planting season approached, farmers in a second area forming a concentric zone around the first, plus those farmers on the fringes of the first area whose superior plants were likely to have been fertilized by wind bearing pollen from outside the area were required to bring in their seed and were given in exchange the improved seed recently received from the first group of farmers. Their inferior grain was ground into meal, and at harvest time reexchanged for improved seed, which was in a like manner given to farmers in a third belt surrounding the second. This cycle continued until the entire area for which a given variety was suitable was covered.

FERTILIZERS

Maize appears to respond fairly strongly to fertilizers throughout tropical Africa; however, commercial fertilizers are so expensive that at several experiment stations the increment of yield achieved has not been enough to cover the cost of fertilizers applied. Most African farmers are considerably more isolated than the experiment stations and must pay much higher transportation costs; therefore it is doubtful if there are many areas where commercial fertilizers can at present be used profitably by Africans. Nor is animal manure widely available in quantity.

Experiment stations nearly always secure considerably greater yields by applying fertilizers. J. Noyen reports yield increases ranging from 144 to 186 percent at Gandajika in southern Congo (Leopoldville). However, the heaviest dose, 1,000 kilograms of phosphate per hectare, was not economic (325, p. 225):

Treatment	Kilograms of maize per hectare		Gain or loss after cost of fertilizer was taken into account (francs per ha.)
	1st harvest	2nd harvest	
Control	1,541	1,681	—

400 kgs. phosphate per ha.	2,417	2,822	+958
600 kgs. phosphate per ha.	2,467	3,025	+660
1,000 kgs. phosphate per ha.	2,226	3,012	−727

R. Lesire's work in the Bas-Congo area of the Congo (Leopoldville) suggests that both compost and mineral fertilizers give improved yields there, the former more than the latter. But only compost applications were economic, possibly because the gains in yield from peanuts grown following maize cannot be separated out in the calculations published (*259*, pp. 71 and 73):

	% yield increase		Gain or loss after cost of fertilizer was taken into account
Treatment	*Maize*	*Peanuts*	*(francs per ha.)*
Compost	141	32	+687
"Mineral fertilizer"	22	2	−178
Compost and "mineral fertilizer"	185	29	−878

R. Hardy gives no figures, but reports that fertilizing is not economic at Kiyaka, about midway between Bas-Congo and Gandajika (*194*, p. 11). At the Nioka experiment station, near Lake Albert, only a 15 percent increase in maize yields was obtained with 30 metric tons of manure per hectare; and somewhat less, an increment of 11 percent, was achieved with 263 kilograms of bicalcium phosphate per hectare (*475*, p. 669).

Studies in Rhodesia suggest that both phosphate applications and green manuring increase yields, but no data are given on whether the gain is enough to offset fertilizer costs (*376*, p. 3):

Method	*Bags of maize per acre*
Maize and green manure grown in alternate years 300 lbs. superphosphate per acre applied to maize	17.4

No fertilizer	12.0
Maize grown continuously 300 lbs. superphosphate per acre given each second year	5.8
No fertilizer, but one ton of lime per acre applied each fourth year	6.2

Other experiments in Rhodesia also show considerable yield improvement from green manuring, but provide no data on its profitability (*360*, p. 5):

Method	Bags of maize per acre
Maize grown continuously, 1928–50	6.01
Maize and green manure grown alternately, 1928–50	13.53

Fertilizer experiments reported by the Kenya Department of Agriculture in 1932 provide a little data on the economics of green manuring. In the Highland areas of Kenya green manuring gave about an 18 percent yield increase (*244*, p. 1). Other results cited in the same report show costs and returns of three areas of European agriculture in the Kenya Highlands to vary considerably, but green manuring was profitable in every instance (*244*, pp. 10–11):

Costs and returns	Shillings per acre		
	Kama Koia	*Kitale I*	*Kitale II*
Cost of green manuring	14.32	15.62	14.48
Increment return	24.00	23.74	15.55
Profit	9.68	8.12	1.07

Research in Nigeria illustrates the great variation in response of maize to fertilizers in areas with different soils and climates, but no data are provided on the cost of fertilizing. In Ilorin Province applications of nitrogen increased yields less than 1 to 13 percent in 1956 and from 24 to 30 percent in 1957 (Table 12-1); in Oram-Aran the increase was from 7 to 20 percent in 1956, and from 31 to 43 percent the following year. At Oke-Ode, however, plots given nitrogen yielded 2 to 11 percent less than the control plot in 1956 but gave 30 to 36 percent more in 1957. Application of phosphate reduced yields at Ilorin in both years; at Oke-Ode phosphate

TABLE 12-1 — NIGERIA: RESPONSE OF MAIZE TO NITROGEN AND
PHOSPHOROUS IN ILORIN PROVINCE, AT ORAM-ARAN, AND AT
OKE-ODE, 1956 AND 1957
(Maize yields: lbs of grain per acre)

Year and Area	Nitrogen treatment			Phosphorus treatment		
	Control	50 lbs. ammonium sulphate per acre	100. lbs ammonium sulphate per acre	Control	50 lbs. super-phosphate per acre	100. lbs super-phosphate per acre
1956						
Ilorin	719	813	725	799	661	796
Oram-Aran	1,267	1,367	1,525	1,344	1,441	1,375
Oke-Ode	490	483	437	454	467	493
1957						
Ilorin	514	640	671	631	629	592
Oram-Aran	929	1,225	1,333	1,053	1,183	1,252
Oke-Ode	638	827	872	798	745	794

Data from Northern Region of Nigeria, Ministry of Agriculture, *Annual Report . . . 1956/57* (Kaduna), pp. 89–90.

increased yields slightly in 1956 but reduced them the next year; and in Oram-Aran phosphates gave a slight increase in 1956 and a sizable one in 1957 (19 to 74 percent).

At Kabba the pattern was reversed: application of 75 pounds of ammonium sulphate per acre reduced yields, but yield increases were obtained on plots receiving 50 pounds of superphosphate per acre (*321*, p. 90):

Treatment	Yield (lbs. grain per acre)	
	Kabba	Osara
Nitrogen treatment		
Control	805	310
75 lbs. ammonium sulphate per acre	785	558
Phosphorus treatment		
Control	745	335
50 lbs. superphosphate per acre	818	584

Experiments at Osara, however, showed strong response to both fertilizer treatments: a yield increment of 80 percent for nitrogen and 74 percent for phosphate.

Trials at Abeokuta indicate fairly strong response to both nitrogen and phosphorous, but only a slight yield increment from potassium (*150*, p. 14):

Treatment (per acre)	Increment in maize yield (percent per acre)	Yield level (lbs. of grain per acre)
100 lbs ammonium sulphate	23	506
200 lbs. ammonium sulphate	26	518
100 lbs. superphosphate	38	533
200 lbs. superphosphate	34	518
100 lbs. potassium muriate	4	468
200 lbs. potassium muriate	12	507

In Zambia, experiments near Lusaka indicate substantial response to nitrogen (*346*, p. 85). Reports of research at Urambo and Nachingwa experiment stations in Tanganyika suggest the response to nitrogen is much the same there (*181*, p. 67): "a dressing of 50–100 lbs of sulphate of ammonia per acre produces economical increases in yield which offset the expense incurred in the purchase of the fertilizer; and the same applies at Kongwa on certain soils."

An exceptionally detailed survey of the response of maize to nitrogen and phosphorous fertilizers has been made by the Malawi Department of Agriculture. The results of 118 experiments in 13 districts show considerable variation, but in a majority of trials application of nitrogen was economic, while the return from phosphorous was not (Table 12-2). According to the Department of Agriculture of Uganda, maize also responds to nitrogen there, but data on the profitability of applying fertilizers are not provided (*426*, p. 9).

Reports from Malawi indicate application of farmyard manure gives "impressive results" (*331*, p. 8). At Ukiriguru, Tanganyika, N. V. Rounce, J. G. M. King, and D. Thorton obtained sizable increases in maize yields with cattle manure (*370*, p. 36):

Cattle Manure (tons per acre)	Maize Yield (lbs. per acre)	% Increase
0	390	. . .
3	1,042	173
6	1,440	278

TABLE 12-2 — NYASALAND: THE PROFITABILITY OF APPLYING NITROGEN AND PHOSPHOROUS FERTILIZERS TO MAIZE, BY DISTRICT, 1952/53–1956/57

District	Number of trials	Response to 75–100 lbs. of ammonium sulphate per acre			Response to 75–150 lbs. of superphosphate per acre		
		% economic[a]	% borderline[b]	% uneconomic[c]	% economic[a]	% borderline[b]	% uneconomic[c]
Central Province							
Lilongwe	31	61	26	13	22	20	58
Dowa (plateau)	11	46	27	27	0	27	73
Dowa (lake shore)	3	34	33	33	0	0	100
Northern Province							
Karonga	8	38	25	37	0	12	88
Rumpi	7	57	14	29	43	14	43
N. Mzimba	7	57	43	0	0	14	86
S. Mzimba	9	67	22	11	44	33	23
Nkata Bay	4	75	25	0	25	25	50
Southern Province							
Fort Johnston	11	55	10	35	18	18	64
Blantyre	9	90	10	0	0	22	78
Cholo	6	66	34	0	50	33	17
Mlanje	10	40	10	50	20	20	60
Lower River	2	0	50	50	0	0	100

Data from Nyasaland, Department of Agriculture, *Annual Report, 1956/57*, Pt. 2 (Zomba, 1958), p. 18.

a Over 400 lbs. of increment in maize yield per acre.

b 200–400 lbs. of increment in maize yield per acre.

c Less than 200 lbs. of increment in maize yield per acre.

Experiments in Kenya and Ghana also suggest maize responds well to fertilizers (*151*, p. 198; and *332*, p. 44).

Wider application of fertilizers should be fairly easily achieved, once they are cheap enough to be clearly profitable. Fertilizers and composts have long been used by many, perhaps most, African peoples.[2]

CULTURAL PRACTICES

Although there is considerable scope for increasing maize yields through superior cultural practices throughout tropical Africa, the yield increment better cultural methods can provide appears often to be less than that which can be obtained with either superior seed or fertilizers. This is what one would expect considering that selecting by trial and error the cultural practices suited to the environment faced and the techniques available is feasible even with a crude technology, whereas plant breeding or production of low cost fertilizers is not.

Irrigation

How much yields can be improved through irrigation has not been well studied in tropical Africa, but more valuable crops appear to respond as well or better to irrigation than maize does; hence in the foreseeable future irrigation is probably not an efficient means of increasing yields.

Pests and Diseases

Research on yield improvement through pesticides has been focused mainly on storage pests. Efforts to control field insects have concentrated on breeding resistant maize varieties. Success of such breeding programs varies greatly from area to area, and the severity of loss to field pests among African farmers is known only vaguely; reasonably trustworthy quantitative estimates are not available on the amount of yield increase that can be achieved by such programs.

More is known about breeding resistance to disease because of extensive programs in recent years to develop maize varieties with resistance to *Puccinia polysora*, an American rust. Ironically, African varieties seem to have developed resistance to this disease by natural selection about as quickly as plant breeders in western tropical Africa, the area where attack by *polysora* appears to have been the most severe, could develop resistant varieties in the laboratory (*86*).

Planting and Cultivation

Yields are greatly affected by such cultural practices as the date of planting, the density of plants per acre, and the number of weedings. However, except for planting techniques in Ethiopia, there is no evidence that African farmers fail to follow optimum cultural practices for their present technology.

Ethiopian maize farmers broadcast their maize seed, a practice unknown in the rest of tropical Africa, and one that appears to be clearly inferior. Experiments at Jima, Ethiopia, show row-planted maize to yield more than twice as much (5,681 compared to 2,627 kilograms) per hectare as broadcast maize (77, p. 38).

THE ORGANIZATION OF AGRICULTURE
FOR INTRODUCTION OF NEW TECHNIQUES

Although most African farmers probably have good knowledge of when to plant, optimum distances between plants, and how often to weed, introduction of improved seed, fertilizers, and superior tools can be expected to require a new set of cultural practices. The speed and efficiency with which new techniques of this sort can be introduced can often be greatly increased by innovations in the organization of agriculture, provided organizational changes can be achieved without generating resistance among the farmers involved.

The creation of *paysannats indigènes* in the Congo (Leopoldville) represents a method that could greatly facilitate introduction of superior cultural practices. In this vast scheme over 120,000 families were resettled in an effort to place their fields in a systematic layout and set the center of the community nearer existing roads. This was done to aid the use of machinery, to facilitate introduction of fertilizers, pesticides, superior rotations, and new varieties, and to make supervision and guidance easier.

If the African is to be primarily a supplier of labor in an enormous agricultural factory where no premium is placed on initiative or freedom, such schemes, which are hardly more than an extension of the plantation system, have much to recommend them. They may give impressive short term gains, but they are not likely to bring permanent changes and continuing increments in productivity unless the farmers involved voluntarily adopt new techniques and are given incentives to make innovations of their own.

Provision of credit, improvement of transportation, and extensive educational programs, put into effect without resettlement, seem to be far more certain means of permanently raising the productivity of tropical African farmers. Maize areas where plows, maize mills, and improved seed have been most widely adopted and where the most striking gains in productivity, as judged from increases in the amount of maize sold per farmer, have been achieved — the maize areas of Zambia, Rhodesia, Kenya, and Mozambique (Chapter 9)— are also areas in which resettlement has not been important. African production techniques in these areas were changed by price incentives, extension services, and improvement of roads.

These less direct programs not only arouse less resistance to change among farmers but make maximum use of the knowledge African peasants have of the problems facing them. The waste of much-needed development capital in projects like the Tanganyika Groundnuts Scheme, the Gambia Poultry Scheme, and the Mokwa Scheme in Nigeria, all of which failed largely because of inadequate understanding of the agronomic and social problems involved, serves as a dramatic reminder of the hazards in trying to increase the productivity of African peasants without drawing on their knowledge of what is feasible.

STORAGE METHODS

Of methods for increasing agricultural productivity commonly discussed, reducing waste — especially storage losses — is usually given high priority. Storage losses are commonly thought to be enormous in tropical Africa; speculation that they are on the order of 20 to 30 percent is often encountered in conversations with agricultural officers and research workers, and estimates of this magnitude have been published (96, p. 568; 2, p. 148; and 327, p. 75). However, recent research demonstrates that such figures are gross exaggerations for most areas, although there is a great deal of variation among areas, according to the variety of maize grown, the climate, and the technique of storage employed.

In general, losses are greater for the merchant than for the producer, and are higher in the wet forest areas than in the savannas, and for flour or dent varieties than for flints.

Rodents, the rice weevil (*Calandra oryzae*), and several other insects are the important pests; the rice weevil is thought to be the major culprit among insect pests, while the rat is the most troublesome rodent. In most tropical African areas only the rice weevil does enough damage to attract the attention of those describing storage problems.

Study of African storage techniques shows that the African farmer almost always attempts to protect maize from weevils. A careful search of the anthropological and agricultural literature shows that throughout tropical Africa stored maize is smoked periodically, and in some areas it is conserved in hermetically sealed stores (e.g. underground pits in Northern Nigeria and Somalia and, among many ethnic groups, earthen pots plugged with mud). Where storage bins are sealed, weevils cannot live because of the high concentration of carbon dioxide that builds up from metabolism of the grain. Fumigation with smoke discourages weevils, and the fire helps to keep the moisture content low.

Knowledge of African methods of storage suggested the hypothesis put forward in 1958 that, on the average, storage losses and waste were less than 5 percent (*289*, p. 9) and not 20 or 30. By 1959 two researchers, working independently and by slightly different methods (see Appendix III), brought forth data indicating that losses to the rice weevil in two small areas — one in an open forest area and the other in a tall grass savanna zone — are not more than 5 percent for the average storage period, and are often not more than half that. In 1958 and 1959 their results were verified for several locations in other vegetation zones. In Table 12-3 losses in these locations for storage periods of four and eight months are shown. Only in the savanna areas is maize likely to be held in store as long as eight months. Elsewhere, more than one crop is grown a year and maize rarely needs to be, or is, stored for more than four months.

Once maize moves into commercial channels, losses are thought to be much greater. In western Nigeria, for example, merchants reported that as soon as maize is shelled and bagged losses mount quickly. In one attempt to get a quantitative estimate, losses were found to be as much as 5 percent in the first month; and the rate probably rises sharply after that (*92*). Western Nigerian middlemen recognize this and attempt to dispose of maize as quickly as possible; they report that they rarely hold stocks more than two months. Of course they could reduce losses considerably by using insecticides, but in the humid forest zone it is difficult to keep bulk storage losses below 10 percent for a six months' period even with liberal use of pesticides (*443*). In the drier areas, such as former British East Africa, Zambia, Malawi, and Rhodesia, losses incurred in bulk storage seem to be kept to 1 or 2 percent with proper treatment. Available evidence suggests, then, that storage losses are low enough with the techniques currently employed for changing storage techniques to deserve low priority, if any, in development programs.

PROCESSING METHODS

Techniques of processing maize vary greatly throughout tropical Africa, but wherever maize is an important item of diet, reduction of the grain to meal or flour usually accounts for most of the processing costs. One of the traditional methods of crushing grain — putting it in a mortar hewn out of a log and pounding it with a heavy wooden pestle — seems to be used throughout tropical Africa. Stone grinding — placing the grain on a large, flat rock and rotating a smaller rock upon it — is less widespread

TABLE 12-3 — MAIZE: ESTIMATED STORAGE LOSSES TO THE RICE WEEVIL IN PEASANT GRANARIES FOR SELECTED TROPICAL AFRICAN AREAS, 1953–60

Vegetation Zone	Losses to rice weevil		No. of communities sampled	No. of samples taken	Year	Country
	After 4 months' storage (% loss by weight)	After 8 months' storage (% loss by weight)				
Closed forest	3	...	2	4	1959	Belgian Congo
Open forest[a]	1	4	1	27	1958	Nigeria
Open forest	1[c]	...	18	52	1958	Nigeria
Open forest	1[c]	...	1	9	1959	French Cameroons
Tall-grass savanna	1[c]	...	7	25	1958	British Cameroons
Tall-grass savanna[b]	1[c]	1	1	...	1953–55	Belgian Congo
Tall-grass savanna	1	...	1	4	1959	Uganda
Tall-grass savanna	1[c]	...	10	28	1959	Northern Rhodesia
Tall-grass savanna	1[c]	...	2	7	1959	Nyasaland

Except as otherwise noted, data are from samples taken by the writer, using Caswell's technique (see App. III).
[a] Unpublished data provided by H. Caswell, University College, Ibadan, Nigeria.
[b] Unpublished data provided by E. de Prêter, INÉAC, Gandajika, Belgian Congo.
[c] One percent or less.

and where known is usually a supplementary technique. Both processes are entirely manual and require a great deal of labor.

Cushman says that in central Angola, with traditional techniques, "Usually it takes about from four o'clock in the morning until noon to get a bushel of the fine corn meal [maize meal] that is the week's supply for the ordinary family . . ." (*113*, p. 77). Mrs. G. M. Culwick gave special attention to processing techniques in a dietary survey of the Azande in southwestern Sudan, where, she reports, 6.75 hours were required to pound and sieve 22 pounds of grain by the most common method employed (*111*, p. 115). A more complex technique sometimes used required 9.5 hours for the same quantity of grain. Williamson estimates that in Malawi the pounding alone (there is no grinding, but considerable winnowing, soaking, etc.) of "About 30 lbs. of grain (three mortarfuls) . . . enough to last an average household four or five days . . ." takes one woman about 13 hours (*467*, pp. 128 and 192). Not more than half an hour is required to grind the same amount by hand mill; and perhaps not more than 10 to 15 minutes would be required with a motorized mill, depending on the size and kind of mill.

Labor is relatively scarce seasonally over most of tropical Africa, and the grinders of grain — the women — typically do most of the agricultural work. Perhaps one of the greatest increments in the productivity of agricultural workers that can be easily achieved is, therefore, by spread of more efficient grinding techniques. A good deal has already been done in this direction, particularly in recent years, and all the evidence suggests that Africans are quick to adopt grinding mills wherever they can be obtained. Although few and only untrustworthy estimates of their numbers exist, I have seen mills of one sort or another, or have records of them, throughout southern parts of Ivory Coast, Ghana, Togo, Dahomey, Nigeria, and Cameroun; the Congo Basin; British East Africa; and Zambia, Malawi, and Rhodesia; there is nothing to suggest that they are not to be found throughout most of the rest of tropical Africa, as well.

In towns, motorized mills are often heard, if not seen, and they may be found in villages, although there hand mills are more general. In a number of instances, introduction of mills, especially motorized mills, has followed organization of cooperatives.

The sort of achievements that can result from saving and investing through cooperatives, if the rural economies are well understood and extension officers are energetic, is illustrated by the record of the Bamenda Highlands, Cameroons.[3] Even hand mills were reportedly unknown in this fairly isolated region in 1954 when government extension officers began to organize cooperatives. Maize-mill societies of around a hundred members were formed, and each society collected three to six pence per member each month to pay for a hand grinding mill (the purchase cost was £16).[4] Mills were installed and serviced by the organizing body.

The first societies were considered highly successful by their members, and the mills were often used from 5 or 6 A.M. until late at night. The demonstration effect was dramatic. Societies were soon formed in neighboring areas, and at the same time some of the wealthier individuals of the community began to demand mills. Local trading companies which had apparently originally assumed that there was no effective demand for mills began to stock them. Within four years 106 societies had been formed and were operating mills; another 60 were formed but had not yet received their mills; and an unknown number of mills were privately owned.

CONCLUSIONS

Contrary to a widely held assumption, the scope for increasing the productivity of African farmers through introduction of new on-farm storage techniques is small. Potential productivity gains are large, however, in maize processing, and in many areas continuance of the spread of mechanized maize processing is the innovation most likely to be achieved in the near future. Although there is much latitude for improving the return from maize by introduction of better seed, superior cultural practices, and wider or greater application of fertilizers, as has been strikingly demonstrated by the work of experiment stations in tropical Africa, introduction of these measures is obstructed by their costs or lack of extension services or lack of understanding of African farming by extension workers.

13

MARKETING

T HERE are striking differences in the organization of maize marketing
in tropical Africa. In western tropical Africa, maize marketing is
characterized by almost complete laissez faire, and stands in sharp contrast to eastern Africa, the Congo (Leopoldville), Angola, Zambia, and
Rhodesia, where every phase of marketing is rigidly controlled.

NIGERIA[1]

The organization of maize marketing in western tropical Africa is best
known in the Western Region of Nigeria, which appears to be typical of
the main maize areas along the coast of western tropical Africa.

The general features of commerce in Western Nigeria discussed in Chapter 5 are also characteristic of maize and can be summarized as follows:
(1) considerable competition in the rural markets (those meeting every
fifth or every ninth day); (2) much less competition in many, if not most,
daily markets, associations of sellers sometimes colluding to prevent
market entry, especially by producers; (3) haggling over price; (4) price
adjustment more through alteration of quantity given than through varying the amount of money charged per unit; 6) marketing highly organized, with a number of intermediaries and an extensive system for
gathering and disseminating market information; (7) traders often aware
of profitable price spreads (i.e. spreads greater than the cost of transportation and a normal return to the seller); (8) middlemen typically not
owning their own transportation but renting it after supplies have been
secured; (9) foodstuff processing essentially a cottage industry, housewives obtaining their foodstuffs in the market, processing them at home,
and selling the finished product at home, in the market, at roadside stands,
or by hawking it in the streets.

246

There is considerable difference in the marketing of green and dry maize; the latter, being more complex, will be described first, and then differences that apply to the green crop will be noted.

Dry Maize

It is necessary first to distinguish between small and large producers. Small producers often attempt to sell their own maize in the nearest market, making the trip themselves or sending a wife. If, however, a trader offering an attractive price is encountered en route, the grain may be sold before it gets to market. This seems to be the usual procedure if the farmer needs cash. If he is not pressed he will typically wait for the normal seasonal price rise. When he considers the price to be at its maximum, or when weevil damage begins to be noticeable, he will send for a middleman. In times of scarcity middlemen may seek him out in their search for supplies.

Large producers, i.e. those selling bags of about 200 pounds rather than baskets (which are only a fourth or fifth as large), seem to rely more on regular customers. Something of a tacit contract is often involved. Many such buyers are large traders from distant towns, and they not infrequently advance cash on the crop prior to harvest, agreeing at that time how many bags must be given in payment.

Large farmers also sell through brokers located in the larger towns, paying a commission and often specifying the price they expect to obtain. Under such arrangements brokers seem to keep anything they get above the price the farmer expects. If the producer has set his price too high, and his grain does not sell, he must still pay storage when he removes his produce.

Middlemen seem to be of three categories: collectors, small traders, and large traders. Collectors, as we have said, customarily meet the farmer or his wife early in the morning, buy the produce on a bush trail, and transport it — usually on foot — to the nearest market, where they sell their headloads to larger traders. Collectors are not always small traders. At Agbor a dealer was found who collects from four- or eight-day markets; shells, bags, and sells the grain to large traders, who take it to the Eastern Region, Lagos, and Ibadan. He indicated that there are many traders around Agbor doing the same thing.

Small traders usually travel to a different rural market each day, buying there and selling to wholesalers and processors. Or they may work permanently in a daily market, buying from wholesalers and retailing. They differ from the collector in more frequently having a permanent place to sell their wares and in having more capital.

Large traders buy from large markets to sell in other large markets, or they may buy directly from farmers who can supply them with the quantities they need. For them the basic unit is the bag, not the basket, and they are often prepared to advance cash to assure supply. They may pay informants to tell them where maize is to be found in quantity, and may hire a measurer to avoid or reduce discussion with the sellers about the size of the "standard" unit of measure. This class of trader can be further differentiated according to the amount of fixed capital employed. Some have invested in stalls, but many avoid this expense and pay rent and commission to those owning stalls. A common rate is one shilling per bag rent and a shilling sales commission. Sometimes the buyer pays an additional shilling commission.

Some large dealers employ agents to secure supplies, paying them a commission and supplying the working capital needed. In Ibadan, Lagos, and Ilorin the largest traders sell only at wholesale, but in other areas they sell at retail as well. Dealers in Ibadan and Lagos not only sell maize to local retailers but may send it as much as a hundred miles away.

Maize is stored primarily by farmers. Traders store only involuntarily as a result of overestimating market activity, and rarely for more than two months. Although quantitative data are not available, it appears from the rate of interest charged that a trader cannot afford to tie up his capital in stocks, for the rate of price rise is probably less than the rate of return he could obtain on his capital by loaning it.[2] The difference is magnified by the high storage losses which are apt to be incurred when traders — rather than farmers — hold stocks any length of time.

Traders who hold grain usually deal in bags, and these are rapidly riddled by weevils if not sold. Unlike the producer, the trader has no effective method of combating insects. The only treatment attempted seems to be spreading the grain in the sun periodically. Considerations are very different for farmers; they usually have little or no capital to invest and hence are not concerned with the rate of interest; and their storage losses appear to be very small owing to the practice of storing maize on the cob and fumigating it with smoke.

Whole grain sold in the market typically undergoes considerable processing before it is consumed; hence, other than traders, it is the processors who account for the bulk of market purchases.

Green Maize

The green maize season is relatively short in most areas: maize may be harvested from one planting for a period of three weeks to a month, depending on variety (i.e. the period from milk stage to dry maize is three weeks to a month.) (No clear picture was obtainable of exactly in what stage most green maize is consumed, but what could be learned indicates it is consumed more in the dough stage than in the milk stage.) Because planting dates vary among fields and from farmer to farmer, and because each community has at its disposal both early and late varieties, the green maize season can be expected to extend over more than a month. Two months or so was named in many areas, and in Benin City green maize seems to be available the year round, although it is scarce at three different periods of a month or so each.

Since green maize is a perishable product, it must be handled with care and speed if it is transported any distance. There is a serious loss in quality if it is held more than 24 hours after harvest. On the other hand, it is a highly popular dish and one that is easy to prepare: no discrimination seems to exist between yellow and white grain or against hard starch varieties; and almost anyone can boil or roast the cobs, a quick and easy process. Nor are complementary flavors required in its consumption; it is often simply eaten from the cob as a snack.

It is not surprising then, considering its perishability, that green maize passes through few hands between producer and consumer. Usually one of the producer's wives will sell it in a local market, or a trading woman will come to the farm to buy and harvest her needs for either a local or distant market.

Buying and selling seem to be competitive; when informants reported restrictive practices in dry maize marketing, they often noted that these did not apply to the portion of the crop sold fresh. Near large urban centers, producers often specialize in green maize production.

IVORY COAST

A study not complete when this section went to press provides some information on maize marketing in the Ivory Coast,[3] where, as in Western Nigeria, the organization of maize commerce is complex and requires transportation of maize over considerable distances.

Data available suggest that maize is a major component in the diet of very few Ivory Coast peoples — and none of those covered by consumption surveys — but there are large numbers of foreign consumers, or consumers of foreign origin, from areas where maize is of greater importance as a foodstuff.[4] Coffee and cocoa plantations of middle and southern Ivory Coast require much more labor than is locally available, labor which is supplied mainly by migrants from Upper Volta and Mali. In addition to these and the unskilled laborers required by other enterprises, there are also relatively important maize consumers of the same origins who have been attracted to southern Ivory Coast by the commercial opportunities found in and near urban centers there.

Most of the maize for Abidjan and the lagoon area, the principal population concentration in the country, comes directly from supply areas 240 to 360 miles to the north. (There is sometimes also considerable trade within the surplus zone because of quality differences in the maize grown.) Producers or their wives in the supply areas carry maize in baskets to weekly rural markets, not infrequently walking as much as ten miles. At the marketplace maize grain, or flour from it, is usually sold to wholesalers from urban areas, who sometimes have employees with them to aid in sacking and loading their purchases. As in Nigeria, wholesalers may be women; they may come directly from towns or cities in the deficit zone or may be based in one of the towns in the supply area, where they sell principally to wholesalers from the south who do not want to bother with buying in weekly markets or who have been unable to secure otherwise all the supplies they need.

Once maize has reached the warehouse of the wholesaler in the deficit area it may be sold to local retailers, including the wholesaler's wife (or wives), to retailers from nearby villages, or to wholesalers from other towns in the deficit zone.

Many wholesalers have relatives or friends in the supply zone who provide them market information and assist in securing shipments. Like traders in Western Nigeria, they can quickly quote prices and relevant transportation costs for several places in the supply area, which suggests that they are aware of the development of geographical differences in price spreads that they might profitably exploit.

BAMENDA PROVINCE (FORMER BRITISH CAMEROONS)

In Bamenda Province of former British Cameroons, roughly 250 air miles east of the Western Region of Nigeria, interregional trade is strikingly less important than in Western Nigeria and is organized differently.[5]

Although there is considerable trade in certain items, e.g. cattle and manufactured goods, commerce in staple foods appears to be small and local, except for small quantities of maize and Irish potatoes sold in markets as much as 250 road miles away. The classical assumption of a predominantly agricultural economy, with each household producing nearly all the calories it consumes, fits well. Lacking are the large non-self-supplying populations and the large traffic in staple foods which are characteristic of Western Nigeria. The degree of specialization is different, too. Not only are fewer staple food products marketed, but in the Nsaw area at least, and probably elsewhere as well, women specializing in these preparations are distinctly a minority, and often engage in their speciality only sporadically (*240*, pp. 132–37).

Organization of Marketing

Except for the daily market at Makon, markets meet every seventh day; and, as in Western Nigeria, the days alternate in such a way that for any particular village some market is almost always within walking distance. (There is a small extramarket trade, but this seems to be limited mainly to sales of maize beer at the brewers' homes.)

Most sellers are occupied with their own production, and rarely carry more than a headload to market. Only a few middlemen buy for resale in a distant market or sell produce they have obtained directly from producers at their farms or from other traders; however, resale does seem to occur commonly with maize sold for beer making, and often the trader partially processes it (by germinating the grain) before resale to the brewer. Middlemen were reported to be more active and to deal in a greater range of staples during the preharvest period when stocks are low; and quantities offered in the market sometimes differ considerably from one locale to another.

All evidence suggests that Bamenda markets are fairly competitive, and organized much like the rural markets of Western Nigeria. Prices are determined by haggling over the quantity received for the going price — especially over the amount added by the seller after bargaining is officially finished — but bargaining appears not to be nearly as lengthy or intense as in Western Nigeria.

EASTERN AND CENTRAL AFRICA

In Kenya, Angola, the Congo (Leopoldville), Zambia, and Rhodesia organization of maize marketing differs greatly from that described for Nigeria or southwestern Cameroons, the outstanding difference being the virtually complete regulation of all phases of the distribution process by the government.

The extreme examples are to be found in Kenya, Zambia, and Rhodesia, where government statutory marketing monopolies buy and sell all maize, at fixed prices; sales to consumers or purchases from producers by anyone except agents of this monopoly are prohibited. Producer and consumer prices are established each season, usually with a large gap between the two which is designed to cover operating costs of the monopoly, and sometimes costs of projects the government is sponsoring, such as building central storage facilities.

Announced producer prices are the same to European and African farmers, but actual prices to the latter are much lower. African farmers are charged for transportation, handling, storage, at a fixed rate, deducted from the price received, whereas European farmers are allowed to make their own arrangements for these services and to pay for them directly. In addition, a tax is often deducted from the price paid African maize growers to help finance government programs designed to improve the productivity of African agriculture. In Kenya a further deduction is made to defray the expenses of district councils. Both this tax and that used for the betterment of African agriculture vary in amount from area to area. Because interdistrict differences in prices are sometimes greater than transfer costs, it is illegal to sell maize outside the district in which it is produced.

In Malawi prices are fixed by the government but apply only to maize offered to it by producers at special government-established buying stations (the government attempts to influence where maize is grown by location of these buying stations; maize is not purchased in areas considered poorly suited to this crop). No attempt is made to regulate trade between Africans.

In Uganda regulation of prices was discontinued in 1953. Maize for urban areas typically is bought directly from farmers by Indian wholesalers. Data are not available on the organization of marketing in rural areas.

In the Congo (Leopoldville) the government sets minimum prices for maize purchased by officially recognized traders. Data are not available for the northern areas, but in Kasai and Katanga provinces, the areas which appear to account for most of the trade in maize, there are three categories of traders. Traders in chieftaincies and rural commercial centers — often Portuguese or Greek but sometimes African — usually have a store at which they buy maize from African producers whenever it is brought in. Sometimes buyers of this sort are merely agents for wholesalers in urban areas. A second category is buyers at markets which are held especially for purchase of African produce at times and places designated by the administration. Such special markets are often frequented by wholesalers from nearby towns. In addition there are, in some areas, cooperatives through which the African producer in effect sells directly to mining companies or wholesalers in urban areas.

Outside this network are indigenous markets, organized much like those described for Western Nigeria, which serve for exchange of maize in rural areas among Africans. Little of the maize sold through these channels reaches urban areas. Maize is found in many forms in these markets:

maize grain, maize meal or flour, sometimes distilled drinks derived from maize, and numerous maize dishes. Little heed is paid to official prices except when a visit by a government official makes it prudent to do so.

The organization of maize marketing in Angola and Mozambique cannot be determined from data available;[6] however, prices are fixed by the government and marketing is tightly regulated.

STATUTORY MARKETING MONOPOLIES AND THEIR RATIONALE

The principal argument offered in defense of maize control schemes such as those of Kenya, Zambia, and Rhodesia centers on the allegedly noneconomic response of African farmers to changes in maize prices. Other arguments rest on the belief that existing markets are so imperfect — and many African sellers so inexperienced in selling cash crops — that uncontrolled marketing would work to the disadvantage of producers as well as consumers.

Price Response

Unreliability of African-produced supply is often given as the basic justification for subsidies paid to European farmers in Zambia, Rhodesia, and Kenya, and has been given official expression.[7] A Kenya Sessional Paper on the maize industry published in 1958 asserts:

In order to feed the colony's African labour force together with their families, especially in the two major towns of Nairobi (pop. 210,000) and Mombasa (pop. 98,000), it would be most imprudent to rely solely on deliveries by peasant growers. African farmers in Kenya plant maize primarily for family subsistence and only secondarily for cash. The result is . . . [that] the surplus available for delivery to markets is only a fraction of the whole and is liable to fluctuate widely from season to season according to weather conditions. Table A, p. 15, shows over the last five years high and low deliveries from the non-scheduled areas [i.e. non-European areas] of 691,000 and 1,483,000 bags, a fluctuation of over 100 per cent. Deliveries are even less dependable in Uganda and Tanganyika, in both of which territories there are maize shortages at present, not for the first time since control of maize was relaxed a few years ago. Since these deliveries cannot be relied on, the only other sources of maize are from overseas or from farmers in the Scheduled Areas. But delivery from this source can only be ensured provided a reasonably economic price is guaranteed from year to year. If there is not this element of stability, both production and prices will fluctuate widely from year to year when local surpluses have to be exported and when as a consequence of the low return accruing from export, production is reduced and import is subsequently necessary. The Government therefore considered that it is in the general interest of the Colony to continue to ensure internal requirements by encouraging the delivery of a stated quantity of maize and to this end it is necessary to retain organized marketing for maize and to ensure that the maize grower is paid a reasonable price. It would not be in the general interest to abolish all guarantees and to revert to an entirely free market (*246*, pp. 8–9).

This statement about the variability of African marketings is misleading. If Europeans and Africans received the same price, or if effective prices were more closely linked, inferences about relative reliability of the two sources could be made with a reasonable degree of confidence. But the data presented cannot be so interpreted. The Africans' price has varied because of decisions by both the government maize-marketing monopoly and district councils. Before the above argument can have any validity regarding the economic behavior of African producers of Kenya, one must establish the relationship between effective prices to Africans and their marketings by district, and one must be able to demonstrate that these relationships are, when aggregated, characterized by less regularity than European marketings.

The statement about the variability of deliveries from Uganda and Tanganyika is also open to question. For the former it ignores that marketings varied with price changes; and for the latter it is irrelevant since in recent years Tanganyika has usually had little exportable surplus, in fact has had difficulty in meeting its own requirements.

In Uganda, Angola, and Malawi, where effective prices to the producer have been permitted to vary, marketings have also varied and in the same direction (Chart 13-1 shows prices and marketings for Buganda Province, Uganda's principal area of commercial production).

A superficial inspection of the data for Angola (Chart 13-2) suggests that there is little response to price: the correlation between maize prices and maize exports [8] is only 0.05 with no lag, and 0.10 with a one-year lag. In west-central Angola, the area where most of the exported maize is produced, beans are also an important cash crop, and practically the only other one grown by Africans (see Chapter 10, p. 192). Beans and maize require almost identical soil and climatic conditions; the amount of maize sold can be expected to be a function not only of the price of maize but also of the price of beans. Resources can be transferred into bean production when bean prices are relatively high, and back to maize when they are lower.[9] Amounts of maize exported have generally followed the curve of prices paid for maize, except in 1947, 1948, 1951, 1952, and 1953, all years when the price of beans was high compared with 1942–46 (Chart 13-2).

Data are not adequate to construct a chart for Malawi, but comments by administrators suggest that the price response of maize producers is normal. The 1947 report of the Department of Agriculture stated that "The amount of surplus maize purchased in the native produce markets fell . . . . Adverse weather conditions were mainly responsible . . . but the markedly increased interest in the high prices of the tobacco crop also had its effect on the quantity of maize produced and sold" (*328*, 1947, p. 7). The price paid producers did not change from 1948 to 1957; but when it was lowered by one-third in 1957, marketings declined to one-fifth of average marketings over the preceding five years. Agricultural officials interpreted this as principally a response to the lower price: "Largely as a result of the Government's decision to reduce the producer price of maize at Agricultural Production and Marketing Board markets to two-thirds of a penny per lb., only 5,784 tons were purchased . . . . The reason for the reduction in the price was to bring it more in line with the world prices; . . ." (*328*, 1957, p. 4).

In Zambia and Rhodesia the question of African price response can be approached more directly by comparing the responses of African and European maize growers. Although lack of data prevents estimation of the production of these two groups, we do have records of the amounts marketed by African and European farmers.

In the main areas that market maize in Zambia, the areas served by rail, African and European farms are adjacent and have largely the same phy-

CHART 13-1 — UGANDA: MAIZE PRICES AND MAIZE MARKETINGS
IN BUGANDA PROVINCE, 1943–56

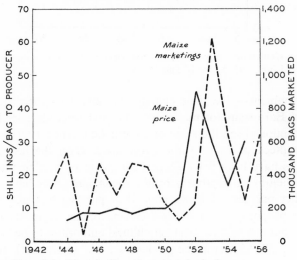

Data from files of the Uganda Department of Agriculture.

256   MAIZE IN TROPICAL AFRICA

CHART 13-2 — ANGOLA: MAIZE PRICES AND EXPORTS, AND BEAN
PRICES, 1942–53 (1,000 metric tons and centavos per kilogram)

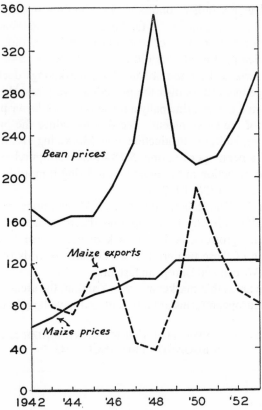

Data from Centro das Actividades Económicas de Angola, *O milho na economia
de Angola* (Lisbon, 1954), pp. 14 and 28–29.

sical environment—the same climate and soil. The prices paid to Africans and Europeans for maize over the past three decades have with minor exceptions been the same or were linked. Since 1936 prices have been guaranteed or fixed by the government. Over the last decade, at least, prices have been fixed. Since 1946 Africans participating in government schemes for improvement of African agriculture have received a bonus either per acre of maize planted or per bag of maize marketed. The exact proportion of farmers receiving bonus payments cannot be computed, but it is said by local agricultural authorities to be "small relative to . . . all African maize producers . . ." (*361*, p. 4). In the Plateau Tonga area, from which the bulk of maize marketed by Africans comes, farmers receiving bonuses were estimated in 1950 to represent about 3 percent of the families and perhaps as much as 20 percent of African maize acreage (*229*, p. 19; and *105*, p. 72).

Given approximately equivalent environment and price changes, a test of the orthodoxy of African price response would be to calculate the correlation between marketings by African and by European farmers; the orthodoxy of African price response in Zambia would be roughly proportional to how near the correlation coefficient is to one. This test was employed for 1933–35 and 1937–57, the period over which data were available, and the correlation coefficient was 0.958. The curves of African and European marketings are almost parallel to each other (Chart 13-3).

The correlation would probably be even higher if Africans had as much machinery at their disposal as the European farmers. A large part of the divergence in the two curves occurred in trough years, times when African marketings fell much more, proportionally, than those of European farmers (the average difference between European and African marketings is

CHART 13-3 — NORTHERN RHODESIA: RECORDED EUROPEAN AND AFRICAN MAIZE MARKETINGS IN AREAS SERVED BY RAIL, 1933–35 AND 1937–57 (1,000 bags of 200 lbs.)

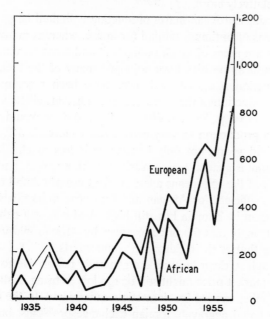

Data from Northern Rhodesia, Department of Agriculture, *Annual Report*, various issues.

2.2 times larger in trough than in peak years), which could be explained largely by the difference in the degree of mechanization between the two groups of farmers.

In this part of Zambia, the area served by rail, rainfall is just sufficient for a crop of maize. If planting is delayed at the beginning of the rainy season in a year when rainfall is below average, the rains stop at a critical period for the maize plant — the period when the ear is forming — with the result that yields are severely depressed. European maize cultivation is almost completely mechanized, while many African farmers do not have plows, harrows, cultivators, and the draft power to pull them. Most of those without equipment borrow or hire it from other Africans after the owners have planted their own fields. Therefore a much larger portion of the African than of the European maize acreage is planted late. When the season is favorable the late acreage, which is largely African, does about as well as that planted early, but in bad years late maize yields very little. Thus one would expect that in good years, when late maize yields well, increases in European and African marketings would be of similar relative magnitudes, and that in bad years both European and African productions would fall, but the latter, with its greater share of late maize, would fall relatively more.

In Rhodesia, European maize production is limited largely to the best soils and areas of optimum rainfall for maize, whereas many of the African reserves are areas of much poorer soil and scant rainfall. In fact, local agricultural authorities have adjudged many of the areas of African maize production marginal, and there have been recommendations to encourage production of the more drought-resistant millets and sorghums in such areas (*134*, p. 53; and *464*, pp. 83, 84). One would therefore expect African production to vary considerably more than European production in bad years, not only because it is less mechanized but also because rainfall is generally more variable in those areas, and because the lower quality of the soil means a less efficient use of rainfall received. The correlation coefficient for African and European marketings, 0.849, is a little lower than in Zambia but still high. And it is still sufficiently high to suggest strongly that the price response by African maize producers is as normal as that of their European counterparts.

Even though African farmers are generally responsive to price incentives, a free market price might still be too low to bring forth the quantity of maize supplies needed for domestic requirements. In the long run this conceivably could aggravate foreign exchange problems, but at present, with sizable maize surpluses in Uganda and Malawi and an enormous maize surplus in North America, maize imports are not likely to be costly.

CHART 13-4 — SOUTHERN RHODESIA: RECORDED EUROPEAN AND
AFRICAN MAIZE MARKETINGS, 1933/34–1956/57

(1,000 bags of 200 lbs.)

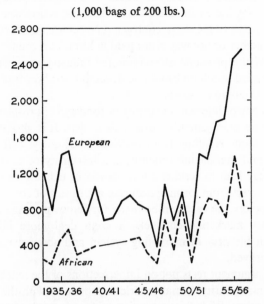

Data from Federation of Rhodesia and Nyasaland, *Report of the Grain Market-ing Board* . . . (Salisbury), various issues.

The argument that European maize farmers are entitled to a "reason-able price" in order to guarantee supplies is hard to defend on grounds of national welfare if adequate and reliable supplies can be obtained from overseas more cheaply. Furthermore, a "reasonable" price as defined by agencies which are dominated by producers or political considerations is likely to be consistently higher than is needed to call forth the required supplies; and in the past the Kenya Maize Control has frequently been obliged to export "surplus" maize at about half the supported price pre-vailing in the protected domestic market.

Other Arguments

In many countries of tropical Africa the development of widespread marketing systems is comparatively recent and by no means complete. Under these circumstances existing market imperfections may make di-rect governmental intervention necessary to assure appropriate distribu-tion and production of essential parts of the food supply. If statutory marketing is conducted wisely and honestly it may be more efficient than the uncontrolled open markets. That this is not always so, however, is demonstrated by the experience in Kenya. There, high prices for maize that were considered necessary to maintain European production raised wages directly by increasing the costs of the basic ration which employers provided as a part of the wage contract. The economic effect is the same, of course, whether or not wages are paid in kind. In a country like Kenya, where one of the principal attractions for industry is cheap labor, this must have tended to inhibit economic development; how much, of course, it would be difficult to measure.

The efficiency of internal marketing of foodstuffs in tropical Africa has only recently received attention from economists. It is altogether possible that imperfections resulting from restrictions of entry, collusion, inadequate price and market information, and insecurity of contract may be great, and may lead to serious misallocation of existing supplies or may prevent producers from forming accurate appraisals of consumer requirements. But before the case can be made for removing some commodities from ordinary marketing channels, a great deal more information is needed about the present marketing system and about ways in which it might be improved.

A related argument rests not on imperfections of the marketing system but on the unfamiliarity of many African producers with the workings of a money economy. Wide fluctuations in prices of a cash crop may unduly discourage such farmers from continued production for sale. If shortages in one year raise prices much above normal levels, these high prices may be taken as the proper price for future years, with consequent disappointment, and unrest, when prices fall. A similar reaction may result when market gluts cause prices to fall. But here again more information is needed to determine whether price fluctuations discourage production or whether they may at times stimulate producers to try new ventures. Moreover, even statutory marketing schemes must periodically adjust producer prices in accordance with changes in the underlying supply-demand conditions; and it is possible that such administrative changes in prices will provoke greater disappointment or unrest than the continuing adaptation of market prices to changing conditions.

14

SUMMARY

MAIZE is grown and consumed in various forms in one season or another in most of tropical Africa. It is probably the third most important source of calories in tropical Africa as a unit, ranking behind millets-sorghums and manioc but ahead of such starchy-staples as wheat, rice, yams, taro, sweet potatoes, bananas, and plantains or breadfruit. Maize is the dominant staple of African diets in several areas along the western African coast and in the Cape Verde Islands; on the Bamenda Plateau of Cameroun; in central Angola; in parts of the northern and southern extremes of the Congo Basin; in portions of Tanganyika, Somalia, Ethiopia, the Malagasy Republic, and Réunion; and in large sections of Kenya, Zambia, Rhodesia, Malawi, and Mozambique.

In most of the areas where maize is a staple it is also a major cash crop; and in Uganda, Kenya, Zambia, Rhodesia, Mozambique, the Malagasy Republic, and Angola it either is or has been a major export.

Maize played a key role in the establishment of many of the first white settlements in Angola, Kenya, Zambia, and Rhodesia; and it has had a prominent place in the economic history of these countries since 1900. In Kenya, Tanganyika, Zambia, Rhodesia, Angola, and Mozambique, from one-fourth to one-half of maize marketings still comes from European producers.

In western tropical Africa maize was a major cash crop at the height of the slave trade in the seventeenth and eighteenth centuries, being used to provision slave ships and communities where slaves were assembled prior to shipment overseas. Its importance as a cash crop declined with elimination of the slave trade in the late nineteenth century, but a brief revival came with attempts to develop it as an export crop in Nigeria, Dahomey, and Togo in the first and second decades of this century. Since 1950

261

West Africa as a region has been a net importer of maize, as growing deficits in Senegal and Ghana became larger than could be met by the small exports from Dahomey and Togo.

Current methods of maize production and processing by African farmers are crude compared with those characteristic of the world's major maize producers. In most of tropical Africa, hoe culture prevails; mechanical and animal draft power is used by African farmers only in fairly small zones of eastern and central tropical Africa, and largely in areas having white settlers. Most fields or plots are cleared with axes and knives — frequently with the aid of fire. The soil is broken with a hoe; methods of weeding, harvesting, and transportation from the field are likewise crude. Fields are irregular and temporary. Typically, after a few seasons (usually not more than two or three) the soil is so exhausted that a new plot of forest or bush is sought and the old one reverts to natural vegetation for an indefinite period.

Almost everywhere maize is grown in gardens around the farmer's hut, in valley bottoms, or along streams, where it is often interplanted with various vegetables and gourds. In these garden plots it usually gets some organic fertilizer or refuse, and the soil is exhausted much more slowly than in fields.

Garden maize, and in some areas part of the field maize, is consumed in an immature state, boiled or roasted on the cob. Mature maize is usually stored on the cob, by methods ranging from suspending bunches of ears from a tree to placing grain in underground pits. By the most common method maize is kept in granaries under which a smoky fire is built from time to time. Evidence available suggests that storage techniques on African farms are much more efficient than has been assumed by most agronomists, although storage losses by traders and others who store maize in towns and cities may be large.

Maize is marketed through an intricate system of small rural markets connected with large urban markets in the main maize areas of western tropical Africa, and marketing is sometimes fairly competitive. In the principal maize areas elsewhere in tropical Africa most maize marketing is tightly regulated by statutory marketing monopolies that fix prices to both producers and consumers. Prices to African farmers are set somewhat lower than to European producers. The official reason for the lower price to Africans is that they are not allowed to deliver their grain directly to central depots.

One of the justifications for abandoning free maize marketing in eastern and central Africa is that African maize producers are alleged not to respond to price. Settlers and administrators argue that a free-market price would be too low to maintain a high level of European maize production and that African producers cannot be depended on regularly to adjust production in accordance with changes in the market prices. All available data suggest that on the contrary African producers respond to price stimuli in an orthodox fashion. If their production is more irregular than that of European producers, it is probably because the African reserves are usually areas of poorer soil and less regular rainfall. Moreover, in recent years in most areas maize could have been imported at a price considerably below that guaranteed to European producers.

Among European farmers maize is of some importance as a livestock feed, but almost none of the maize grown by Africans is so used.

Nearly all tropical African maize dishes made from mature maize require reducing the grain to meal or flour, traditionally done by various techniques of pounding the kernels in a wooden mortar with a wooden pestle. An alternative method among some ethnic groups was to grind between two flat stones, one stationary and the other held with both hands. Today hand mills, and in the more prosperous areas motorized grinders, are increasingly replacing the traditional processing methods. In urban areas a large portion of Africans buy maize meal or flour and do no grinding themselves.

There is considerable geographical variation in the ways in which maize is eaten. The products most widely made from ground maize grain are a cooked paste or mush, eaten while still warm, and a thick beer of low alcoholic content. Chunks of the paste or mush are broken off and dipped into stews or sauces of meat, fish, insects, or vegetables before eating. In some areas maize mush is fried or baked, but not in the North American forms of cornbread or tortillas. Other major dishes of tropical Africa are maize fritters, whole maize cooked with beans, fermented and flavored maize starch, parched or popped maize, dehydrated immature maize boiled just before eating, thin maize mush, maize gruel, flavored weak maize beer, and distilled maize drinks.

The total maize requirements of tropical African consumers have risen strikingly during this century, and especially since World War II, in areas for which we have quantitative data. Qualitative information suggests that this is generally true for urban areas, and probably more widely. Per capita maize consumption has also increased in some areas, especially in towns and mining communities. Maize has gained principally at the expense of the millets, sorghums, and manioc. In other areas per capita maize consumption may have declined as people have become more familiar with manioc and sweet potatoes, crops that are less vulnerable to insects and irregular rainfall, and that are often cheaper sources of calories.

Trends in maize consumption or production in earlier centuries cannot be established, but maize clearly has been central to the economic change of many tropical African economies in one period or another. Over the span of the last four and a half centuries maize has been introduced to most African peoples, and it has been one of the factors that has brought about great increases in agricultural productivity. While we cannot be certain that the maize plant was brought to Africa by Europeans, we can be sure that new and higher-yielding varieties were introduced by them, and that these innovations worked to the disadvantage of indigenous crops like millets, sorghums, yams, and a multitude of now rarely noticed edible wild plants, such as *Pachyrrhizus angulatus* and *Maranta arundinacea*, which were once dietary mainstays. Higher-yielding varieties of the indigenous crops have not been widely adopted, nor has their improvement in recent years by departments of agriculture been as successful as maize-breeding programs.

Exploitation of mineral and agricultural resources under European supervision, as well as the establishment and maintenance of colonial administrations, required large numbers of African laborers; this created a market for cheap staple foodstuffs, of which the principal one was maize, for reasons relating to its characteristics as a plant and as a commodity.

In the short run of the next decade or two maize will probably continue to be of increasing importance in the diet, gaining at the expense of at least the millets and sorghums, and perhaps also some of the other starchy-staples. Budget surveys suggest, however, that it will lose ground to rice, bread, and nonstarchy foods. Whether total per capita maize utilization will rise or fall will also depend on the extent to which maize becomes a feed as the livestock feeding industry expands, or a raw material for the distilling industry. Maize is an excellent feed and very possibly will eventually be used in large quantities for livestock rations.

The potential for increasing maize production through adoption of known techniques is striking and is probably sufficient to meet projected consumption and industrial needs. There is, however, a large disparity between the potential increment in maize production and that which reasonably can be expected. Plant breeders have frequently developed varieties with higher yields but lacking important qualities that African producers or consumers desired, with the result that African farmers have often ignored higher-yielding seed available to them. Hybrid varieties, the dissemination of which has so dramatically raised yields in temperate countries, especially the United States, cannot be easily incorporated into the farming systems employed by Africans because of their cost and because of lack of the extension and educational services needed to establish successful use of hybrid seed. Commercial fertilizers, likewise, are too expensive for most African farmers, often giving not enough increment in yield to offset their cost.

African farmers seem typically to know the best planting and weeding times, optimum spacing, and the best crop combinations under present conditions; but introduction of commercial fertilizers, better tools, and improved seed will require a new set of cultural methods. Colonial administrators have often relied on resettlement schemes and coercion of various kinds to obtain desired changes in agriculture, but such policies seem unlikely to achieve the maximum rate of economic growth which is possible. They may give impressive short-term gains, but they are not likely to generate continuing increases in productivity — if the response of African maize producers is typical of what can be expected. The largest gains in productivity — produced by adoption of plows, maize mills, and improved seed — came where price incentives, extension services, and improvement of transportation were the major facets of development policy.

Such indirect programs arouse less resistance to change among farmers than do resettlement or coercion, and make maximum use of the African farmers' knowledge of their own areas and problems. The waste of development capital in the Tanganyika Groundnuts Scheme, the Gambia Poultry Scheme, and the Mokwa Scheme of Nigeria, which failed largely for lack of adequate understanding of African agricultural systems, is testimony to the risks of attempting to increase the productivity of African farmers without making use of their knowledge of what is feasible.

REFERENCE MATERIAL

APPENDIX TABLE 1 — NAMES OF COUNTRIES

Colonial name	Colonial power	Year self-government gained	Current name
Angola	Portugal	—	—
Bechuanaland	Great Britain	—	—
Belgian Congo	Belgium	1960	Congo (Leopoldville)
British Cameroons	Great Britain	1961	Nigeria, Cameroons[b]
British Somaliland	Great Britain	1960	Somalia
Comoro Islands	France	—	—
Cape Verde Islands	Portugal	—	—
Ethiopia	—	*ca.* 2,000 B.C.	—
French Cameroons	France	1960	Cameroons or Cameroun
French Equatorial Africa (Chad, Ubangi-Chari, Gabon, Moyen Congo)	France	1960	Chad, Central African Republic, Gabon, Congo (Brazzaville)
French Somaliland	France	—	—
French Togo	France	1960	Togo
French West Africa (Mauritania, French Guinea, Sudan, Senegal, Ivory Coast, Niger, Dahomey, Upper Volta)	France	1958,[a] 1960	Mauritania, Guinea, Mali, Senegal, Ivory Coast, Niger, Dahomey, Upper Volta
Gambia	Great Britain	—	—
Gold Coast	Great Britain	1957	Ghana
Kenya	Great Britain	1963	—
Liberia	—	1847	—
Mauritius	Great Britain	—	—
Madagascar	France	1960	Malagasy Republic
Mozambique	Portugal	—	—
Nigeria	Great Britain	1961	—
Northern Rhodesia	Great Britain	1964	Zambia
Nyasaland	Great Britain	1964	Malawi
Portuguese Guinea	Portugal	—	—
Réunion	France	—	—
Ruanda-Urundi	Belgium	1962	Rwanda, Burundi
São Tomé and Príncipe	Portugal	—	—
Sierra Leone	Great Britain	1961	—
Seychelles	Great Britain	—	—
Italian Somaliland	Italy	1960	Somalia
Southern Rhodesia	Great Britain	—	Rhodesia
Spanish Guinea and Fernando Po	Spain	—	—

Colonial name	Colonial power	Year self-government gained	Current name
Anglo-Egyptian Sudan	Great Britain	1956	Sudan
Tanganyika	Great Britain	1961	Tanzania
Uganda	Great Britain	1962	—
Zanzibar and Pemba	Great Britain	1963	Tanzania

[a] French Guinea became independent in 1958; the rest of French West Africa in 1960.

[b] The northern part of the country merged with Nigeria at independence; the southern part joined Cameroons.

Country	Total population (thousands)	Population per square kilometer
Nigeria	35,091	38
Ethiopia	20,000	17
Congo (Leopoldville)	14,150	6
Sudan	11,770	5
Tanganyika	9,239	10
Rhodesia and Nyasaland	8,130[a]	7[a]
Ghana	6,691	28
Uganda	6,517[a]	27[a]
Kenya	6,340[a]	11[a]
Mozambique	6,310[a]	8[a]
Malagasy Republic	5,393	9
Ruanda-Urundi	4,780[a]	88[a]
Angola	4,550[a]	4[a]
Upper Volta	4,400[b]	16[b]
Mali	4,100	3
Cameroun	4,097	9
Ivory Coast	3,230	10
Guinea	3,000	12
Senegal	2,973[b]	15[b]
Niger	2,870	2
Chad	2,639	2
Sierra Leone	2,450	34
Somalia	1,990	3
Dahomey	1,934	17
Togo	1,440	25
Liberia	1,290	12
Central African Republic	1,227	2
Congo (Brazzaville)	900	3
Mauritania	727[a]	1[a]
Mauritius	621[a]	333[a]
Gabon	444	2
Bechuanaland	337[a]	1[a]
Réunion	324[a]	129[a]
Zanzibar and Pemba	304[a]	115[a]
Gambia	301[a]	29[a]
French Somaliland	70[a]	3[a]

Data from UN *Demographic Yearbook, 1961* (New York, 1961), pp. 101–2, and UN *Economic Bulletin for Africa*, 2, No. 2 (June, 1962), 61.

[a] 1959

[b] 1960–61

APPENDIX TABLE 3—MANUFACTURING IN SELECTED
TROPICAL AFRICAN COUNTRIES, ABOUT 1958

Country	Year	*Percent of total manufacturing*		
		Food, beverages, and tobacco	*Textiles and footwear*	*Wood furniture*
Sudan (net output)	1955/56	74	—	2
Tanganyika (net output)	1958	59	3	21
Ethiopia (net output)	1958	58	19	3
French Cameroons (gross output)	1956	44	8	15
Ghana (net output)	1958	41	—	34
Former Fed. of Rhodesia and Nyasaland (net output)	1958	30	11	6
Kenya (net output)	1958	25	6	9
Guinea (employment)	1956	23	7	60
Congo (Leopoldville) (employment)	1959	16	11	8

Data from UN, *Economic Bulletin for Africa*, 2, No. 2 (June 1962), 13.
a Percentages have been rounded.

Paper print- ing	Leather and leather goods	Con- struction materials (non- metallic)	Chemi- cals	Metals and metal products	Miscel- laneous	Total
			Percent of total manufacturing			
3	—	8	5	6	2	100
—	—	—	2	11	4	100
2	3	7	—	—	8	100
1	1	2	17	12	—	100
7	1	1	3	7	6	100
7	—	11	5	28	2	100
8	—	8	7	31	6	100
—	—	—	—	10	—	100
2	—	4	46	12	—	99a

APPENDIX TABLE 4 — LABOR MIGRATION IN SELECTED AFRICAN COUNTRIES, ABOUT 1956

(Thousands of workers)

Country of origin	Country of employment						
	Northern Rhodesia (1956)	Southern Rhodesia (1956)	Nyasaland (1956)	Belgian Congo (1956)	Tanganyika[a] (1957)	Uganda (1957)	Republic of South Africa[b] (1957)
Northern Rhodesia	217.8	42.3	0.4		4.0		⎫
Southern Rhodesia	2.2	300.2	0.1				⎬ 61.0
Nyasaland	20.7	132.6	155.4		3.8		⎭
Belgian Congo				1,121.3		6.2	
Ruanda-Urundi				25.0	14.2	29.6	
Kenya					4.4	16.5	
Uganda					0.6	163.3	
Tanganyika					290.6	3.0	
Angola ⎰ (Tanganyika & Angola)	9.2	125.2	7.7		12.6		
Mozambique							99.3
Bechuanaland							11.5
Republic of South Africa							108.1
Other	13.3	9.7	0.7	51.6	1.1	9.3	45.5
Total	263.2	610.0	164.3	1,197.9	331.3	226.9	325.4

Data from UN, *Economic Survey of Africa since 1950* (New York, 1959), p. 49.

[a] Males only.

[b] Africans employed in gold and coal mines only.

APPENDIX I

The Adequacy of Data on Tropical Africa

Hardly more than a century ago much of Africa was a blank space on the geographers' maps; now those embarrassing voids are filled with names, lines, and symbols suggestive of knowledge, although they are, in fact, not infrequently a poor guide.

On the maps of the economic scientist the dominant features are still voids; and probably much of the data found, more than sometimes seems to be realized, is a deceptive guide for those who would chart a way out of the forest of backwardness, or correct economic injustices, or promote a more stable economy. There are very few reasonably complete descriptions of how scarce resources are transformed into products for the satisfaction of needs and desires, of how such products get distributed, stored, consumed, and invested in further production. Neither the volume nor the composition of production is more than vaguely known over most of tropical Africa. For a few of the goods and services produced largely for consumption outside of Africa, or for European use within Africa, production is determinable, although one must often rely on unpublished data; but for the remainder only very rough estimates exist.

The official explanation of how production statistics for 1950 were derived in Northern Ghana tells us (*140a*; see Gold Coast):

acreages and production have been extrapolated from agricultural surveys conducted between 1931 and 1936 in different limited areas; . . .

in Sierra Leone (*140a*; see Sierra Leone):

Certain acreage statistics (for cacao, coffee and some swamp rice) come from eye estimates while others are merely intelligent guesses, cross-checked by reference to other sources. . . .

For Nyasaland (*140a*; see Nyasaland):

The acreages were deduced from a count of the total number of gardens under each crop and measurement of the area of 5–10 per cent of them by pacing. It is thought that the resulting estimates are not very accurate.

Speaking of what was formerly French Africa, Theodore states (*412*, p. 28): "food-crop production is often estimated with a margin of error of plus or minus 50%. . . ." In Nigeria, where a sample census of agricultural production was taken in 1950–51, the estimate was that there was a 5% chance that the margin of sampling error was more than 50% for the global estimates of maize production (the error was larger for

275

subunits within Nigeria, e.g. provinces, because there was less chance of errors offsetting). And when one adds the bias that seems to be incurred in tropical countries from cutting a sample plot and projecting the results (see *208a*, pp. 60–61), and from observation and recording errors, it is not unlikely that the total margin of error is 50% or more. I doubt if there are many data associated with peasant agriculture, except possibly those related to international trade, for which the margin of error is much smaller.

Some idea of the size of the population and the composition of the labor force is supplied by censuses, but little is really known about the rate of population increase, a key variable in the rate of economic growth.

There is no adequate analysis of internal trade, and very little has been done on the structure of markets or the organization of commerce. Of course without knowledge of production and trade, there is no possibility of determining consumption indirectly, and only a feeble beginning has been made at direct estimates, e.g. food consumption surveys.

There is little basis for any kind of intelligent guessing about national income, much less propensities to save or invest. One reason for this has been the greater or more obvious urgency for solutions to purely agricultural or political problems. Once an epidemic disease begins to take a large toll of plant or animal yields, or once there is political unrest, the virtues of research are easily seen. Economic ills are often more difficult to diagnose, and administrators seem prone to believe the cure can be effected without the help of a specialist.

Traditions within the ranks of economists have also been important. Anthropologists, sociologists, geographers, and historians have as part of their purpose of study of all areas and all people of the world. Economists, on the other hand, have had no tradition of studying all types of economies, and, until the recent interest in developing countries, have been content to build most of their theory from European and North American data. Still another contributing factor is lack of data needed for economic research. Since economics is more quantitative in method than the other social sciences, a lack of reliable, or reasonably reliable, quantitative data is graver and can seriously inhibit research: neither economic structure nor economic trends, unlike social or political structure or trends, can have much meaning without fairly good quantitative data.

That data are pitifully few and poor stems from multifarious causes, and does not necessarily reflect the ability or industry of those assigned statistical chores. With communications poor, trained personnel few, and a large portion of the population not capable of, or not disposed to, giving accurate account of their activities, collection of data is slow and costly.

Tropical environments seem to militate against efficiency, too, in sapping the energy of administrators and investigators, and in adding to the difficulty of communications.

For some questions even very rough data are useful, however, and through economic research the reliability of questionable data can often be checked or useful estimates made to fill gaps. A primary objective of this study has been to amass and assess as much relevant data as possible, at the risk of boring the reader with documentation and data description.

It is only through some such process that first approximations can be refined, and conclusions made less tentative.

APPENDIX II

Construction of Map 6-1, "Maize in Tropical Africa about 1950"

Map 6-1, an attempt to portray the geographical distribution of maize production in sub-Saharan Africa about 1950, is based on official statistics when they were available. For five territories, these were from sample censuses, which were part of the 1950 world census of agriculture.

The margin of error is undoubtedly large. Where transportation is poor and commercial production of the commodity concerned is small, one would expect estimation to be difficult and subject to considerable error; in addition, underdeveloped areas almost universally are too poor to afford good statistical services, and colonial budgets have tended to be tight. Since several of these governments have not published statistics for all postwar years, an average of 1949–51, the period desired, was frequently impossible; only two of these three years were available in several instances, and for some territories data of a single year had to be used. Nor was it possible always to obtain data within the 1949–51 range; 1946 was the earliest dating of any figures used, 1953 the latest.

Data were taken from *Anuário de Guiné Portuguesa 1948* (Publicação do Governo da Colónia, Lisbon); France, Ministère de la France d'Outremer, *Annuaire statistique de l'Union Française 1939–46* (Paris, 1949), Chap. F.; Haut Commissariat de l'Afrique Occidentale Française, *Annuaire statistique de l'Afrique Occidentale Française, Vol. 2* (Paris, 1951); *Marchés tropicaux du monde*, Nov. 24, 1956; Gold Coast, Department of Agriculture, *Annual Report . . . 1st April 1952 to 31st March 1953* (Accra, 1954); Nigeria, Department of Statistics, *Report on the Sample Census of Agriculture 1950–51* (Lagos, 1952); *Ager*, Boletín de la Dirección de Agricultura de la Guinea Española, Vol. 4, Jan.–June 1954; Belgium, Ministère des Colonies, *L'Agriculture au Congo Belge et Ruanda-Urundi de 1948 à 1952* (Brussels, 1954); *idem, Plan décennal pour le développement économique et social du Ruanda-Urundi*, Vol. 1 (Brussels, 1951); FAO, *Yearbook of Food and Agriculture Statistics 1953*, Pt. 1: Production (Rome, 1954); UN, *Non-Self-Governing Territories, 1952* (New York, 1953), Vol. 2; Uganda, Department of Agriculture, *Annual Report, 1951* (Entebbe, 1952); Tanganyika, *Tanganyika Blue Book for the Year Ended December 31, 1948* (Dar es Salaam, 1950); Southern Rhodesia, *Seventh Report on the Agricultural and Pastoral Production of European Farmers, 1952–53* (Salisbury, 1954); and data made available by M. J. Miège, formerly of the territorial government of the Ivory Coast;

278

M. Thomas of Dahomey; and the Northern Rhodesia Department of Agriculture.

For Mozambique, production was estimated from a description of the importance of maize in the diet given by the Department of Agriculture (40% of staple foods consumed — information provided by R. Smith Simpson, American consul general of Mozambique), assuming that staples contribute 70% of total calories and that, on the average (including children), 1,800 calories are consumed per capita per day.

For Uganda, production was calculated from acreage and average yield data. The following yield estimates were used (in quintals per hectare) based on average statistics for all of Uganda and on rainfall data: Buganda, 14; Eastern, 11; Western, 8; and Northern, 8. Within these provinces yields were assumed to be uniform.

For Zanzibar, production was estimated from acreage, assuming a yield of 10 quintals per hectare.

Where data could be obtained for small administrative divisions, distribution was assumed to be uniform within each local unit to which the data referred. For most of French West Africa these were *cercles*; for Uganda and Tanganyika, districts; for Nigeria and the Belgian Congo, provinces; for Portuguese Guinea, Ghana, French Cameroons, French Equatorial Africa, Ruanda-Urundi, and Northern Rhodesia, only a breakdown by major subdivisions could be obtained. Where no breakdown of statistics was available — for Gambia, Rio Muni, Sierra Leone, Zanzibar and Pemba, Nyasaland, Liberia, Sudan, Ethiopia, Kenya, Somalia, Mozambique, Angola, and Southern Rhodesia — the method of distributing dots depended on the size of the territory. The first five of these are no larger than some of the provinces in other territories, hence dots were distributed uniformly. But for the sizable territories, the last eight named, nonstatistical information — descriptions of agriculture in the various regions (including descriptive maps), letters from administrators, rainfall and population maps, and the location of centers of European agriculture — was utilized to obtain a rough first approximation of the geographical distribution of maize.

APPENDIX III

Measuring Storage Losses to Rice Weevil

Data in Table 12-3, except for the tall-grass savanna of the Belgian Congo, are first approximations based on a method devised by Harry Caswell, entomologist, University College, Ibadan, Nigeria, about 1958. He decided that study of the eating habits of the rice weevil would be a fruitful approach, and found that each weevil eats roughly 7 percent of an average-size Nigerian kernel of maize.

The female rice weevil bores a tiny hole and lays her egg, then seals the hole, moves on, and drills again. Upon hatching, the young weevil begins to eat the walls of his chamber, and by the time he reaches adulthood has burrowed a tunnel terminating in a hole, where he emerges from the kernel, seeks a mate, and starts the cycle again.

Thus by counting the number of telltale holes in a sample of maize grains, multiplying them by .07, and dividing by the number of grains in the sample, one gets an approximation of the percentage of the weight of the sample that has been consumed by rice weevils.

Actual loss is somewhat higher, of course, because of additional quantities the weevils contaminate, but these are probably not large, and in any case appear to be considerably less than what is actually consumed.

With Caswell's method an estimate of weevil damage can quickly and easily be obtained by sampling stores. In practice precision is lost when weevil damage is exceptionally heavy, because holes overlap and cannot be counted accurately. Adjustments must also be made, of course, for variations in the average size of grain. In addition, not only the holes must be counted but also tunnels without openings (usually detectable as a white line on the kernel just beneath the pericarp).

Starting a few years earlier (1953) in the Belgian Congo, E. de Prèter tried a similar approach. Assuming the weevils are indiscriminate in choosing kernels of the same variety, i.e. they show no preference for any particular size of grain, he calculated the average difference in weight of weeviled kernels and undamaged ones, and expressed the difference as a percentage of the weight of the second kernels. Samplings from one location, taken from 1953 to 1955, showed this to be consistently 7 to 8 percent. If the average number of weevils per damaged grain is one, as de Prèter thinks it is (although unfortunately this information was not recorded in his experiments), this is strikingly close to Caswell's findings.

280

NOTES

Chapter One

1 Throughout this study *Zea mays* is referred to simply as "maize," the most widely understood common name for it, and the only English one which phonetically suggests the botanical term. Moreover, it closely resembles many of the various names that have been applied to *Z. mays* over the centuries. Columbus came back from the New World exhibiting a wonder he called *Mahiz*. "Corn" (or sometimes "Indian corn"), the usual name now given to maize in the United States, is fairly new as a specific term; it is found in historical records, in the main, only when the author was too careless to note what kind of corn (i.e. food grain) he intended.

2 Because of its large kernels, arranged around a rather large core, the cob, ears of maize can be fed on the ground with little waste. Moreover, maize can be efficiently harvested by livestock. In the American Corn Belt, livestock, swine particularly, may be turned in on a mature but unharvested field and left to feed at will, a practice often referred to as "hogging off" or "hogging down" the crop.

3 Edgar Anderson considers this classification "worse than useless," at least for Mexican maize, because flint and flour maize, for example, differ by a single gene; where both kinds are being grown in the same locality, "This single difference may occur in the same field and on the same ear so that shelled kernels from a single ear would have to be classified in two groups by this system" (*7*, p. 148). Anderson proposes a new system of classification based on the degree of dent and the amount of point in the grain.

4 Excessive moisture can result in soil conditions in which seeds rot rather than germinate, and can damage the young plants as well (*243*, p. 322); but this seems to be mostly a theoretical consideration. It is doubtful that excessive moisture actually is detrimental to maize over any considerable area in Africa. Most regions with heavy rainfall also have a dry season, even if a short one, and it is at the beginning of the rainy season (or seasons), a time when rainfall is neither particularly heavy nor regular, that maize is usully planted. The bulk of the rains, and the really wet parts of the year, come after maize is a well-established, thriving plant.

   In the Caribbean, excessive rainfall and low yields appear to be positively correlated, but just how higher-than-optimum rainfall affects the plant is not well understood (*90*, pp. 28, 53, and 109).

5 Tropical-temperate yield comparisons are not strictly valid. Because intercropping is commoner in the tropics, the number of maize plants per unit of land can be expected to be less than in the temperate zones; official estimates should correct for this, but it is not always clear that they do. Even so, other factors, such as improved seed, fertilizers, greater care and frequency of cultivation, and the better control of insects and diseases, are probably responsible for most of the superiority of the temperate regions.

281

Chapter Two

1 Some malnutrition is found among Africans. Most publicized is *kwashiorkor*, a protein deficiency disease found among children. Some Africans undoubtedly would be healthier if they changed either the quantity or quality of their food intake; but the same statement can be made of any population. We do not have good enough data to know even roughly how much better or worse African diets are than our own. Nutritional science is not yet sufficiently advanced to say with any precision what the nutritional needs of African peoples are; only feeble efforts have been made to measure food consumption in tropical Africa, and, in any case, investigators have not been able to measure accurately enough to make meaningful generalizations; food production and trade statistics are so fragmentary and unreliable that an indirect approach to accurate estimation of food consumption is not possible; and there is no evidence that nutritional deficiency diseases — the only sure indicator of inadequate diets, under these circumstances — are at all prevalent. In addition to carelessness about the reliability of available data and unrigorous analysis and interpretation of them, there seems to have been a general tendency to assume that people of a vastly inferior technology ipso facto have inferior diets. Subjective (or ethnocentric) bias may be of no small importance, too. But although African foods are often unappetizing to Western eyes, it remains to be demonstrated that this is reason to judge them nutritionally inferior.

Chapter Three

1 See Chapter 5, and the literature it cites, for discussion of the extent and character of nonmarket trade.

2 The importance of European settlers is generally considerably greater than their numbers suggest. In Rhodesia 49% of the land — and generally the better land — is occupied by Europeans; corresponding data for some other areas are the Congo (Leopoldville), 9%; Kenya, 7%; Bechuanaland, 6%; and Malawi, 5% (*440*, p. 27).

3 Over 750 ethnic groups are found in Africa (*310*, p. 82). Most tropical African countries have over a dozen and a number have over fifty.

4 Gross Domestic Product is a measure of total production within a specified geographic area. It differs from Gross National Product by the volume of production in any country that is contributed by foreigners or foreign-owned enterprises.

Chapter Four

1 See Chap. 8.

2 Pulses, although not starchy, are staples in much of Rwanda and Burundi and are of considerable importance in much of the rest of tropical Africa. Breadfruit (*Artocarpus incisa*) and jackfruit (*A. heterophyllus*) are the principal starchy-staples in the Seychelles but, except for the Comoro Islands, are not important in the diet elsewhere in Africa (*142*, p. 2; and *384*, p. 7), although in the 1930's Belgian colonial administrators vigorously tried to get Congolese farmers to adopt breadfruit (*171*, p. 901; and *383*, p. 906).

3 If goats are kept, the fields may be located far enough away so that these voracious animals will not find the crops.

4 The fertility of uncleared land is often judged by the type of natural vegetation it supports (see *298*).

5 Dogs seem to be kept now mainly for hunting; but in some areas, as among the Poto of the Congo Basin, they were traditionally fattened for slaughter, a practice similar to that reported for preconquest Middle America.

6 The growth period of the starchy-staples varies from as little as two months for some varieties of maize, millets, and sorghums to 18 months or more for some varieties of taro and plantain.

Chapter Five

1 Although the slave trade began to decline early in the 19th century, it was not completely suppressed until the beginning of the present century.

2 This sharp upward trend in fish trade reflects not only the forced substitution of fish for meat but also rapidly rising per capita purchasing power, and a principle that M. K. Bennett of the Food Research Institute of Stanford University finds to be generally valid in any culture. Bennett maintains that as levels of living rise, i.e. as purchasing power rises, people substitute relatively expensive foods, particularly meat and fish, for starchy-staples (*50*, pp. 213–22). All available evidence suggests that with economic growth in tropical Africa, and particularly during this century, many Africans have experienced great rises in real per capita income and have substituted meat and fish for starches for reasons of income, and fish for meat for reasons of price (shortages of meat have made that considerably dearer).

3 "Western Nigeria" with a capital W refers here, and hereafter, to the Western Region of Nigeria.

   This section is based mainly on observations during three and a half months in Nigeria. Much of the data was obtained from a tour of the major markets Nov. 3–9 and Dec. 18–20, 1958. Most of the Western Region was covered, and markets were visited in or near Ifé, Ondo, Ede, Ilesha, Ekiti, Akure, Lokoja, Ubiaja, Agbor, Benin City, Ibadan, Oyo, Ogbomosho, Ilorin, Ilaro, Agege, Lagos, and Ijebu-Ode. During this tour traders were interviewed through an interpreter; to check the information they gave, similar questions were put to nearby farmers and processors. See *274* for additional information on the operations of women traders.

4 About 46% of the population was in towns and cities of over 5,000, excluding Lagos, the second largest city in the area (1952/53 census; *198*, p. 65).

5 For a few quantitative data on the extent to which raw materials are purchased see Galletti, Baldwin, and Dina, *Nigerian Cocoa Farmers* (London, Oxford Univ. Press, 1956), Table 212 and App. Tables 47–49. Unfortunately these data, as presented, will not allow estimating the proportion of housewives who specialize in food processing. However, the following statement is made: "The processing and cooking of food for the market form the principal occupation for many of the women. Ijebu women specialize in the production of a gari (a manioc product), while the women of Ibadan specialize more in cooked food for the market, especially the maize products *agidi* and *eko* or the bean cakes called *akara*. They do not depend on the family farms for their raw material but purchase it by the bag or in smaller quantities as required from time to time" (*163*, p. 425).

6 "Middlemen" is used throughout to refer to sellers who buy goods for resale; in fact, however, in western tropical Africa most of them are women.

7 Frequently these organizations have a recognized head, and in some of the larger markets there is a head of all guilds. Such organizations perform considerably more than an economic function; they are powerful politically in some instances, and have an important place in the social activities of members, who appear obligated to attend naming ceremonies, funerals, etc., of other members. Hodder (*202*, p. 114) suggests that for the Akinyele area, at least, guilds were much more important "in earlier years of the present century."

8 The collection of papers on African commerce edited by Paul Bohannan and George Dalton (*Markets in Africa*, Evanston, Ill., 1962) contains chapters which touch on the organization of commerce in several areas of tropical Africa (see Chaps. 1, 2, 5, 9, 10, 14, 21, 22, and 26–28), but information in these accounts is not sufficient for further generalization on geographical variation in the organization. N. A. Cox-George, *Report on African Participation in the Commerce of Sierra Leone* (Freetown, 1960), provides a lengthy discussion of the organization of commerce in Sierra Leone; and J. Binet ("Marchés en pays Soussou," *Cahiers d'études Africaines*, 2, 4ᵉ Cahier [1962], 104–14) reports in detail on the organization of markets in a neighboring area of Guinea.

9 In a survey of 473 Zambian Copperbelt vendors I made in September and December 1959, 63% of the sellers displayed only one item; 20% had two; and 17% had three or more. See *295*, p. 711 for description of this survey.

10 Storekeepers say African consumers prefer to buy small quantities rather than to store foodstuffs. In Zambia, for example, they sell sugar, salt, oil, fish, kerosene, and most other items in three-penny lots. The reason for this seems to be largely fear of excessive borrowing by friends or relatives that could arise because of obligations to share with them. Consumers seem to find it advantageous to buy little more than enough for immediate consumption and pay the higher price per unit charged for small amounts than to buy in bulk and have a large portion of their purchases disappear in the hands of friends or kinsmen.

11 Whether basela is given is a function of one's skill in bargaining, the commodity, conditions of supply and demand, the kinds of competition one faces, and whether the buyer is known or liked.

12 One of its activities, I am told, is to plead with the government for elimination of competition from Europeans on the ground that Africans do not have, and cannot easily get, enough capital to compete with whites.

13 See *295*, p. 711, for further details on how the survey was conducted and its results.

14 The actual number of ethnic groups in Accra markets is somewhat greater than the survey indicates. The Accra survey did not report the composition of "Other Akans," "Northern Region," "Nigerians," "French," and "Others." The Nigerians are, however, apparently almost entirely Yoruba, and the other categories not broken down represent only 13% of the vendors surveyed.

15 The same seems to be true of Accra. In the Accra survey, only 21% of vendors initially started their trading with borrowed money, almost all of which came

from nonrelatives, and 52% got their start with a gift (*334*, p. 32). Parents supplied 61% of such gifts, and husbands and other relatives supplied 26 and 13% respectively.

Chapter Seven

1 The Cameroun and all of sub-Saharan Africa to the west.

2 Frank Willett speculates that an editor probably added the illustration, although he is not able to prove it (*466*, p. 3).

3 See *466*, pp. 1–13, and *297* for a critical appraisal of evidence on the introduction of maize to Africa in pre-Columbian times.

4 *Milho zaburro* is now used by the Portuguese for sorghum or millet, but as late as 1873 Domingos Vieira, in his *Thesouro da lingua portugueza* (*449*), said it was a synonym for *milho grosso* (5:1029), which he identified as *Zea maiz* (4:241).

5 "Eerstelijk groeit daer rijs, ook Turksche tarruw, *Mays* by d'Indianen genaemt, die de Portugesen allereerst uit Westindien, daer het overvloedelijk wast, na het eilant *Sinte Thomé*, en van daer na de Goutkuste tot hun nootdrust gebraght, en onder de zwarten verdeelt hebben. . . ."

6 Dapper lists maize as the most common grain in the vicinity of Cape Verde, but does not mention it between Cape Verde and Liberia (*117*, p. 389).

7 Another economic motive, introduction of maize to supply Portuguese sailors on ships engaged in the spice trade by the newly discovered route to the Orient, seems unlikely. It is probable that the Portuguese did not readily accept maize as a staple. Gerarde summarizes what was probably the consensus of European attitudes in 1597 with these words (quoted in *457*, p. 45): "We may easily iude [*sic*] that it nourisheth but little, and is of hard and evil digestion, and a more convenient food for swine than men." One of the Portuguese writers of the same period, Duarte Lopez, noted in 1591 that maize was the vilest of grain and only fit for swine (*350*, p. 40). Moreover, descriptions of the diet of ships' crews and of garrison provisions of Mozambique for 1505–07 made no mention of maize (*25*, p. 132); and as late as 1721 maize is described as a provision crews would use only in emergencies (*253*, p. 167). However, this concerns use of maize flour or maize meal; we do not have evidence on when roasting ears, a popular but not staple use of maize, gained acceptance by Europeans. It could well be that maize was grown around provisioning stations at an early date as a vegetable to be used by shore personnel and by ships while they were in port.

8 "Vi è il miglio bianco nominato Mazza di Congo, cioè grano di Congo & il Maiz che è il più vile de tutti che dassi a porci, & cosi anco il riso è in porco prezzo, & al Maiz diccono Mazza Manputo cioè grano di Portugallo, appolando essi Manputo Portugallo" (*350*, p. 40).

9 Correspondence between Sir John Gray and A. C. W. Wright, cited in *471*, p. 64.

10 At another point (*174*, p. 49) Charles Grant, son of the baron, states that Governor de la Bourdonnais had manioc brought from the island of Madeira.

11 "There are also the aloes, indigo, sugar canes, cotton, the anana, the banana, tobacco, the potato, the pumpkin, land and watermelons, cucumbers, and a hundred other plants, fruits, and roots, which grow everywhere, and with-

out cultivation, even on the mountains. Turkey corn, or maize, millet, rice, wheat, barley, and oats, are also experimentally known to flourish there; and a twofold harvest of these grains may be annually gathered. All the plants and herbs of our European gardens have been cultivated there with great success" (*174*, p. 154).

12   See *453*, pp. 37, 91, 189, and 249; *262*, pp. 111, 278, and 498; *84*, p. 474; *153*, p. 136; *397*, pp. 183, 227, 269, and 313; *252*, pp. 113, 187, 189, 221, and 223; and *91*, p. 257.

13   I am indebted to Cyril Ehrlich, University College of East Africa, Kampala, Uganda, for use of a copy he made of this letter.

14   Patterson's parenthetical qualification.

15   See *82*, p. 33; *203*, pp. 18 and 19; *210*; *61*, pp. 38 and 39; *208*, p. 47; and *200*, pp. 16, 27, 37, and 72.

Chapter Eight

1   Agidi is the principal maize dish in Sierra Leone (*6*, p. 49). I have not found reference to it elsewhere outside Nigeria, however, although I have seen a dish much like it along the eastern lagoons of the Ivory Coast.

2   The portion used for beer is about 22% of the original grain; the remainder, 31%, is reportedly waste (*111*, p. 15).

3   A few other helpful references to processing techniques and maize products in tropical African rural economies are *169*, especially pp. 89, 90, 94, 95, 129, 137, 139–51, 154, 165, and 232; *107*, p. 20; *453*, p. 220; *459*, p. 92; *192*, pp. 141 and 146; *304*, pp. 162, 164, and 165; *76*, p. 129; *456*, p. 71; *163*, p. 125; *364*, chap. 4; *261*, pp. 513 and 514; *4*, pp. 95–97; *210*, p. 69; *416*, p. 237; *280*, p. 283; and *235*, pp. 269–70.

4   Based on a rough assumption of 1,800 calories per capita per day, with starchy-staples accounting for 70% of the calorie intake. Variations among ethnic groups resulting from differences in body size, age composition, and other factors are ignored because of lack of any basis for attempting such a refinement.

5   See Chapter 5, p. 62, for description of this survey.

6   Weevil damage is very high once maize is moved from the farm; hence consumers and traders try to keep stocks at a minimum.

7   The mean divided by the standard deviation times 100.

Chapter Nine

1   In 1942, 1945, 1948–51, and 1953 there is record of issuing maize or maize meal in one part or another of Uganda to relieve food shortage (*435*, various issues).

2   It may also have been for some of the migrant labor working for the Baganda, e.g. those from western Kenya; but maize clearly was not used to feed certain other groups of laborers. As late as 1943 people from Ruanda who were questioned about the reasons they had chosen to work for Buganda farmers — rather than for estates, the government, or mines — mentioned, among other things, that they preferred the diet of sweet potatoes or plaintain of Buganda to the maize they were certain to get in other employment (*422*, p. 17).

3   In 1938 only four of the basic industries — sugar, sisal, lumbering, and fuel-cutting — gave rations to all employees. Of the coffee and rubber estates

37.5% gave rations to all workers, and another 25% issued them to a part of their employees; 28% of tea plantations gave rations to all workers and an equal number rationed only a part of their labor force. Less adequate data are available for cotton ginneries and mines, but in 1938 issuance of rations was not universal in either of these industries (*421*, pp. 27–28).

Estimates of unskilled labor employed in Uganda were (*436*, various issues; and *421*, p. 13):

Year	Laborers
1937	83,000
1943–45	66,464
1946–50	55,338[a]
1951–55	106,103
1956 and 1957	106,108

[a] Four-year average; 1947 missing.

4   As late as 1919, average transport costs from farm to rail were reported to be £5 per ton on the Uasin Gishu Plateau (*131*, p. 16). A commission appointed to evaluate the economic potential of British East Africa and make policy recommendations commented in its report (1919) that maize production was being "strangled by absence of communications" (*131*, p. 16).

5   In 1919 the Economic Commisison for the East African Protectorate asserted: "The native population of over 2½ million lives mainly on varieties of grain produced in the country. Maize is the principal crop" (*131*, p. 9). And the same source cites an estimate of the director of agriculture, presumably made in the same year, of 224 pounds of maize production per capita per year, which, if at all accurate, would indicate that maize was the major staple. But production is not known with any accuracy even now, and knowledge in 1919 is not likely to have been any better. Other evidence suggests that maize may have been the staple among the Kikuyu (found around Nairobi) by 1919, and we know it to have been a staple farther south and east even before European administration (see Chapter 7). However, maize probably was not a major staple in western areas until the late 1920's, if then (*200*, pp. 6, 27, 37, and 72; and *210*, p. 62).

6   In a small region around Lake Victoria and in parts of the Rift Valley bisecting the Kenya Highlands, where rainfall is less than about 50 inches annually, sorghum seems to have withstood competition from maize because of its lower rainfall requirements (*338*).

7   The adoption of the plow has varied grealy by area, however; in the Central Province, the area around Nairobi, hilly terrain and fragmentation of holdings resulting in extremely small fields seem to have prevented widespread plowing until the last ten years or so (*204*, p. 3068).

8   The six crops shown in Map 9-1, Sec. B, account for most of Mozambique's plantation agriculture; in 1949–51 and 1952–55 they represented 85% of agricultural exports by value (*300*, various issues).

9   Data on 1945–46 to 1947–48 were not available to me.

10   Based on information given me in 1959 by 74 Plateau Tonga, 34 Senga, 20 Nsenga, and 5 Soli informants, all of whom claimed to be old enough to remember life before British rule. See also *168; 124*, p. 99; and *402*, p. 77.

11   European farmers typically took up land on the rail line or very near it; there-fore improvements in transportation had little effect on their capacity to produce. It was not until it became profitable to bring maize by truck nearly 400 miles from the Eastern Province in the 1940's that they were much affected by transportation improvements.

12   African farmers along the railway had no plows as late as 1905 (*305*, p. 260); it probably was in 1914 that the first plow was sold to an African (*229*, p. 3). However, one ethnic group alone, the Plateau Tonga, had an estimated 91 tractors, 21,168 plows, 4,516 oxcarts, and 45 power-operated mills by 1958 (*322*), besides an unknown number of cultivators, harrows, and like equipment.

13   According to Hobson, "The 1915–16 report for Northern Rhodesia states the calculated monthly consumption of the troops on the Northern border was 335,000 lbs., and General Northey wanted a six-month reserve on top of it . . ." (*201*, p. 25). This works out to 20,064 bags of grain a year, not includ-ing the reserve. One cannot establish what normal needs were at the time, but this is just over 50% of average estimated normal needs six years later (*287*, p. 6), which were very likely greater than in 1915, considering the general trend in mining activity.

14   The other possibility — an increase in the total acreage cultivated but no in-crease in per capita acreage or yields per acre — seems improbable. Floyd speaking of the 1890–1958 period, asserts: "The African areas have grown no larger, but the native population has increased rapidly" (*154*, p. 4). According to Barber, the reason Africans did not shift toward tobacco as many European farmers did is that it was discouraged, if not prohibited, by the government, which wanted a European monopoly on export crops (*29*, pp. 27–28).

15   Creole merchants were shipping rice, cattle, and presumably other foodstuffs to Mauritius and Réunion as early as 1800 (*216*, p. 101).

16   Louis Chevalier estimates that between Tananarive, the capital in the center of the island, and the coast, transportation charges were 1,200 francs per metric ton at the beginning of French rule, but fell to 800 fr. per metric ton once a mule trail was built and to 250 fr. per metric ton when the first road was opened (*102*, pp. 109–10).

17   Shortage of labor and of other factors of production during World War II is cited as the major cause of a general reduction in agricultural output (*101*, p. 349).

18   Hildebert Isnard says that the sharecropper usually is given about 3.5 hectares to devote to cash crops and, in addition, garden plots for his subsistence; he is advanced seed and taxes by the landowner, and is given credit as he needs it at the landowner's store; all work is done by the sharecropper, who receives from one-half to two-thirds of the harvest as his share (*214*, p. 103).

19   In the east and southwest, descriptions of the cultivation of unirrigated maize suggest that no manure is applied (*367*, p. 8; and *412*, p. 443). On the central plateau the Malgache have long manured rice fields and in some areas are now beginning to buy chemical fertilizers (*216*, p. 202); Rollot implies that in this region other crops are less likely to be fertilized than is rice (*368*, p. 158).

20   In 1938 only 11% of cultivated land was irrigated, but by 1949 irrigated crops represented 36%, and in 1960 about half (51%), of arable land and per-manent crops (*102*, p. 347; *143*, 1953, p. 9; and *143*, 1961, pp. 7–9).

    Rice acreage also increased because of shifts in population. In the western third of the island — an area growing mainly manioc, arrowroot, and maize, but little rice, at the beginning of colonial rule (*102*, p. 56; and *386*, p. 295) — rice production has been greatly expanded by settlement of rice-growing peoples from the central plateau who have migrated westward in recent decades (*102*, pp. 145–52).

21 Sweet potatoes and yams are not exported; hence, unless yields are offsetting, the smaller area given to these crops reflects less production. Manioc is an export crop, and in the early postwar period exports were declining with acreage. In recent years, however, the trend in manioc exports seems to have reversed, and the decline in acreage has been coupled with a considerable increase in exports; this suggests that, barring an unusual increase in yields, domestic utilization of manioc is declining relative to other starchy-staples (*102*, pp. 206–7; *288*, pp. 347 and 359; and *193*, p. 268):

	Exports (1,000 metric tons)	
Year	Dry manioc and tapioca	Flour and starch
1926–35	35.4	2.7
1934–38	30.6	. . .
1941–45	2.0	8.9
1946–50	12.7	4.5
1951–55	13.4	3.4
1956	15.0	1.4
1957	17.0	1.2

Other data suggest that manioc has never been a preferred staple in much of the Malagasy Republic. The increase in the acreage of manioc relative to other starchy-staples prior to 1934–38 that is suggested by Table 9-8 apparently does not represent a preference for manioc as a food, although it does reflect something more than the trend in manioc exports. During this period manioc acreage grew (1) partly because manioc plots were planted as famine reserves, and (2) because of increased familiarity with the crop. That migrant workers brought manioc home with them after working for settlers or plantations, for example, is the reason given for the rise of manioc in southern Malagasy and the decline of millet in recent decades from a major to a very minor starchy-staple (*122*, p. 265). Now, however, many of the same innovators are adopting rice wherever they can develop irrigation (*ibid.*; and *386*, p. 295).

Chapter Ten

1 For sectors I and VI, Map 10–1, a similar census was conducted the preceding 36 months. In sector I, 1957/58 maize trade was considerably smaller than it had been in the three preceding years (5,028 metric tons net imports compared with an average of 8,963 metric tons in 1954–57); but in sector VI it was slightly more in 1957/58 (3,214 metric tons net imports compared with an average of 2,937 metric tons in 1954–57). Other than these data, there is little evidence as to how representative 1957/58 was for maize trade, except

that movements into sector IX were larger than usual because of poor crops there caused by drought.

2   Based on the author's observations and survey of the organization of staple-food marketing in Western Nigeria, Sept. to Dec. 1958.

3   Data provided by the Maize Marketing Board show only 2 metric tons of maize exported from this region in 1949 and none from 1950 to 1957. Figures from the economic section of Banco de Angola suggest that an export surplus is now developing, however; 1,246 metric tons of maize were sold to the Maize Marketing Board in 1959 and 13,953 in 1960 (9, April–June 1961, p. 5).

4   In 1949–56, 1959, and 1960 this region accounted for between 85 and 95% of maize exports; in 1957, a year of exceptionally low overseas sales, it accounted for only 59% of maize exported. The percentage of total maize exports coming from the only other sizable exporting region, Luanda-Malange (Map 10-3), tends to vary inversely with the size of total exports, and ranged from 36% in years of exceptionally small marketings to 3.4% in the year of peak exports (187).

5   Whether Angola got a larger share of the metropolitan market or found new markets cannot be determined from data available to me.

Chapter Eleven

1   For evidence of normal economic behavior by Africans, see 238, 292, 293, 295, 296, and 314.

2   See 231, pp. 144–47, for discussion for some of the food preferences reported in western tropical Africa.

3   An average of 110,500 unskilled laborers was recorded for the 1953–57 quinquennium (436, various issues). The aggregate population of Kampala, Jinja, and Entebbe, the three principal cities, has never been accurately counted, but was estimated to be about 60,000 in 1958 (431, p. 9).

4   Data from Ghana and Katanga Province, Congo (Leopoldville), the only area for which there are reasonably complete data on quantities of starchy-staples moving in internal commerce, show maize and manioc to be the main commodities marketed:

	Percent of total starchy-staple trade	
	Katanga Province, Congo (Leopoldville) 1954–58	*All Ghana 1957–58*
Maize	46.5	42.9
Manioc	40.0[a]	34.7[a]
Rice	6.9	2.4
Millets-sorghums	1.6	2.4
Yam	0.0	3.4
Taro	0.0	0.8
Bananas-plaintains	3.3	10.5
Other	1.7	2.9
Total	100.0	100.0
Total Trade (*metric tons*)	61,000	140,100

Data are from Belgium, Ministère des Colonies, Province du Katanga, Affaires Économiques, *Rapport économique* (Elisabethville), various issues; and files of the Ghana Government Statistician. They are dry equivalent basis; i.e. actual tonnages were multiplied by the following index:

$$\frac{\text{calories per 100 grams of commodity}}{\text{calories per 100 grams of maize}}$$

to adjust for differences in water content.

* Fresh manioc and manioc flour, mostly the latter. Manioc flour was assumed to have the same number of calories per 100 grams as maize.

5 Why hybrid maize varieties cannot markedly change African maize productivity, in the short run, is discussed in Chapter 12.

Chapter Twelve

1 See Jones, *Manioc in Africa*, pp. 93–94, for discussion of Belgian efforts to make African agriculture more like that of Europe.

2 Examples at hand are the following: There is record of composting in Malawi, Mozambique, Zambia, Tanganyika, and the Congo Basin (*72*, p. 118; *184*, p. 24; *127*, p. 814; *254*, p. 101; *381*, p. 478; *400*, p. 23; *410*, p. 39; *302*, p. 422; *339*, p. 253; and *470*, p. 92). Animal manures are applied to some crops, at least, in parts of Nigeria, Rwanda-Burundi, Tanganyika, Zambia, Malawi, Somalia, and the Congo Basin (*3*, p. 12; *118*, p. 112; *128*, p. 153; *172*, p. 153; *186*; *404*, p. 49; *370*, p. 36; *371*, p. 3; *373*, p. 53; *408*; *452*, p. 91; and *461*, p. 132). In two parts of Nigeria, at least — among the Hill Pagans of Dikwa Emirate and among the Ezzas in Abakaliki and Afikpo divisions of Ogoja Province — night soil is an important fertilizer (*452*, p. 91; and *461*, p. 132). Ash fertilizers are widely used (*32*, p. 11; *118*, p. 112; *133*, p. 183; *270*, p. 112; *410*, pp. 9, 27, and 39; and *461*, p. 132).

3 The following is based on communication with Elizabeth O'Kelley, British Cameroons, Dec. 1958.

4 After the maize mill cooperatives became popular, some motorized mills were purchased.

Chapter Thirteen

1 This section is based on observations made during three and one-half months in the Western Region of Nigeria in 1958; see Chap. 5, p. 67, for description of method of study and areas visited. See Chap. 5, pp. 67–70, for a general description of the organization of trade in Western Nigeria.

2 A number of informants reported interest rates of 200–300% per year.

3 This section is based on my research on the organization of internal commerce in major commodities and on market structure in the Ivory Coast in 1965, and in particular on data obtained between the beginning of field work in March and the end of April, when this section went to press.

4 A food consumption survey at Bongouanou in central Ivory Coast (see Chap. 8, p. 118) found maize to account for less than 1% of starchy-staple calories among the local population, whereas among the foreigners — 76% of whom were from Upper Volta, Mali, Guinea, or Niger — maize was second only to rice as a supplier of calories, accounting for 26% of starchy-staple calories

consumed (J. L. Boutillier, *Bongouanou, Côte d'Ivoire*, Paris, 1960, pp. 146, 154, and 216).

5   This section is based on a tour of markets I made Dec. 24, 1958 to Jan. 1, 1959, visiting Bali, Ngemba, Makon, Jakero, and Wum markets. Additional data were obtained from the provincial agricultural officer and informants in the Bafut and Ndop areas.

6   The organization of Mozambique maize marketing for 1936–44 is described in Chap. 9, pp. 149–50; information on changes since 1944, if any, is not available.

7   See *191* and *290* for further discussion of Kenya's maize control scheme.

8   Portuguese officials of the grain-marketing monopoly in Lisbon are of the opinion that exports fairly closely approximate marketings.

9   Adding the price of beans as a variable, and assuming no lags, gives a multiple correlation coefficient of 0.457 (with r_{13}, the correlation coefficient of bean prices and maize exports, -0.43; and r_{23}, the correlation coefficient of bean and maize prices, 0.18).

CITATIONS

1   A. Adandé. "Le maïs et ses usages dans le Bas-Dahomey," *Bull. de l'IFAN*, Vol. 15, No. 1 (Jan. 1953).

2   F. N. Ahl. *Wings over the Congo*. Boston, 1956.

3   W. Allan. *Studies in African Land Usage in Northern Rhodesia*, Rhodes-Livingstone Papers, No. 15. Oxford, 1949.

4   K. W. Allen. "The Monotonous Diet of Africans," *E. Afr. Med. J.*, Mar. 1955.

5   João de Almeida. *Sul de Angola*. Lisbon, 1936.

6   T. J. Alldridge. *A Transformed Colony, Sierra Leone* . . . . London, 1910.

7   Edgar Anderson. "Maize in Mexico — A Preliminary Survey," *Ann. Mo. Bot. Gard.*, Vol. 33 (1946).

8   M. Angelo and Denis De Carli. "A Voyage to Congo in the Years 1666 and 1667," in John Pinkerton, ed., *A General Collection of the Best and Most Interesting Voyages and Travels in All Parts of the World*, Vol. 16. London, 1814.

9   Banco de Angola, Repartição de Estudos Económicas. *Boletim Trimestral*.

10   Angola Institute. *Angola, Portuguese Province in Africa*. Luanda, 1953.

11   Angola, Repartição de Estatística Geral. *Anúario estatístico*. Luanda.

12   Anonymous. "Benguella e seu sertão," in Luciano Cordeiro, ed. *Viagens explorações e conquistas dos Portuguezes*. Lisbon, 1881.

13   ————. "La Riziculture à Madagascar," *Bull. Écon.* (Madagascar), No. 1 (1909).

14   ————."Les Progrès économiques des protectorats allemands de l'Afrique," *Bull. Agr. Congo Belge*, Dec. 1910.

15   ————. "L'Agriculture du Congo Belge," *ibid.*, June 1924.

16   ————. "L'Agriculture du Congo Belge en 1936," *ibid.*, Mar. 1937.

17   *Ibid.*, "en 1937," Sept. 1938.

18   *Ibid.*, "en 1938," Mar. 1939.

19   S. La Anyane. Communication from Accra, Ghana, Oct. 1958.

20   Anacleto Apodaca. "Corn and Custom: The Introduction of Hybrid Corn to Spanish American Farmers in New Mexico," in Edward H. Spicer, *Human Problems in Technological Change*. New York, 1952.

21   E. W. Ardner. Communication, Dec. 1958.

22   F. S. Arnot. *Garenganze*. New York, 1889.

23   Association for Promoting the Discovery of the Interior Parts of Africa. *Proceedings*. London, 1791.

24   J. Atkins. *A Voyage to Guinea, Brasil and the West Indies*. London, 1737.

25   E. Axelson. *South-East Africa 1488–1530*. London, 1940.

26   F. Alyward. *Interim Report to the Government on Foods and Nutrition*. Processed, FAO, Rome, 1961.

27   Fon of Bafut. Communication from Bamenda, British Cameroons, Dec. 1958.

28 E. Baillaud. *La Situation économique de l'Afrique Occidentale, Anglaise et Française*. Paris, 1907.

29 W. J. Barber. *The Economy of British Central Africa*. Stanford, Calif., 1961.

30 J. Barbot. "A Desciption of the Coasts of North and South Guinea: and of Ethiopia Inferior, Vulgarly Angola . . . ," in A. Churchill, comp., *A Collection of Voyages and Travels*, Vol. 5. London, 1725.

31 A. R. Barlow. "Evidence from Early Explorers and Travelers," in Kenya, *Land Commission Evidence*, Vol. 1. Nairobi, 1933.

32 J. A. Barnes. *The Material Culture of the Fort Jameson Ngoni*. Livingstone, Northern Rhodesia, 1948.

33 W. R. Bascom. "Yoruba Cooking," *Africa* (Oxford), Jan. 1951.

34 ———. "Yoruba Food," *Africa* (Oxford), Apr. 1951.

35 P. Bascoulergue and J. Bergot. *L'Alimentation rurale au Moyen-Congo*, French Equatorial Africa, Service Commun de Lutte contre les grandes endémies. 1953.

36 Perrier de la Bathie. "Les Plantes introduites à Madagascar," *Rev. Bot. App. et Agr. Trop.*, Sept.–Oct. 1931.

37 B. A. Beadle, trans. "Journey of the Pombeiros . . . from Angola to Tette on the Zambeze . . . ," in R. F. Burton, trans., *Lacerda's Journey to Cazembe in 1798*. London, 1873.

38 J. B. Bebiano. "Considerações sobre algunas problemas fundamentais de Cabo Verde," in Junta de Investigações do Ultramar, *Colóquias Cabo-Verdianas*. Lisbon, 1959.

39 Belgium, Ministère des Colonies. *Rapport . . . au Conseil de la Société de Nations au sujet . . . du Ruanda-Urundi pendant l'année 1925.* 1926.

40 *Ibid., 1928.* 1929.

41 ———. *Plan décennal pour le développement économique et social du Congo Belge*, Vol. 1. Brussels, 1949.

42 ———. *La Situation économique de Congo Belge*. Brussels.

43 ———, Province du Kasai, Affaires Économiques. *Rapport économique*, Luluabourg.

44 ———, Province du Katanga, Affaires Économiques. *Rapport économique*, Elizabethville.

45 ———. *Rapport annuel sur l'administration du Congo Belge pendant l'année 1931.* 1932.

46 *Ibid., 1936.*

47 *Ibid., 1937.*

48 *Ibid., 1950.*

49 *Ibid., 1951.*

50 M. K. Bennett. *The World's Food*. New York, 1954.

51 E. Berg. "French West Africa," in W. Galenson, ed., *Labor and Economic Development*. New York, 1959.

52 ———. "Backward-sloping Labor Supply Functions in Dual Economies — The Africa Case," *Quart. J. Econ.*, Aug. 1961.

53 M. Bervas. "L'Agriculture à la Côte d'Ivoire," in Société d'Études d'Agriculture Tropicale, *L'Agronomie Trop.*, Pt. 1. Louvain, 1911.

54 J. W. Blake, ed. *Europeans in West Africa 1450–1560*, printed for the Hakluyt Society, Vol. 1. London, 1942.
55 E. Böhm. "La Mise en valeur des colonies portugaises." Unpublished doctoral thesis, University of Lille, 1933.
56 O. Boléo. *Moçambique.* Lisbon, 1951.
57 B. W. Bond. Information given in Kenya, *Land Commission Evidence*, Vol. 3. Nairobi, 1933.
58 F. Bontick, trans. *La Fondation de la mission des Capucins au Royame du Congo (1648)*, Louvain, 1964.
59 W. L. Booker. Communication from Accra, Ghana, Oct. 1958.
60 W. Bosman. *A New and Accurate Description of the Coast of Guinea* . . . . London, 1705.
61 P. Bostock. *The Peoples of Kenya, The Tiata.* London, 1950.
62 Sebastião Xavier Botelho. *Memória estatística sôbre os dominíos portuguezes na África Oriental.* Lisbon, 1835.
63 E. W. Bovill. *Caravans of the Old Sahara.* London, 1933.
64 C. R. Boxer. "Maize Names," *Uganda J.*, Sept. 1952.
65 ———. "Background to Angola: Cadorenga's Chronicle," *Hist. Today* (London), Oct. 1961.
66 Garcia Mendes Castello Branco. "Da Mina ao Cabo Negro," in Luciano Cordeiro, ed., *Viagens explorações e conquistas dos Portuguezes.* Lisbon, 1881.
67 V. W. Brelsford. *Copperbelt Markets: A Social and Economic Study.* Government Printer, Lusaka, 1947.
68 F. H. LeBreton. *Up-Country Swahili.* Richmond, Surrey, England, 1956.
69 British South Africa Company. *Maize Growing in Rhodesia.* [1918?].
70 H. Bross. *Somalia Grain Study.* Rome, 1954.
71 R. Bruyère. Communication from Kizozi, Ruanda-Urundi, Apr. 1959.
72 J. Buchanan. *The Shiré Highlands.* London, 1885.
73 *Bulletin of the Imperial Institute* (London), Vol. 8, No. 1 (1910).
74 G. H. Bullock. Great Britain, Dept. of Overseas Trade. *Economic Conditions in Angola, March, 1934*, No. 577. London, 1934.
75 Bureau pour le Développement de la Production Agricole, Comores Archipelago. *Étude agricole et socio-économique de la région de Nioumakele* (Anjouan Island), Vol. 2. Paris, 1961.
76 G. Burel. *La France Equatoriale Africaine.* Paris, 1935.
77 R. H. Burley, ed. *The Agriculture of Ethiopia*, U.S.A. Operations Mission to Ethiopia-Point 4, Vol. 2. Addis Ababa, 1957.
78 R. F. Burton. *Abeokuta and the Camaroons Mountains*, Vol. 1. London, 1863.
79 ———, trans. *Lacerda's Journey to Cazembe in 1798.* London, 1873.
80 W. F. P. Burton. "The Country of the Baluba in Central Katanga," *Geog. J.*, Oct. 1927.
81 C. E. V. Buxton. Information given in Kenya, *Land Commission Evidence*, Vol. 3. Nairobi, 1933.
82 C. Cagnolo. *The Akikuyu.* Nyeri, Kenya, 1931.
83 A. de Calonne-Beaufaict. *Azande.* Brussels, 1921.
84 V. L. Cameron. *Across Africa.* New York, 1877.

85 R. H. Cammack. "Observations of *Puccinia polysora* Underw. in West Africa," in West African Maize Rust Research Unit, *First Annual Report, 1953*. London 1954.
86 R. H. Cammack. Communication from Ibadan, Nigeria, Dec. 1958.
87 Cape Verde Islands. *Annuário estatístico.*
88 H. Capello and R. Ivens. *De Benguella as Terras de Iácca*, Vol. 2. Lisbon, 1881.
89 ———. *De Angola a Contra-Costa*, Vol. 1. Lisbon, 1886.
90 Caribbean Commission, Committee . . . of the Caribbean Research Council. *Grain Crops in the Caribbean*, Crop Inquiry Series, No. 3. Washington, D.C., 1947.
91 C. Casati. *Ten Years in Equatoria*. London, 1898.
92 H. Caswell. Communication from Ibadan, Nigeria, Dec. 1958.
93 Centro das Actividades Económicas de Angola. *O milho na economia de Angola*. Lisbon, 1954.
94 P. B. Du Chaillu. *Explorations and Adventures in Equatorial Africa.* New York, 1861.
95 R. Chambon and M. Alofs. *Le District agricole du Tanganyika.* Belgium, Ministère des Colonies, Brussels, 1958.
96 R. Chambon and A. Leruth. "Monographie des bena Muhona, Territoire de Kongolo — District du Tanganyika," *Bull. Agr. Congo Belge,* June 1954.
97 C. Chatfield. *Food Composition Tables for International Use*, FAO, Nutr. Stud. No. 11. Rome, 1954.
98 A. Chevalier. "La Culture du maïs en Afrique Occidentale et espécialement au Dahomey," *J. Agr. Trop.*, Aug. 1910.
99 ———. "Les Productions végétales du Sahara et ses confins Nord et Sud, passé, present, avenir," *Rev. Bot. App. et Agr. Trop.*, Sept.–Oct. 1932.
100 ———. "Les Iles du Cap Vert," *ibid.*, Oct.–Nov. 1935.
101 ———, ed. "Cinquante années d'efforts scientifiques et sociaux pour le développement de l'agriculture Malgache," *ibid.*, Supplement, Sept. 1946.
102 L. Chevalier. *Madagascar, population et resources*. Paris, 1952.
103 H. L. Chung. "The Sweet Potato in Hawaii," *Hawaii Agr. Exp. Stat. Bull.*, No. 50. Washington, D.C., 1923.
104 E. S. Clayton. "Research Methodology and Peasant Agriculture," *Farm Economist* (Oxford), Vol. 8, No. 6 (1956).
105 E. Colson. *Marriage and Family among the Plateau Tonga of Northern Rhodesia*. Manchester, 1958.
106 G. Condominas. *Fokon'olona et collectivités rurales en Imerina.* Paris, 1960.
107 Conseils au Moniteurs. *Enseignement pratique agriculture.* N.p., 1942.
108 José de Araujo Correia. "Possibilidades económicas de Angola," *Boletim da Agência Geral das Colónias*, Apr. 1926.
109 G. Cours. "La Revue de Madagascar," *Le Courrier Agricole d'Afrique,* 14 Feb. 1946.

110 J. A. Crutchfield. *Report to the Government of Uganda on Fish Marketing in Uganda*, FAO Report No. 998. Processed, Rome, 1959.

111 G. M. Culwick. *A Dietary Survey among the Zande of the Southwestern Sudan*. Sudan, Ministry of Agriculture, 1950.

112 Oscar Reis Cunha. "Monografia agrícola de manica e sofala." Unpublished manuscript, Beira, Mozambique, 1957.

113 M. F. Cushman. *Missionary Doctor*. New York, Harper and Bros., 1944.

114 Dahomey, Department of Agriculture. Information from the files.

115 ———. *Rapport annuel 1957*. 1958.

116 A. Dalzel. *The History of Dahomey*. London, 1793.

117 O. Dapper. *Naukeurige Beschrijuinge der Afrikaensche* . . . . Amsterdam, 1668.

118 J. G. Davies. "The Gyel Farm Survey in Jos Division," *Farm and Forest* (Nigeria), Nov. 1946.

119 R. Decary. *L'Androy*, Vol. 1. Paris, 1930.

120 *Ibid.*, Vol. 2. Paris, 1933.

121 ———. *L'Ile Nosy Bé de Madagascar*. Paris, 1960.

122 H. Descamps. *Les Migrations interieures passées et présentes à Madagascar*. Paris, 1959.

123 J. Despois. "Des montagnards en pays tropical Bamiléké et Bamoun," *Rev. Géog. Alpine*, Vol. 33 (1945).

124 C. M. Doke. *The Lambas of Northern Rhodesia*. London, 1931.

125 I. S. Van Dongen. "The Port of Luanda in the Economy of Angola," *Boletim da Sociedade de Geografia de Lisboa*, Jan.–Mar. 1960.

126 M. Douglas. "The Lele of Kasai," in C. D. Forde, ed., *African Worlds: Studies in the Cosmological Ideas and Values of African Peoples*. Oxford, 1954.

127 V. Drachoussoff. "Essai sur l'agriculture indigène au Bas-Congo," *Bull. Agr. Congo Belge*. (Belgium, Ministère des Colonies), Sept. and Dec. 1947.

128 G. C. Dudgeon. *The Agriculture and Forest Products of British West Africa*. London, 1922.

129 I. Dugast. *The Banen, Bafia, and Balom of the French Cameroons*. International African Institute, Ethnographic Survey of Africa, Vol. 3, Pt. 9. London, 1954.

130 East African Protectorate. *Annual Colonial Report, 1906–07*.

131 ———, Economic Commission. *Final Report, Pt. 1*. Nairobi, 1919.

132 C. Ehrlich. "The Economy of Buganda, 1893–1903." *Uganda J.*, Mar. 1956.

133 Encyclopédie Coloniale et Maritime. *Encyclopédie de L'Afrique Française*. Paris, 1951.

134 Sir Frank Engledow. *Report to the Minister of Agriculture . . . on the Agricultural Development of Southern Rhodesia*. Salisbury, 1950.

135 Baron Ch. de l'Epine. "L'Historie des famines et disettes dans l'Urundi," *Bull. Agr. Congo Belge*, June 1929.

136 E. Everaerts. "Monographie agricole du Ruanda-Urundi." *ibid.*, Dec. 1939.

137 FAO, *World Food Survey*. Washington, D.C., 1946.

138 ———. *Food Balance Sheets*. Rome, 1949.

139 ———. *Maize and Maize Diets*, Nutr. Stud. No. 9. Rome, 1953.

140 ———. *Food Balance Sheets*. Rome, 1955.

140a ———. *Report on the 1950 World Census of Agriculture*. Rome, 1955.

141 ———. "Food and Agriculture Developments in Africa South of the Sahara," *The State of Food and Agriculture, 1958*. Rome, 1958.

142 ———. "Preliminary Results of the 1960 World Census of Agriculture: 7th Issue," *Monthly Bull. Agr. Econ. and Stat.*, June 1962.

143 ———. *Yearbook of Food and Agricultural Statistics*, Pt. 1: Production. Rome.

144 ———. *Yearbook of Food and Agricultural Statistics*, Pt. 2: Commerce. Rome.

145 A Fauchèrie. "L'Agriculture," in M. Loisy, *Madagascar*. Paris, 1914.

146 O. T. Faulkner and J. R. Mackie. *West African Agriculture*. Cambridge, England, 1933.

147 S. H. Fazan. Information given in Kenya, *Land Commission Evidence*, Vol. 1. Nairobi, 1933.

148 Federation of Rhodesia and Nyasaland, Central African Statistical Office. *Second Report on Urban African Budget Survey Held in Northern Rhodesia, May to August, 1960*. Salisbury, Jan. 1961.

149 Federation of Rhodesia and Nyasaland. *Report of the Grain Marketing Board . . .* , Salisbury.

150 Federation of Nigeria, Department of Agriculture (Central). *Annual Report for the Year 1952/53*, Pt. 2. Lagos.

151 *Field Crop Abstracts*, Aug. 1956.

152 W. Fitzgerald. *Africa: A Social, Economic and Political Geography of Its Major Regions*, 8th ed. London, Methuen; New York, E. P. Dutton, 1955.

153 W. W. A. Fitzgerald. *Travels in the Coastlands of British East Africa . . . .* London, 1898.

154 B. N. Floyd. "Changing Patterns of African Land Use in Southern Rhodesia." Unpublished paper read before the Social Science Research Committee at the University College of Rhodesia and Nyasaland, Nov. 6, 1958.

155 H. A. Ford, Great Britain, Dept. of Overseas Trade. *Report on the Economic Conditions of Portuguese East Africa, October, 1932*, No. 537. London, 1933.

156 V. C. R. Ford. *The Trade of Lake Victoria*, E. Afr. Stud., No. 3. Kampala, 1955.

157 France. *Annuaire de Madagascar, année 1899*. Tananarive, 1899.

158 France, Secretariat d'État aux Colonies. *Les Exploitations agricoles des céréales de l'Afrique Occidentale . . . .* Paris, 1944.

159 France. *Madagascar*. Paris, n.d.

160 ———. *Madagascar, à travers ses provinces*. Paris, n.d.

161 S. H. Frankel. *Capital Investment in Africa*. Oxford, 1938.

162 N. R. Fuggles-Couchman. "Some Production-Cost Figures for Native

Crops in the Eastern Province of Tanganyika Territory," *E. Afr. Agr. J.*, Mar. 1939.

163 R. Galletti, K. D. S. Baldwin, and I. O. Dina. *Nigerian Cocoa Farmers: An Economic Survey of Yoruba Cocoa Farming Families.* Nigeria Cocoa Marketing Board, London, Oxford Univ. Press, 1956.

164 L. Galtié. "Vakinankarata agricole," *Bull. Écon.* (Madagascar), 1928.

165 G. Geortay. "Données de base pour la gestion de paysannats de cultures vivrières en région équatoriale forestière," *Bull. Inf. de l'INÉAC*, Aug. 1956.

166 Ghana, Office of the Government Statistician. Unpublished data, Oct. 1958.

167 M. Gluckman. *Economy of the Central Barotse Plain*, Rhodes-Livingstone Papers, No. 7. 1941.

168 Max Gluckman. Communication from Manchester, England, July 1958.

169 Gold Coast. *Gold Coast Nutrition and Cookery*. Edinburgh, 1953.

170 A. H. H. Goodwin. "The Origin of Maize," *S. Afr. Arch. Bull.*, Mar. 1953.

171 V. Gossens. "Multiplication de l'arbre à pain (*Artocarpus incisa*) pour le ravitaillement des indigènes," *Bull. Agr. Congo Belge*, Sept. 1930.

172 Government of Italy and United Nations Technical Assistance Programme. *The Trust Territory of Somaliland under Italian Administration.* New York, 1952.

173 A. Grandidier, ed. *Collection des ouvrages anciens concernant Madagascar*, Vol. 5. Paris, 1903.

174 C. Grant. *The History of Mauritius . . . .* London, 1801.

175 Great Britain. *Report by Consul Hopkins on the Trade, Commerce, Navigation etc., of the Province of Angola and Its Dependencies for the Year 1874.*

176 ———, Foreign Office, Historical Section. "Cape Verde Islands," No. 117 in *Portuguese Possessions*, Peace Handbooks, Vol. 19. London, 1920.

177 ———. *French African Possessions*, Peace Handbooks, Vol. 17. London, 1920.

178 ———. "Mozambique," No. 121 in *Portuguese Possessions*, Peace Handbooks, Vol. 19. London, 1920.

179 Great Britain, Colonial Office. *Colonial Research, 1954–55.* London, Nov. 1955.

180 Great Britain, Dept. of Overseas Trade. *Overseas Economic Surveys, Portugal, June, 1954.* London, 1955.

181 Great Britain, Overseas Food Corporation. *Report and Accounts for 1954–55.* London, 1956.

182 Great Britain. *Basutoland, Bechuanaland Protectorate and Swaziland: Report of an Economic Survey Mission.* London, 1960.

183 G. A. Van de Goor. *Agronomic Research on Maize in Indonesia.* Contributions of the General Agricultural Research Station, Bogor, No. 135. Bogor, Indonesia, Sept. 1953.

184 G. De Greef. "Monographie agricole de la région de l'Urundi," *Bull. Agr. Congo Belge*, Mar.–Dec. 1919.

185 L. P. Green and T. J. D. Fair. *Development in Africa*. Johannesburg, 1962.

186 M. Greenwoal. "The Peasant Use of Fertilizers in Northern Nigeria," *E. Afr. Agr. J.*, July 1950.

187 Grémio do Milho do Ultramar, Lisbon. Data from the files.

188 Grémio do Milho do Ultramar, Angola. *Relatório e contas da direcção e parecer do conselho fiscal relativos ao exercício*. Lisbon.

189 P. H. Gulliver. "The Evolution of Arusha Trade," in Paul Bohannan and George Dalton, eds., *Markets in Africa*. Evanston, Ill., 1962.

190 Lord Hailey. *An African Survey*. Oxford, 1939.

191 A. A. Haller. "A Rejoinder to Mr. Miracle's Article," *E. Afr. Econ. Rev.*, Dec. 1959.

192 W. D. Hambly. *The Ovimbundu of Angola*, Anthropological Series of the Field Museum of Natural History, Vol. 21, No. 2. Chicago, 1934.

193 W. A. Hance. *African Economic Development*. London, 1958.

194 R. Hardy. "L'Activité de la Station de Kiyaka," *Bull. Inf. de l'INÉAC*, Feb. 1954.

195 F. Hargot. "Monographie agricole du Maniema," *Bull. Agr. Congo Belge*, Feb. 1955.

196 A. S. Hartley. Information given in Kenya, *Land Commission Evidence*, Vol. 3. Nairobi, 1933.

197 M. R. Haswell. *Economics of Agriculture in a Savannah Village . . .* , Great Britain, Colonial Office, Col. Res. Stud. No. 8. London, 1953.

198 J. Heads. "Urbanization and Economic Progress," in *Proceedings of the Annual Conference of the Nigerian Institute of Social and Economic Research 1958*. Ibadan, 1959.

199 F. Hellot. *La Pacification de Madagascar*. Paris, 1900.

200 C. W. Hobley. *Eastern Uganda, an Ethnographical Survey*, Anthropological Institute of Great Britain and Ireland, Occasional Papers, No. 1. London, 1902.

201 R. H. Hobson. *Rubber: A Footnote to Northern Rhodesian History*, Occasional Papers of the Rhodes-Livingstone Museum, No. 13. 1960.

202 B. W. Hodder. "The Yoruba Rural Market," in Paul Bohannon and George Dalton, eds., *Markets in Africa*. Evanston, Ill., 1962.

203 A. C. Hollis. *The Nandi*. Oxford, 1909.

204 A. Holm. Information given in Kenya, *Land Commission Evidence*, Vol. 3. Nairobi, 1933.

205 L. von Holmel. *Discovery of Lakes Rudolf and Stefanie*. London, 1894.

206 P. F. Hone. *Southern Rhodesia*. London, G. Bell and Sons, 1909.

207 G. R. Horner. *Traditional Society and Social Change among the Bulu*. Unpublished manuscript, Boston University, 1958.

208 N. Humphrey. *The Liguru and the Land*. Nairobi, 1947.

208a K. E. Hunt. *Statistics for African Agriculture*. Processed, FAO, Rome, 1953.

209 T. Hunter and T. V. Danso. "Notes on Food Farming at Ejura," in Gold Coast, Department of Agriculture, *Year-book, 1930*. Accra, n.d.

210 G. W. B. Huntingford. *Nandi Work and Culture*, Great Britain, Colonial Office, Col. Res. Stud. No. 4. London, 1950.

211 A. B. Hutcheon, Great Britain, Department of Overseas Trade. *Report on the Economic Conditions in Angola (Portuguese West Africa), dated March, 1923*. London, 1923.

212 ———. *Report on the Economic Situation in Angola (Portuguese West Africa) June, 1925*. London, 1925.

213 E. Huxley. *No Easy Way*. Nairobi, 1958.

214 H. Isnard. "La Colonisation agricole à Madagascar," *Rev. Géog. Alpine*, Vol. 39. 1951.

215 ———. "La Réunion: Problèmes démographiques économiques et sociaux," *ibid.*, Vol. 41, 1953.

216 ———. *Madagascar*. Paris, 1955.

217 Institut National pour l'Étude Agronomique du Congo Belge. Data from the files.

218 ———. "Plantes vivrières, rapport synthétique général sur l'exercice 1957." Unpublished manuscript, Yangambi, Belgian Congo, 1958.

219 International Bank for Reconstruction and Development, *The Economic Development of Nigeria*. Baltimore, 1955.

220 C. Ivens. "L'Angola méridional," *Bull. de la Société d'Études Coloniales*, Sept.–Oct. 1898.

221 Ivory Coast, Conseil Supérieur des Recherches Sociologiques Outremer. *Enquête nutrition — Niveau de vie (Subdivision de Bongouanou, 1955–1956)*. Paris, 1958.

222 B. R. Jackson. Communication from Dire Dawa, Ethiopia, Jan. 1958.

223 H. E. Jacob. *Six Thousand Years of Bread*. New York, 1944.

224 N. Jasny. *Competition among Grains*. Food Research Institute, Stanford, Calif., 1940.

225 M. D. W. Jeffreys. "The History of Maize in Africa," *S. Afr. J. of Sci.*, Mar. 1954.

226 ———. "The Origin of the Portuguese Word Zaburro as Their Name for Maize," *Bull. de l'IFAN*, Ser. B., Vol. 19. 1957.

227 M. T. Jenkins. "Corn Improvement," in USDA, *Yearbook of Agriculture*, 1936.

228 ———. "Influence of Climate and Weather on the Growth of Corn," *ibid.*, 1941.

229 C. E. Johnson. *African Farming Improvements in the Plateau Tonga Area of Northern Rhodesia*, Northern Rhodesia, Department of Agriculture, Agr. Bull. No. 11. London, 1956.

230 R. M. W. Johnson. "African Agricultural Development in Southern Rhodesia: 1945–1960," *Food Res. Inst. Stud.*, Food Research Institute, Stanford, Calif., Vol. 4, No. 2, 1964.

231 B. F. Johnston. *The Staple Food Economies of Western Tropical Africa*, Food Res. Inst. Stud. in Trop. Devel., No. 1. Stanford, Calif., Stanford Univ. Press, 1958.

232 ———. *The Outlook for Wheat and Flour Imports in Tropical Africa*, USDA, Foreign Agricultural Service, FAS-M-48. Feb. 1959.

233 Sir Harry Johnston. *British Central Africa*. New York, 1897.

234   ———. Letter to the British Foreign Office, July 10, 1901.

235   E. B. Jones. "Foods from Southern Rhodesia," in Great Britain Colonial Office, *Malnutrition in African Mothers, Infants, and Young Children.* London, 1954.

236   W. O. Jones. "Manioc: An Example of Innovation in African Economies," *Economic Development and Cultural Change* (Chicago, Ill.) Jan. 1957.

237   ———. *Manioc in Africa,* Food Res. Inst. Stud. in Trop. Devel., No. 2. Stanford, Calif., Stanford Univ. Press, 1959.

238. .———. "Economic Man in Africa," *Food Res. Inst. Stud.,* Foor Research Institute, Stanford, Calif., May 1960.

239   W. O. Jones and C. Mérat, "Consumption of Exotic Consumer Goods as an Indicator of Economic Achievement in Ten Countries of Tropical Africa," *Food Res. Inst. Stud.,* Feb. 1962.

240   P. M. Kaberry. *Women of the Grassfields: A Study of the Economic Position of Women in Bamenda, British Cameroons,* Great Britain, Colonial Office, Col. Res. Pub. No. 14. London, 1952.

241   S. E. Kay, Great Britain, Department of Overseas Trade, *Report on the Economic Conditions of Portuguese East Africa, July, 1935,* No. 624, London, 1935.

242   S. E. Kay and C. N. Ezard, Great Britain, Department of Overseas Trade. *Report on the Economic and Commercial Conditions of the Government-Administered Territory and the Territory of the Mozambique Company, in Portuguese East Africa, March, 1938,* No. 702. London, 1938.

243   M. J. Kellerman. "Essais sur la fréquence des arrosages dans la culture irriguée du maïs," in Union Nationale des Coopératives Agricoles de Céréales, *Le Maïs.* Paris, Dec. 1949.

244   Kenya, Department of Agriculture. *Maize Yields and Green-Manuring, 1932,* Bull. No. 3 of 1933. Nairobi.

245   Kenya. *Food Shortage Commission of Inquiry Report, 1943.* Nairobi, 1943.

246   ———. *The Maize Industry,* Sessional Paper No. 6 of 1957/58 Nairobi, 1958.

247   ———. *Report of Proceedings of Maize Conference Held at Nairobi, 1922.* Nairobi, n.d.

248   ———, Department of Agriculture. *Annual Report.* Nairobi.

249   ———, East African Statistical Office. *The Pattern of Income, Expenditure and Consumption of Africans in Nairobi, 1957/58.*

250   G. H. T. Kimble. *Tropical Africa,* Vol. 1. New York, Twentieth Century Fund, 1960.

251   K. H. W. Klages. *Ecological Crop Geography.* New York, Macmillan, 1942.

252   J. L. Krapf. *Travels, Researches, and Missionary Labours during Eighteen Years' Residence in Eastern Africa . . . .* Boston, 1860.

253   J. B. Labat. *Nouvelle relation de l'Afrique Occidentale.* Paris, 1728.

254   M. Lacombez. "L'Agriculture chez les Mangbetu de l'Ituri," *Bull. Agr. Congo Belg.,* Mar.–Dec. 1918.

255   M.-A. Leblond. *Madagascar, création française.* Paris, 1934.

256 M. H. Lelong. *Mes Frères du Congo*, Vol. 2. Brussels, 1946.
257 E. Leplae. "Histoire et développement des cultures obligatoires de coton et de riz au Congo Belge de 1917 à 1933," *Congo*, May 1933.
258 A. M. Leroy. "Le Maïs dans l'alimentation animale," in Union Nationale des Coopératives Agricoles de Céréales, *Le Maïs*. Paris, Dec. 1949.
259 R. Lesire. "Essai de fumure, premiers résultats," *Bull. Agr. Congo Belge*, Feb. 1953.
260 P. Leurquin. *Le Niveau de vie des populations rurales du Ruanda-Urundi*. Louvain, Belgium, 1960.
261 G. Lindblom. *The Akamba*. Uppsala, 1920.
262 David and Charles Livingstone. *Narrative of an Expedition to the Zambesi and Its Tributaries*, . . . , London, 1865.
263 A. Lyall. *Black and White Make Brown*. London, 1938.
264 R. N. Lyne. *Mozambique: Its Agricultural Development*. London, Unwin, 1913.
265 Augusto Reis Machado, ed. *Livro em que dá relação do que viu e ouviu no Oriente Duarte Barbosa*. Lisbon, 1964.
266 D. R. Mackenzie. *The Spirit-ridden Konde*. Philadelphia, 1925.
267 Madagascar, Agence Générale des Colonies. *Bulletin*.
268 C. Maher. Information given in Kenya, *Land Commission Evidence*, Vol. 2, Nairobi, 1933.
269 J. Maina. Communication from Stanford, Calif., June 1961.
270 L. P. Mair. *An African People in the Twentieth Century*. London, 1934.
271 G. Mallien. *Travels in the Interior of Africa to the Sources of the Senegal and Gambia* . . . , London, 1820.
272 M. Manoukian. *Tribes of the Northern Territories of the Gold Coast*, International African Institute, Ethnographic Survey of Africa, Vol. 3, Pt. 5. London, 1952.
273 J. Montalvão Marques, *Esboço para uma monografia agrícola do posto-sede dos Muchopes e de alguns regulados do Chibuto*, Memórias de Junta de Investigações do Ultramar, No. 22. Lisbon, 1960.
274 G. A. Marshall. "The Marketing of Farm Produce: Some Patterns among Women in Western Nigeria," Nigerian Institute of Social and Economic Research, *Conference Proceedings March 1962*. Ibadan, 1963.
275 W. S. Martin and B. Griffith. "Uganda Soils," in J. D. Tothill, ed., *Agriculture in Uganda*. London, 1940.
276 Mauritius, Department of Agriculture. *Annual Report*.
277 G. B. Masefield. "Maize Names," *Uganda J.*, Mar. 1950.
278 R. Masseyeff and A. Cambon. *Enquêtes sur l'alimentation au Cameroun, Part I: Evodoula*, IRCAM. Yaoundé, 1955.
279 R. Masseyeff, A. Cambon, and R. Bergeret. *Enquête sur l'alimentation au Cameroun, Pt. 3: Golompoui (Subdivision de Yagoua)*, IRCAM. Yaoundé, n.d.
280 R. C. F. Maugham. *Portuguese East Africa*. New York, 1906.
281 J. E. Meade and others. *The Economic and Social Structure of Mauritius*. London, 1961.

282 A. P. Merriam and others. "The Concept of Cultural Clusters Applied to the Belgian Congo," *Southwestern J. Anthr.*, Winter 1959.

283 Y. Mersadier. *Budgets familiaux africains*, Études Sénégalaises, No. 7. Saint-Louis, Senegal, 1957.

284 J. M. Th. Messen. *Ituri*. Brussels, 1951.

285 O. F. Metzger. *Unsere alte Kolonie Togo*. Neudamm, Germany, 1941.

286 J. Middleton. "Trade and Markets among the Lugbara of Uganda," in Paul Bohannan and George Dalton, eds., *Markets in Africa*, Evanston, Ill., 1962.

287 S. Milligan. *Report on the Present Position of the Agricultural Industry* . . . . Livingstone, Northern Rhodesia, 1931.

288 J. Minelle. *L'Agriculture à Madagascar*. Paris, 1959.

289 M. P. Miracle. "Maize in Tropical African Agriculture," *Trop. Agr.*, Jan. 1958.

290 ———. "An Economic Appraisal of Kenya's Maize Control." *E. Afr. Econ. Rev.*, Dec. 1959.

291 ———. "Plateau Tonga Entrepreneurs in Historical Inter-Regional Trade," *Rhodes-Livingstone Inst. J.*, Dec. 1959.

292 ———. Review of P. J. Quin, "Foods and Feeding Habits of the Pedi," *ibid.*, Dec. 1959.

293 ———. " 'Seasonal Hunger': A Vague Concept and an Unexplored Problem," *Bull. de l'IFAN*, Ser. B, Vol. 22, Nos. 1–2. 1961.

294 ———. "Aboriginal Trade among the Senga and Nsenga of Northern Rhodesia," *Ethnology*, Apr. 1962.

295 ———. "African Markets and Trade in the Copperbelt," in Paul Bohannan and George Dalton, eds., *Markets in Africa*. Evanston, Ill., 1962.

296 ———. "Response to Economic Incentives in Central Africa." *Proceedings of the Thirty-Sixth Annual Conference of the Western Economic Association*. 1962.

297 ———. "Interpretation of Evidence on the Introduction of Maize into West Africa." *Africa*, April 1963.

298 ———. *Traditional Agricultural Methods in the Congo Basin*. Mimeographed monograph, Food Res. Inst., Stanford, Calif., Oct. 1964.

299 Mozambique, Direcção dos Serviços de Economia e Estatística. *Anuário estatístico*. Lourenço Marques.

300 ———. *Estatística agrícola*. Lourenço Marques.

301 Mozambique. *Relatório do Chefe dos Serviços de Agricultura 1940–1944*, Pts. 2 and 3. Lourenço Marques, 1946.

302 D. Van Moesieke. "Monographie agricole du district de la Lulonga (Equateur)," *Bull. Agr. Congo Belge*, Sept. 1929.

303 T. Monod, Teixeira da Mota, and R. Mauny, *Description de la côte occidentale d'Afrique (Sénégal au Cap de Monte, Archipels), par Valentim Fernandes* (1506–1510) [Bissau, 1951].

304 J. J. Monteiro. *Angola and the River Congo*. New York, 1878.

305 J. Moreau. "The Economic Life of the Natives . . . ," *Zambesi Mission Rec.*, Oct. 1947.

306 F. B. Morrison. *Feeds and Feeding*. Ithaca, N.Y., Morrison Pub. Co., 1951.

307 A. Teixeira da Mota. Communication. 1958.
308 W. G. B. Mountmorres. *The Congo Independent State.* London, Williams and Norgate, 1906.
309 Pedro Muralha. "Os valores económicas da África Portuguesa," *Boletim da Agência Geral das Colónias,* June 1926.
310 G. P. Murdock. *Africa.* New York, 1959.
311 N. P. Neal and A. M. Strommen. *Supplement to Wisconsin Corn Hybrids,* Wisconsin Agricultural Experiment Station Bull. No. 476, Supplement. Jan. 1956.
312 J. H. Neill. Information given in Kenya, *Land Commission Evidence,* Vol. 3. Nairobi, 1933.
313 *The New Gold Coast Farmer,* Aug. 1956.
314 S. D. Neumark. "Economic Development and Economic Incentives," *South African J. of Econ.,* Mar. 1958.
315 B. M. Nicol. "The Nutrition of Nigerian Peasants, with Special Reference to the Effects of Deficiencies of the Vitamin B Complex, Vitamin A and Animal Protein," *Brit. J. Nutr.,* Vol. 6. 1952.
316 ———. "The Calorie Requirments of Nigerian Peasant Farmers," *ibid.,* Vol. 3. 1949.
317 ———. "Nutrition of Nigerian Peasant Farmers, with Special Reference to the Effects of Vitamin A and Riboflavin Deficiency," *ibid.,* Vol. 3. 1949.
318 Nigeria, Department of Agriculture. Information from the files.
319 E. A. Nobbs and F. Eyles. "Statistics for Crops Grown by Europeans in Southern Rhodesia for the Season 1917–18," *Rhodesian Agr. J.,* Vol. 15, No. 6. Dec. 1918.
320 T. R. Noon. Communication from Nairobi, Kenya, July 1959.
321 Northern Region of Nigeria, Ministry of Agriculture. *Annual Report, . . . 1957/58.* Kaduna.
322 Northern Rhodesia. *Annual Report of the Southern Province* (Lusaka).
323 ———. Department of Agriculture. *Annual Report.* Lusaka.
324 J. Noyen. "Considérations sur les possibilités d'amélioration du rendement travail dans le milieux paysan," Typescript. Gandajika, Belgian Congo, Mar. 5, 1949.
325 ———. "Possibilités d'augmentation des rendements des principales cultures indigènes au Lomami," *Bull. Agr. Congo Belge,* Sept.–Dec. 1949.
326 Nyasaland, Agricultural Production and Marketing Board. *Annual Report, 1958.* Zomba, 1959.
327 ———, Department of Agriculture. *African Agriculture in Nyasaland.* Textbook. Zomba, 1959.
328 ———. *Annual Report.* Zomba.
329 ———. Data from the files, Oct. 1959.
330 ———. "Notes on T. R. Ellis's Paper: Maize Types of Nyasaland." Unpublished manuscript. Zomba.
331 *Nyasaland Farmer and Forester,* Nov. 1955.
332 P. H. Nye. "A Survey of the Value of Fertilizers to the Food-farming Area of the Gold Coast. Part 3: The Voltain Sandstone Region and the Southern Maize Areas," *Empire J. Exp. Agr.,* Vol. 22 (1954).

333 A. A. Nyirenda. "African Market Vendors in Lusaka with a Note on the Recent Boycott," *Rhodes-Livingstone Inst. J.*, 1957.
334 A. Nypan. *Market Trade*, University College of Ghana, African Business Series No. 2. Accra, 1960.
335 C. O. Oates. Information given in Kenya, *Land Commission Evidence*, Vol. 1. Nairobi, 1933.
336 M. Oliver. *Six ans de politique sociale à Madagascar.* Paris, 1931.
337 F. O'Meara, Great Britain, Dept. of Overseas Trade. *Report on the Economic and Commercial Conditions of Angola, February, 1937*, No. 667. London, 1937.
338 S. A. Ominde. Communication from Kampala, Uganda, Apr. 1959.
339 C. Van Overbergh. *Les Mangbetu*, Brussels, 1909.
340 T. A. Oxley. *Grain Storage in East and Central Africa*, Great Britain, Colonial Office, Col. Res. Pub. No. 5. London, 1950.
341 Rui Miller Paiva. "Agricultura na África," *Boletim de Agricultura* (São Paulo), 1950.
342 M. Park. *Travels in the Interior of Africa.* Everyman's Library. London, 1907.
343 V. M. Patiño. "El Maíz Chococito," *Amer. Indigena*, Oct. 1956.
344 J. H. Patterson. *The Man-Eaters of Tsavo* . . . . London, Macmillan, 1907.
345 F. M. Pauwels. *Landuishoudkundig Onderzoek bij de Japaliri.* Ghent, 1960.
346 E. Pawson. "The Composition and Fertility of Maize Soils in Northern Rhodesia," *Empire J. Exp. Agr.*, Apr. 1957.
347 P. Pelissier. "Les Paysans Sérères," *Les Cahiers d'Outre-mer*, April–June 1953.
348 A. J. Pena. "Tentative d'établissement du bilan alimentaire de l'Angola," paper presented to Third Inter-African Nutrition Conference, CCTA, Luanda, 1956.
349 J. Périssé. *Une enquête alimentaire sur les populations agricoles du Sud-Togo B: Résultats du pays Ouatchi (Sud-Togo)*, France, Office de la Recherche Scientifique et Technique, Outre-mer, Institut de Recherches, Togo. Lomé, n.d.
350 F. Pigafetta. "Relatione del reame di Congo . . ." (Rome), quoted in Conde de Ficalho, *Plantas uteis da África Portugueza.* Lisbon, 1884.
351 A. W. Pim and S. Milligan. *Report of the Commission Appointed to Enquire into the Financial and Economic Position of Northern Rhodesia*, Great Britain, Colonial Office, Colonial No. 145. London, 1938.
352 B. S. Platt. *Tables of Representative Values of Foods Commonly Used in Tropical Countries*, Medical Research Council. London, 1945.
353 H. L. Poisson. "Culture des plantes forragères dans le Sud-Ouest de Madagascar," *Rev. Bot. App. et Agr. Coloniale*, Mar. 1943.
354 T. T. Poleman. "The Food Economies of Urban Middle Africa: The Case of Ghana," *Food. Res. Inst. Stud.*, Food Research Institute, Stanford, Calif. May 1961.
355 R. Portères. "L'Introduction du maïs en Afrique," *J. Agr. Trop. et Bot. App.*, Nos. 5–6 (1955).

356 P. G. Powesland. *Economic Policy and Labour*, E. Afr. Stud. No. 10. Kampala, 1957.

357 E. de Prêter. Communication from Gandajika, Belgian Congo, June 1959.

358 Abbé Proyart. "History of Loango, Kakongo, and Other Kingdoms of Africa," in John Pinkerton, ed., *A General Collection of the Best and Most Interesting Voyages and Travels in All Parts of the World*, Vol. 16. London, 1814.

359 J. Pyke, Great Britain, Department of Overseas Trade. *Economic Conditions in Portuguese East Africa, December, 1929*. London, 1930.

360 A. G. H. Rattray and B. S. Ellis. "Maize and Green Manuring in Southern Rhodesia," *Rhodesian Agr. J.*, July–Aug. 1952.

361 A. M. M. Rees and R. H. Howard. *An Economic Survey of Commercial African Farming* . . . , Northern Rhodesia, Department of Agriculture, Agr. Bull. No. 10. Lusaka, 1955.

362 *Rhodesian Agr. J.*

363 J. Richard-Molard. "Essai sur la vie paysanne au Fouta-Dialon," *Rev. Géog. Alpine*, Vol. 33 (1945).

364 A. I. Richards. *Land, Labour, and Diet in Northern Rhodesia* . . . . London, 1939.

365 J. L. Robert. "Monographie agricole du District du Lac Léopold II," *Bull. Agr. Congo Belge*, Sept. 1952.

366 J. A. Alves Roçadas. *La Main d'Oeuvre indigène*. Paper presented to Third International Tropical Agriculture Congress, London, 1914. Lisbon, 1914.

367 C. Rollot. "Le Maïs à Madagascar," in Madagascar, *Bull. Écon.* Supplement, 1925.

368 ———. "Le Manioc à Madagascar," *Rev. Bot. App. et Agr. Coloniale*, Feb.–Mar. 1926.

369 R. De Rouck. *Atlas géographique et historique du Congo Belge* . . . , 4th ed. Brussels, n.d.

370 N. V. Rounce, J. G. M. King, and D. Thorton. *A Record of Investigations and Observations on the Agriculture of the Cultivation Steppe of Sukuma and Nyamwezi* . . . , Tanganyika, Department of Agriculture, Pam. No. 30. Dar es Salaam.

371 N. V. Rounce and D. Thorton. *Ukara Island and the Agricultural Practices of the Wakara*, Nairobi, n.d. (A revised version of an article with the same title that appeared in *Tanganyika Notes and Records*, Mar. 1936.

372 W. Van Royen. *The Agricultural Resources of the World*, USDA, Bureau of Agricultural Economics, and University of Maryland. New York, Prentice-Hall, 1954.

373 E. R. Russell. "Primitive Farming in Nigeria; the Mumuye Tribe," *Empire J. Exp. Agr.*, Vol. 8 (1940).

374 Armando Salbany. "Dos tipos de postos em Angola," *Agronomia Angolana*, No. 10, 1956.

375 M. H. Santos. "Subsidios para o estudo agro-economica de agricultura de Cabo Verde, anno 1934," manuscript.

376 D. H. Saunder and R. C. Salmon. "Phosphate in Rhodesian Soils," *Rhodesia Agr. J.*, May–June 1952.

377 P. de Schlippé. "Sous-station d'essais de l'INÉAC à Kurukwata (Extraits du premier rapport annuel)," *Bull. Agr. Congo Belge*, June 1948.

378 ———. *Shifting Cultivation in Africa*, London, 1956.

379 B. F. Schneider. "The Nutritive Value of Corn," in American Society of Agronomy, G. F. Sprague, ed., *Corn and Corn Improvement*, New York, Academic Press, 1955.

380 G. Schwab. "The Customs of the Bassa," ed. by G. R. Horner. Unpublished manuscript, Boston University, 1958.

381 B. Schwab. "An Experiment in Resettlement in Northern Nigeria," in H. M. Taf and P. G. Franck, eds., *Hands across Frontiers*. Ithaca, N.Y., 1955.

382 G. Schweinfurth. *The Heart of Africa*, Vol. 2. London, 1874.

383 Colonel Servais. "La Culture de l'arbre à pain dans des camps de la Force Publique au Congo-Kasai," *Bull. Agr. Congo Belge*, Sept. 1930.

384 Seychelles, Department of Agriculture. *Annual Report, 1949*, Victoria, 1949.

385 H. L. Shantz. "Agricultural Regions of Africa," Pt. 2: Vegetation and Potential Productivity of the Land, *Econ. Geog.* (Worcester, Mass.), Oct. 1940.

386 G. A. Shaw. *Madagascar and France*. London, 1885.

387 J. H. Shollenberger and C. M. Jaeger. *Corn, Its Products and Uses* USDA. Sept. 1943.

388 J. Sibree. *Madagascar before the Conquest*. London, 1896.

389 E. W. Smith and A. M. Dale. *The Ila-speaking Peoples of Northern Rhodesia*, Vol. 1. London, 1920.

390 Jerome Merolla da Sorrento. *A Voyage to Congo*. N.p., n.d.

391 A. W. Southall. "Alur Migrants," in A. I. Richards, ed. *Economic Development and Tribal Change*. Cambridge, England [1955?].

392 A. W. Southall and P. C. W. Gutkind. *Townsmen in the Making*, E. Afr. Stud. No. 9. Kampala, 1957.

393 Southern Rhodesia. *Report of the Maize Enquiry Committee*. Salisbury, 1930.

394 ———. *Seventh Report on the Agricultural and Pastoral Production of European Farmers, 1952–53*. Salisbury, 1954.

395 ———, Department of Agriculture. *Annual Report*. Salisbury.

396 J. H. Speke. *Journal of the Discovery of the Source of the Nile*. London, 1864.

397 ———. *What Led to the Discovery of the Source of the Nile*. London, 1864.

398 L. D. Stamp. *Africa. A Study in Tropical Development*. New York, 1953.

399 W. R. Stanton. "Progress Report on a Maize Survey of West Africa, Pt. 2." Unpublished manuscript, Moor Plantation, Nigeria, 1958.

400 A. S. Stenhouse. "Agriculture in the Matengo Highlands," *E. Afr. Agr. J.*, July 1944.

401 E. Van Der Straeten. *L'Agriculture et les industries agricoles au Congo*

Belge, Publication de la Compagnie du Congo pour le Commerce et l'Industrie. Brussels, 1945.

402 D. W. Strike. *Barotseland: Eight Years among the Barotse*. London, 1922.

403 G. H. Stringfield. "Corn Culture," in G. F. Sprague, ed., *Corn and Corn Improvement*. New York, 1955.

404 J. E. T. "Termite Mounds Used for Manure," *Farm and Forest* (Nigeria), Mar. 1942.

405 Tanganyika, East African Statistics Office. *The Pattern of Income, Expenditures and Consumption of African Labourers in Dar es Salaam, August, 1950*. Nairobi, Jan. 1951.

406 Tanganyika Department of Agriculture. Information from the files.

407 ———. *Annual Report*. Dar es Salaam.

408 A. Taton. Communication from Mulungu, Belgian Congo, June 1959.

409 A. C. Justino Teixeira. "Milho de Angola," *Agronomia Angolana*, No. 4 (1950).

410 M. Tew. *Peoples of the Lake Nyasa Region*. London, 1950.

411 G. M. Theal. *Records of South-Eastern Africa*, Vol. 2. Capetown, 1898.

412 G. Théodore. "Le Statisticien face au développement," *Développement et civilisations* (Paris), June 1960.

413 G. le Thomas. "Les Plantes cultivées par les Indigènes dans le Sud du Madagascar," in A. Chevalier, ed., "Cinquante années d'efforts scientifiques et sociaux pour le développement de l'agriculture Malgache," *Rev. Bot. App. et Agr. Trop.*, Supplement, Sept. 1946.

414 J. Thompson. *Through Massai Land*. N.p., 1883.

415 ———. *To the Central African Lakes and Back*. London, 1888.

415a B. P. Thomson. *Two Studies in African Nutrition*, Rhodes-Livingstone Papers, No. 24. Manchester Univ. Press, Manchester; and New York, 1954.

416 D. H. Thwaites. "Wanyakyusa Agriculture," *E. Afr. Agr. J.*, Apr. 1944.

417 P. Tissot. "Situation actuelle du maïs dans le monde. Position de la France et des colonies françaises," *Rev. Bot. App. et Agr. Trop.*, May–June 1939.

418 E. Torday. *On the Trail of the Bushongo*. London, 1925.

419 G. T. Trewartha and W. Zelinsky. "Population Patterns in Tropical Africa," *Ann. Ass. Amer. Geog.*, June 1954.

420 *Uganda Argus*, Nov. 24, 1955.

421 Uganda, Department of Labour. *Report of the Committee of Enquiry into the Labour Situation in Uganda Protectorate, 1938*. Entebbe, 1938.

422 ———. *Organization of the South-western Labour Migration Routes*, Second Report of the Labour Advisory Committee. Entebbe, 1943.

423 Uganda [East Africa High Commission] East African Statistical Department. *The Pattern of Income, Expenditure and Consumption of African Labourers in Kampala, September, 1950*. May 1951.

424 ———. *The Pattern of Income and Expenditure and Consumption of African Unskilled Labourers in Kampala, September, 1951*. Jan. 1952.

425 ———. *The Pattern of Income, Expenditure and Consumption of Unskilled Labourers in Jinja, November, 1951*. Aug. 1952.

426 Uganda, Department of Agriculture. *Notes on the Principal Annual Food Crops.* Entebbe, 1952.

427 Uganda [East Africa High Commission], East African Statistical Department. *The Pattern of Income, Expenditure, and Consumption of Unskilled Labourers in Jinja, November, 1952.* May 1953.

428 ———. *The Patterns of Income, Expenditure, and Consumption of African Unskilled Labourers in Kampala, September 1953.* Jan. 1954.

429 *Ibid., February 1957.* June 1957.

430 ———. *The Patterns of Income, Expenditure and Consumption of African Unskilled Workers in Mbale, February, 1958.* July 1958.

431 ———. *Statistical Abstract 1958.* Entebbe, 1959.

432 ———. *The Patterns of Income, Expenditure and Consumption of African Unskilled Workers in Fort Portal, February 1960.* Oct. 1960.

433 Uganda, Ministry of Economic Development, Statistics Branch. *The Patterns of Income, Expenditure and Consumption of African Unskilled Workers in Gulu, February 1961.* [Entebbe], Aug. 1961.

434 Uganda, Department of Agriculture. Data from the files.

435 ———. *Annual Report.* Entebbe.

436 Uganda, Department of Labour. *Annual Report.* Entebbe.

437 UN, *Demographic Yearbook, 1952.* New York, 1952.

438 ———. *Economic Survey of Africa since 1950.* New York, 1959.

439 ———. *Economic Bulletin for Africa,* Vol. 2, No. 2 (June 1962).

440 ———, FAO, ILO. *Progress in Land Reform: Third Report.* New York, 1962.

441 A. W. Urquhart. *Patterns of Settlement and Subsistence in Southwestern Angola,* Nat. Acad. Sci.–Nat. Res. Council Pub. 1096. Washington, D.C., 1963.

442 USDA, Foreign Agricultural Service. *Prospects for Foreign Trade in Food and Feed Grains* . . . . Jan. 1960.

443 R. Van Vaerenbergh. Communication from Yangambi, Belgian Congo, Mar. 1959.

444 J. H. Vandermissen. *Aperçu sur l'économie agricole de la Province du Katanga.* Brussels, 1956.

445 J. Vansina. "Recording the Oral History of the Bakuba, II: Results," *J. Afr. Hist.* (Cambridge, England), Vol. 1. No. 2 (1960).

446 E. Verhulpen. *Baluba et Balubaisés du Katanga.* Antwerp, 1938.

447 M. Vermeesch. "Monographie agricole du district du Lomami (Katanga)," *Bull. Agr. Congo Belge,* Mar. 1924.

448 C. de Melo Vieira. *L'Agriculture* (Mozambique). Published for the Exposition Coloniale Internationale. Paris, 1931.

449 D. Vieira. *Thesouro da lingua portugueza.* 5 vols. Porto, 1871–74.

450 V. M. Wadsworth. "Price and Marketing Aspects of Maize Production," in Federation of Rhodesia and Nyasaland, Ministry of Agriculture, *Proceedings of the Second Annual Conference of the Professional Officers* . . . . Salisbury, 1956.

451 G. Wagner. *The Bantu of North Kavirondo,* ed. L. P. Mair, Vol. 2. London, 1956.

452 J. W. Wallace. "Agriculture in Abakaliki and Afikpo," *Farm and Forest* (Nigeria), Oct. 1941.

453   H. Waller, ed. *The Last Journals of David Livingstone*, Vol. 1, London, 1874.
454   *Ibid.*, Vol. 2.
455   Rachel S. [Mrs. Stuart] Watt. *In the Heart of Savagedom*, London, n.d.
456   A. J. Wauters. *Le Congo illustré*. Brussels, 1895.
457   P. Weatherwax. *Indian Corn in Old America*. New York, 1954.
458   P. Weatherwax and L. F. Randolph. "History and Origin of Corn," in G. F. Sprague, ed., *Corn and Corn Improvement*. New York, 1955.
459   J. K. Weeks. *Among the Primitive Bakongo*. London, 1914.
460   C. M. N. White. *A Preliminary Survey of Luvale Rural Economy*. Rhodes-Livingstone Papers, No. 29. Manchester [England] and New York, 1959.
461   S. White. "The Agriculture Economy of the Hill Pagans of Dikwa Emirate, Cameroons (British Mandate)," *Empire J. Exp. Agr.*, Vol. 9 (1941).
462   W. White. *Journal of a Voyage Performed in the Lion Extra Indiaman . . . .* London, 1800.
463   J. S. Whitmore. "The Marginal Areas of the Orange Free State," *Farming in South Africa*, Jan. 1950.
464   D. Whittlesey. "Southern Rhodesia — An African Compage," *Ann. Ass. Amer. Geog.*, Mar. 1956.
465   E. de Wildeman. "Documents pour l'étude de l'alimentation végétale de l'indigène du Congo Belge," *Mem. d'Inst. Royal Col. Belge*, Coll. 8, Vol. 2, Fasc. 4. Brussels, 1934.
466   F. Willett. "The Introduction of Maize into West Africa: An Assessment of Recent Evidence," *Africa*, Jan. 1962.
467   Jessie Williamson. *Useful Plants of Nyasaland*, ed. P. J. Greenway. Government Printer, Zomba, Nyasaland, 1955.
468   C. T. Wilson and R. W. Felkin. *Uganda and the Egyptian Soudan*, Vol. 1. London, 1882.
469   G. Wilson. *The Land Rights of Individuals among the Nyakyusa*, Rhodes-Livingstone Papers, No. 1. Livingstone, 1938.
470   ———. "Agricultural Practices among the Agoni-Tumbuka Tribes of Mzimba (Nyasaland)," *E. Afr. Agr. J.*, Oct. 1941.
471   A. C. W. Wright. "Maize Names as Indicators of Economic Contacts," *Uganda J.*, Mar. 1949.
472   Joaquim Xabregas and António de Sousa e Santos. "Le Problème alimentaire au paysannat du Vale de Loge." Paper presented to Third Inter-African Nutrition Conference, CCTA, Luanda, 1956.
473   *Zaïre* (Brussels), Mar. 1954.
474   "Notes from the Different Stations." *Zambezi Mission Rec.*, Oct. 1910.
475   R. Zwijsen. "L'Amélioration de la culture du maïs à Nioka," *Bull. Inf. de l'INÉAC*, June 1959.

INDEX

Manioc: importance in tropical Africa,
3; as food, 9, 11, 46, 62, 65, 81, 91,
93, 97, 105, 106, 109, 115–18 *passim*,
120–21, 123, 131, 132, 172, 187, 198,
206, 221, 224, 226, 291; *manihot utilissima*, 46; introduction to Africa,
59, 95, 97; Katanga, 62, 291; Western
Nigeria, 67; trade in, 68, 171; among
Bushong, 93; and maize, 94, 95, 181,
193; in Uganda, 116, 117, 136, 216;
prices of, 136, 216; in Malagasy,
168, 289; Cape Verde Island, 183;
production, 194, 207, 228; costs, 209,
210–14 *passim*, 227, 228; compulsory
acreages, 229; Ghana, 291
Manjoza, 94
Manufacturing, 32
Manures, animal. *See* Fertilizers
Marketing Board, Angola, 191
Markets: distribution of, 29, 55, 56, 57,
66; organization and working of, 54,
55, 58, 66–80 *passim*, 246, 248, 250,
259, 260, 276, 291; list of goods available, 63–65; frequency of, 68, 70,
246, 247, 251; statutory monopolies
for, 72, 165, 226, 251, 254, 259, 260,
292
Massikessi, Mozambique, 144
Matabiche, 72
Matadi, Congo (Leopoldville), 202
Matches, 66
Mauritania, 28
Mauritius, 25, 28, 97, 167, 170–71, 173–
75
Mbale, Uganda, 116
Measures, 59, 69–70, 72, 248
Meat: as food, 47, 52, 60, 99, 103, 110,
224, 226, 227, 229, 283; trade in, 60,
70, 71; shortage of, in tropical Africa,
283
Mechanization, 14, 50, 147, 228, 240,
258. *See also* African agriculture
Mediterrean area, and maize, 88, 89
Melo de Castro, Francisco de, 97
Merchants. *See* Traders
Middlemen, 30, 70, 77, 216, 246, 247,
251, 284
Miège, M. J., 278

Milange *Circunscrição*, Mozambique,
152, 154
Milk, 52, 99, 106, 110
Millets-sorghums: importance in tropical Africa, 3, 81; as food, 9, 11, 44,
65, 93, 94, 98–99, 107, 109, 116, 121,
122, 125, 131, 140, 144, 182, 206,
224, 226; names for, 44, 97, 285; Katanga, 64; Western Nigeria, 67; and
government policy, 72, 229; advantages of cultivation, 83, 141, 163,
208, 258; and maize, 88, 95, 96, 107–
8, 109; costs of, 92, 133, 209–13 *passim*; yields, 92, 94, 208; Kenya, 137,
287; Zambia, 158; Rhodesia, 164;
Angola, 186; growth period of, 283;
Réunion, 286; Malagasy, 289
Milling, 105, 109, 134, 163, 198, 240,
244. *See also* Grinding
Mines: role in African economies, 29,
30, 39–40; employment in, 36, 78;
and development of agriculture, 43,
142, 157–58, 195, 202, 224; Katanga,
86, 160, 162, 193–94, 201, 288; food
consumption by, 133, 201, 227; Ugan-
da, 135, 215, 287; Kivu, 196; Kilo
Moto, 202
Mintja, 106
Mirrors, 66
Moçambique *Circunscrição*, Mozambi-
que, 146
Mocuba *Circunscrição*, Mozambique,
152
Mokwa Scheme, 241
Mombasa, Kenya, 96
Money, as unit of exchange, 29, 55, 58,
59, 70, 71, 72, 158, 260
Monomotapa, 96
Morondava, Malagasy, 172
Morrumbula *Circunscrição*, Mozambi-
que, 154
Mortars and pestles, 50, 66, 103, 104,
110, 242
Mossâmedes, Angola, 186
Mossuril *Circunscrição*, Mozambique,
152
Moyen Congo, Congo (Brazzaville), 122
Mozambique, 97, 279, 285, 287